PRAISE FOR *ON T*

MW01013581

"Comer and Powers's *On the Origin of Being* is a revelation—a captivating exploration of the evolutionary forces that have shaped the human mind, body, and soul. Through compelling storytelling and rigorous scientific inquiry, they unveil the disconnect between our ancestral blueprint and the contemporary landscape, offering invaluable guidance on reclaiming our vitality and purpose."

—**DAVID R. SAMSON,** PhD, associate professor of
anthropology at the University of Toronto, author of
Our Tribal Future, winner of the Writers' Trust Balsillie
Prize for Public Policy, recipient of the Canadian Sleep
Society Roger Broughton Young Investigator Award

"Fantastically clear, easy to read, and deeply researched, *On the Origin of Being* is a must-read book. As an anthropologist, I've often puzzled at the profound tension between our modern lives and our evolutionary trajectories. How we sleep, work, eat, and love is a struggle between millions of years of evolution and a few centuries of recent cultural development. And now, we're often left flailing to figure out how to bridge these contradictory worlds to live a good life. This book helps provide real answers, grounded in a range of academic fields, to the most important question we face every day—how to flourish."

—**CHIP COLWELL,** PhD, associate research professor of
anthropology at University of Colorado Denver,
founding editor-in-chief of *SAPEINS* magazine, author of
*So Much Stuff: How Humans Discovered Tools, Invented
Meaning, and Made More of Everything*

"We all crave the good life, and yet in our modern life it can feel far away. As a coach, I guide clients to be *instinctive* so that they can live their dreams. I'm so excited to recommend *On the Origin of Being* because it's the scientific counterpart that teaches us how to live in a way that works. It's a thoughtful, practical, and hopeful book that will lead you to your good life. And the science is downright captivating, easy to understand, and will ground what you've always known inside."

—**TAMA KIEVES,** bestselling author of *Thriving Through Uncertainty* and *A Year Without Fear*; speaker; and visionary career, success, and book coach

ON THE ORIGIN OF BEING

Understanding the Science of Evolution to Enhance Your Quality of Life

LUKE COMER & JENNY POWERS, PhD

RIVER GROVE
BOOKS

This book is intended as a reference volume only, not as a medical manual. The information given here is designed to help you make informed decisions about your health. It is not intended as a substitute for any treatment that may have been prescribed by your doctor. If you suspect that you have a medical problem, you should seek competent medical help. You should not begin a new health regimen without first consulting a medical professional.

Published by River Grove Books
Austin, TX
www.rivergrovebooks.com

Copyright © 2024 The Aurignacian, LLC

All rights reserved.

Used with permission, and with the authors' gratitude:
- *Disconnected* watercolor (2023) commissioned by the authors from Kan Srijirapon, © 2023 Kan Srijirapon.
- *David and Chimp, Embrace,* and *Charles Darwin* watercolors by Kan Srijirapon, © 2020 Kan Srijirapon.

Thank you for purchasing an authorized edition of this book and for complying with copyright law. No part of this book may be reproduced, stored in a retrieval system, or transmitted by any means, electronic, mechanical, photocopying, recording, or otherwise, without written permission from the copyright holder.

Distributed by River Grove Books

Design and composition by Greenleaf Book Group
Cover design by Greenleaf Book Group
Cover images used under license from
©Shutterstock.com/GANJIRO KUMA;
©Shutterstock.com/Clipart Collectors

Publisher's Cataloging-in-Publication data is available.

Print ISBN: 978-1-63299-769-2

eBook ISBN: 978-1-63299-770-8

First Edition

For Marley and Sam . . . may science and nature always inspire you.

—Jenny

Kan Srijirapon, Disconnected, 2023, watercolor

CONTENTS

SEEKING A GOOD LIFE

The good life is one inspired by love and guided by knowledge.
Neither love without knowledge nor knowledge without love can
produce a good life.

—BERTRAND RUSSELL

How do we live a good life? It's a question everyone will ask at some point in their lives as they navigate the triumphs, the tragedies, and the ordeals of living. For some, it may be easy to live a good life, but for many, it feels illusive, unattainable, and a struggle day after day. We deal with physical and mental health challenges, relationship issues, financial worries, work dissatisfaction, societal stress . . . The list goes on and on. Adding on the desire to be content and satisfied with our lives feels like we are asking too much of ourselves. Then we wonder, *Why is a good life so hard to attain?*

We all possess unique tools we believe will help guide us to a good life. We tend to adopt the paradigms of our upbringing, and they shape our relationships, our sense of self, and our behaviors in the world. Countless philosophies, religions, and economic and political ideologies try to steer our attitudes and behavior. For example, key tenets of Taoism are based around humility with a focus on the individual, simplicity, and nature. Christianity instructs us to follow the teachings of Jesus and the Bible to live a good life, declaring we cannot know ourselves without knowing Him. Capitalism suggests that if we work hard and accumulate wealth, we can have the freedom to elevate our status and have a better life. And nationalism promotes a good life by promoting the interests of one nation's people above all others. The paradigms we adhere to frame our experiences and influence our decision-making in all facets of life.

However, if we look at them critically, many of these life philosophies are flawed and internally inconsistent. They run counter to our instincts, passions, and sense of logic. Instead of encouraging us to live in balance with our own nature, our philosophies may suggest, request, or demand that we either repress our nature or transcend it.

The unique American vision of the good life was shaped by its unusual founding, capitalism, and the principles of freedom and equality. The ideal American can be described as individualistic, self-reliant, pragmatic, and self-improving, as they strive to climb the ladder of success on merit and achievement.[1] Americans believe that anyone can achieve a good life through the embodiment of these virtues. As we relentlessly strive to attain the next rung of this ladder, we are taught to trust that each step brings us closer to the supposed satisfaction of making it all on our own, the epitome of a good life. In this way, hard work and success have become a moral quality, an indication of worth as a human being. As a nation, we idolize the wealthy, the powerful, and the famous because they all supposedly sit at the top of the climb.

Since wealth is how we measure achievement, we consider the countries with the most money to be the most successful. Using gross domestic product (GDP) as the metric, America has always thrived at or near the top. But the long-term gains in American prosperity actually hide the extreme inequalities in income, wealth, and well-being distribution along racial and class lines.[2] According to journalist Lisa Curtis, for many in the United States, "the ladder of success has been reduced to splinters."[3] The United States may still be ranked at the top based on GDP, but of all first-world nations, it is ranked 23rd in a new metric called the Human Development Index, which takes into account life expectancy, education, standard of living, and inequality.[4] Using these new metrics, the American ideology doesn't guarantee a good life either. Is there some way to find a good life that is instinctive and logical, that aligns with our passions, and that allows us to live in equilibrium with our own nature?

Suffering despite progress

According to the numbers, humans have persistently progressed over time; violence and war have declined, democracies are on the rise, gains have been made against poverty, life expectancies have expanded, and medicine is revolutionary. Many lucky Americans now have an unparalleled opportunity to live exactly how they want.[5] You may be asking, "All of this progress supports a good life, so why don't we have it?"

Well, in spite of all that "progress," many aspects of our lives are deteriorating, especially our health. Over 40% of American adults are considered obese,[6] one out of 10 Americans has type 2 diabetes,[7] and a quarter of American deaths are due to heart disease.[8] Why are we so unhealthy? Even though the modern world *seems* better than ever, many of us feel plagued by profound dissatisfaction, depression, addiction, and despair.[9] In 2016, 56.8 million visits to American physicians were due to mental and behavioral disorders.[10] That same year in the United States, one person took their own life every 12 minutes. In the last 20 years, there has been a 33% increase in suicide rates in America, especially among young people.[11] Why are we so desolate? Our modern behaviors—our approach to sleep, food, work, and even the world around us—aren't working. We need a new approach to life—or maybe an extremely old one.

So, why do we still blindly continue down the modern path? According to anthropologist Stanley Knick, it's because "modern culture is powerful: It is mechanized, it moves mountains, it digs canals and drains swamps, it overwhelms, and it is seductive; it glitters, it tastes sweet, it goes fast. And it advertises."[12] We are bombarded with messages that define a good life for us, and we buy into those messages in a very literal way, by buying things to fill the emptiness and to feel fleeting happiness. We are so distracted by the bells, whistles, and excesses of modernity that we don't realize modernity itself may be at the root of our inability to find a good life.

Eudaemonia

A good life isn't necessarily a life of constant happiness, nor is it the absence of negative circumstances. We all enjoy prosperity and endure adversity, and every life has its ups and downs. To be human is to know that our lives will ultimately end. However, from birth to death, one fundamental element of a good life is living in a dynamic state of health.

The notion of health is more complex than simply the body's ability to function without illness. In the mid-twentieth century, the World Health Organization (WHO) introduced the term *well-being* into a more innovative definition of *health*: "a state of complete physical, mental, and social well-being, and not merely the absence of disease or infirmity."[13] But health is still beyond general well-being and the lack of sickness. In the 1980s, the WHO modified this definition again to reflect a more dynamic process. Health is what allows someone to achieve goals, fulfill their needs, and cope with any situation life throws at them. It is a personal resource that is employed to maintain homeostasis, the process that biological systems use to maintain stability and equilibrium while adjusting to external forces. Being able to quickly recover when this equilibrium is disrupted is the basis for physical, mental, and social resiliency.[14] This more active description of physical, mental, and social health encompasses far more than simply being fully functioning and without disease. When good mental and social health overlay onto good physical health, we have fulfilled one important aspect of a good life.

The other aspect of a good life is having vitality, the indefinable undercurrent of power that makes life worth enduring. We've all felt those ephemeral moments of connectedness and flow when our smiles and delight in our hearts are not forced or feigned. We are simply joyful because of life. Joseph Campbell, the American professor of literature famous for his observations of the human experience, said it perfectly: "I think that what we're seeking is an experience of being alive, so that our life experiences on the purely physical plane will have resonances with our own innermost being and reality, so that we actually feel the rapture of being alive."[15] A good life integrates this delight of being alive into our health and well-being.

An all-encompassing idea for the combination of health, well-being, and vitality is Aristotle's concept of *eudaemonia*. Many equate eudaemonia with happiness, but it's more than that. To Aristotle, eudaemonia described the condition of human *flourishing*, of living a full and deeply satisfying life.[16] According to psychologists Edward Deci and Michael Ryan, eudaemonia "maintains that well-being is not so much an outcome or end state as it is a process of fulfilling or realizing one's daimon or true nature—that is, of fulfilling one's virtuous potentials and living as one was inherently intended to live."[17]

There is nothing more "inherently intended" than how the natural process of evolution shaped us to adapt to our environment, survive, and ultimately reproduce. By delving into a study of our collective evolutionary origins and life histories, we can begin to grasp that, unlike other philosophies and ideologies, evolution wrought us to live *within* our natures. Evidence from many scientific fields—anthropology, archaeology, biology, genetics, psychology, primatology, and medicine—support the idea that evolution encoded within us a road map to help us find eudaemonia. All we need is to learn to read the signs.

Thankfully, a shift is already happening. Lisa Curtis sees people transitioning "from climbing the ladder of unfulfilled societal expectations and consumerism to blazing a trail with a life guided by a holistic focus on well-being, community, and sustainability."[18] Deep down, this shift feels right, almost natural. It's as if some forgotten part of us is beginning to surface and let its voice be heard. Do any of our old visions of the good life help us listen to this voice? Can they help us redefine a good life for ourselves and forge a new path, or is our blind adherence to them what got us here in the first place? It's clear that our modern dilemma requires a different approach.

Instead of being mindlessly compelled by modernity, instead of reevaluating and reframing old practices, and instead of constructing a path based on personal experiences, let's focus through the lens of science. Science verifies that we literally evolved to thrive in this world, and the key to a good life is simply living the way we evolved to live.

Our physical and mental health suffer because our world is unrecognizable from the one humans inhabited for most of our existence, the one we evolved in. We thrived in close-knit groups but now live alone in cities of millions. We survived, even prospered, through scarcity but now have unbelievable excess. We slept when we were tired and ate when we were hungry but now follow artificial and rigid approaches to both. Compared with most of human history, modernity seems empty.[19] Journalist Andrew Sullivan sums it up nicely: "As we have slowly and surely attained more progress, we have lost something that undergirds all of it: meaning, cohesion, and a different, deeper kind of happiness than the satisfaction of all our earthly needs."[20]

If we ground our approach to life in Darwin's theory of evolution (figure 0.1), change our behaviors to better match our evolved natures, and trust that nature provided us with the tools we need to be successful, we will be well on our way to achieving eudaemonia. Our evolutionary journey has already created a good life within us. All we must do is rediscover it.

Figure 0.1. Finding a Good Life through the Understanding of Evolution

Kan Srijirapon, Darwin, 2023, watercolor

CHAPTER 1

AN EVOLUTIONARY MISMATCH

Our bodies are adapted for foraging ways of life, but they must contend with psychological, nutritional, and physical stresses of Space Age existence.

–S. BOYD EATON

R ecent human history, especially the last few hundred years, has seen tremendous technological advancements and sweeping changes to our ecologies and cultures. In most cases, we are not adapted to these radically new conditions because our cultural advancement has entirely outpaced our biological evolution. As nutrition scientist and physician Brandon Hidaka explains, "In effect, humans have dragged a body with a long hominid history into an overfed, malnourished, sedentary, sunlight-deficient, sleep-deprived, competitive, inequitable, and socially isolating environment with dire consequences."[1]

Our physical health, mental health, social health, and vitality are compromised because present-day humans are physiologically mismatched to our modern environment, and we are no longer living in accord with our evolved natures. This is a critical barrier between us and a good life. But we can learn to close the gap between our modern and our evolved existence by understanding how our evolutionary journey prepared us to live. If we reintegrate some of these evolved ways of being into our hectic, modern lives, we may find the way to eudaemonia.

The march of evolution

The Earth was formed a mind-boggling 4.5 billion years ago. Less than a billion years later, the first sparks of life appeared in our oceans, and remarkably, we still possess many of the genes found in the first eukaryotes that appeared about 2 billion years ago. Human traits and behaviors are rooted in the beginnings of life itself, so observing the genetics and behaviors of many forms of life—from the single-celled organisms that arose in our ancient seas, to the mammals that appeared when the dinosaurs roamed the Earth, to the human lineage that split from other great apes—will help us understand the underpinnings of evolution. Figure 1.1 is a graphic of Earth's history of life.

Living nonhuman primates, especially chimpanzees and bonobos, are useful to study because in them we recognize the foundations of ourselves. Humans, chimpanzees, and bonobos all shared a common ancestor between five and seven million years ago, and we share over 98% of our DNA with these species. By studying them, we can learn so much about ourselves.

Geographic and climate change forced our ancestors to leave the trees and begin adapting to life on the savannah. We diverged from our primate cousins by becoming bipedal, and the size of our brains increased exponentially. We may have left the trees, yet in many ways, we stayed the same; for example, we remained intensely social.

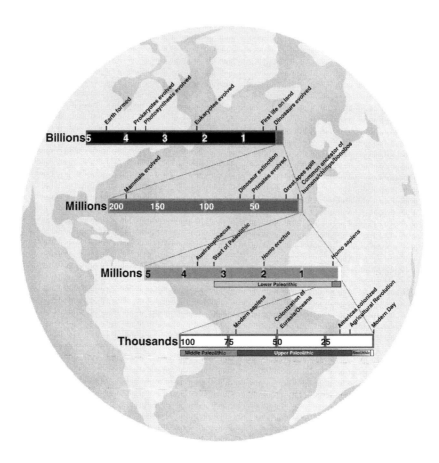

Figure 1.1. The Timeline of Life on Earth

Anatomically modern human beings, *Homo sapiens*, finally evolved between 100,000 and 200,000 years ago. However, it wasn't until after a significant Cognitive Revolution 70,000 years ago, when the attributes of language, abstract thinking, planning, innovation, cooperation beyond close kin, and the development of elaborate structures we now call *culture* developed, that *behaviorally* modern human beings appeared.[2] With these new behavioral and cultural tools at our disposal, humans dispersed from Africa and permanently colonized most continents on Earth, supplanting every other *Homo* species along the way. During this time, nearly two million years after *Homo erectus*, we still thrived as hunter-gatherers, but our cultural advancements allowed us to take life to new levels.

Every step of the way evolutionary forces manipulated our genetic code so it would better direct our cells, bodies, and brains to develop, function, and interact with each other to ensure our survival. Based on what Charles Darwin observed about these natural phenomena, he developed his theory of evolution by natural selection and presented it in *On the Origin of Species* in 1859. This theory describes the process by which small alterations in DNA change a species' physical or behavioral traits over time. A trait that allows an organism to better adapt to its environment increases its survival and its ability to have more offspring, passing that trait to the next generation.

Evolutionary biologist Richard Dawkins describes this process vividly: "The chisels of the sculptor, which is natural selection, work away at carving the shape of the gene pool of the ancestors of every animal and plant alive, carving it into the shape required for the animals concerned to survive in their particular environment."[3] Evolution by the process of natural selection refined our genomes, which defined our physical traits and influenced our root behaviors so we could survive and reproduce. To find our way to a good life, we must focus on learning to recognize the traits and behaviors that were embedded in our genes when we were most well-adapted to our environment, when we were hunter-gatherers.

The model of hunter-gatherers

If we start with *Homo erectus*, which mostly resembled *Homo sapiens*, our ancestors survived as hunter-gatherers for our entire hominin existence. This method of survival was a successful adaptation for millions of years. This long period of consistent, adapted behavior shows hunter-gatherers living in a manner that was in touch with their own evolutionary nature. There are striking parallels between chimpanzees, bonobos, and hunter-gatherers, showing a continuum and a connection through evolution (figure 1.2). We have changed dramatically from our days in the trees, but that continuum still extends to modern humans.

We may expect to see ways of being that seem vastly different from our own, but if we look again after understanding our evolution, we find familiarity. We may even see a way to re-create what we learn in our modern lives by combining all the advancements of modern society with the more natural approach of our ancestors' evolved behavior.

A mere 12,000 years ago, with some exceptions, most humans lived as small-band nomadic hunter-gatherers, where seasons, animal migrations, and plant cycles dictated their movements. Although hunter-gatherer societies were culturally different from each other, tribes of these nomads exhibited similar features, such as cooperation, problem-solving without a central authority, and egalitarianism—the doctrine that all people are equal and deserve equal rights and opportunities.[4] They also shared evolved behaviors surrounding sleep, diet, work, and interactions with

Figure 1.2. Striking Parallels between Chimps and Humans
Kan Srijirapon, Embrace, 2023, watercolor

nature, which suggests they were influenced by the same innate and genetic factors.

The lives of hunter-gatherers were difficult at times, just as ours are. But in 1966, the widespread misconceptions of the "nasty, brutish life" of hunter-gatherers were dispelled at a scientific symposium called "Man the Hunter." In fact, at this conference, Marshall Sahlins dubbed hunter-gatherers the "original affluent society."[5] Hunter-gatherers worked less and had far more leisure time than we do. Their few material wants were easily satisfied, and generally speaking, they lived uncomplicated and fundamentally free lives.[6]

The era of hunter-gatherers ended with the spread of agriculture. Contrary to what some may believe, the shift to farming and the ensuing population explosion actually caused human life expectancies to plummet below that of hunter-gatherers and greatly reduced quality of life. Hunter-gatherers who survived childhood commonly had a full and healthy lifespan of 68 to 78 years. But malnutrition, poor sanitation, and infectious diseases during the transition to agriculture have led some to estimate the average life expectancy at the time to be only 20 years.

When the Agricultural Revolution began, we started to diverge from what had become our species-typical way of life. It was the beginning of the end of our hunting and gathering days. Once our population exploded, we could never go back.

At the beginning of the Neolithic era, the entire human population was estimated to be between 1 million and 15 million people. Imagine the population of New York City (around 8 million people) thinly spread over the entire Earth! Two thousand years ago, the world's population had grown to 200 million, with only half of humans transitioning to an agriculture-based lifestyle. Just 500 years ago, the world population was at 500 million, with only 15% of humans still living as hunter-gatherers.[7] The population reached 1 billion for the first time in the year 1800, and the initial rumblings of the Industrial Revolution were heard. Since then, most humans have transitioned from being farmers and herders into being urban laborers and office workers. The current human population stands at 8 billion people and is growing at a rate of more than 80 million per year. In fact, while this book was being written, the population grew by more than 200 million people (figure 1.3). Although tiny pockets of hunter-gatherers remain, they have been pushed into fringe environments, and their lifestyles are becoming extinct.

Life expectancy slowly crept up since agriculture began, but it only increased significantly in the last century because of a focus on public health and sanitation and the development of antibiotics and vaccines. The WHO's current calculated modern-life expectancy is 72 years. Although we seem to live around the same amount of time as our great-great-great- (and many more greats)-grandparents, the life expectancy of modern industrialized humans is presently trending downward. Modern medicine cannot cure the chronic diseases prevalent in the modern world. Doctors can keep people alive (or "keep people dying longer," as some put it) far beyond when they would've died a hundred years ago. Calculating life

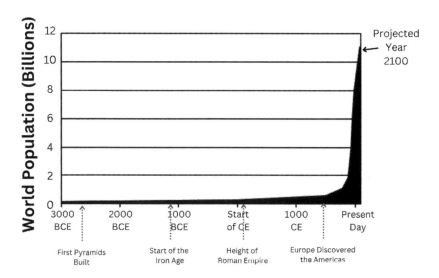

Figure 1.3. World Population Growth Over the Last 3,000 Years

expectancy *without* including the years a person spends dealing with illness shows that the average person has only 63.1 healthy years.[8] Although we may think modern life has us trending toward immortality, we're experiencing quite the opposite.

New pathologies are creeping into our lives. Daniel Lieberman, a professor of evolutionary biology at Harvard, says that today "the average person who walks in to see a doctor is seeing them for a disease that we didn't used to get."[9] For example, the leading cause of death in the modern world—heart disease—was not a problem hunter-gatherers faced.[10] The number of noncommunicable diseases humans get has exploded over the past century. Are they all due to our modern lifestyle? If so, these diseases make it glaringly obvious that we have deviated from how our genes encoded us to live.

Unhitched from evolution

If evolution takes time to adapt an organism to a new environment, this raises an important question: Have humans evolved since the Agricultural Revolution, or are we still genetically Paleolithic people who struggle in our rapidly changing modern environment?

Evolution is a relentless and constant phenomenon, and at times it can be a rapid process. For example, scientists have observed that some squirrels have evolved new breeding times in response to climate change, and some fish species have evolved resistance to toxins dumped in the Hudson River.[11] In humans, the genetic mutation allowing humans to breathe the thin air in the high altitudes of Tibet occurred during the last 4,000 years. This is the strongest and most rapid example of selection known in modern humans.[12] However, these "fast" changes are confined to small populations, and if that change is to persist, the underlying selection force must also persist.

After humans spread to every corner of Earth, the changes required to thrive in these different climates and environments would be considered small in the grand scheme of evolution and would only have affected the populations exposed to them. In general, enduring changes that spread to an entire species are rare, are more gradual, and take on the order of tens to hundreds of thousands of years.[13] Imagine how long it would take for a major modern adaptation to spread to the entire far-flung human race! It has been about 10,000 years since humans began the mass transition from the hunter-gatherer way of life. Is that long enough for us to have genetically evolved to thrive in modernity?

A strong case can be made that our genes haven't had enough time or selective pressure to completely adapt to our modern lifestyles. In his book *Tribe*, journalist Sebastian Junger writes, "The enormous changes that came with agriculture in the last 10,000 years have hardly begun to affect our gene pool."[14] It may take thousands of years for us to know what changes our genes are currently making, if any. However, we can assume that, although we may be living in a modern world, we are still expressing the same predominant genes we had as hunter-gatherers.

Most animal behaviors are dictated by their genes, and animals of the same species behave in similar ways. A significant behavioral change in response to a new environment would require genetic evolution. Humans, however, are not just any animal. After the Cognitive Revolution 70,000 years ago, we could adapt rapidly by consciously altering our behavior to match our needs. According to Yuval Noah Harari, author of *Sapiens*, "This opened a fast lane of cultural evolution, bypassing the traffic jams of genetic evolution." He suggests that, ever since we became behaviorally modern humans, there is no single natural way of life but, rather, a baffling number of choices.[15] We now manipulate our environment with technology to significantly reduce the challenges to our survival and no longer have to wait for evolution. This is why, although we've adapted to survive in the modern world with our intelligence, plasticity, and creativity, we are still genetically similar to our hunter-gatherer ancestors.

The Cognitive Revolution unhitched our survival from the slow creep of genetic evolution, and human behavior is now determined as much by our culture as by our genes. We have created the high-tech, fast-paced world around us through our culture, but we are limited in our ability to physiologically adapt to this new world because our underlying genes haven't changed. This mismatch is the very root of our inability to achieve the good life.

Realigning with our evolved nature

Since we *are*, after all, still genetically Paleolithic people who struggle in our rapidly changing modern environment, who better to learn from than our ancestors themselves? Anthropologist Richard Lee suggests that although hunter-gatherers "stand at the opposite pole from the dense urban life experienced by most of humanity," they "may hold the key to some of the central questions about the human condition—about social life, politics, and gender; about diet and nutrition and living in nature; [about] how people can live and have lived without the state; [about] how to live without accumulated technology; [and about] the possibility of living in nature without destroying it."[16]

From their vantage point, hunter-gatherers would probably think the modern humans could use a lot of help. We've moved into densely populated cities but don't interact with a single person all day. We eat convenient and prepackaged but unhealthy foods while driving to our next commitment in our busy lives. We sit in front of computer screens and television sets every day and night and rarely exercise. Exposed to artificial light all day, some of us never get outside to see the sun or experience nature. Our sleep patterns are irregular, and our work habits are backbreaking. Contemporary life is the root cause of much suffering, and we face observable pathologies as a result. Humans are now more prone to diseases like heart disease, obesity, diabetes, and musculoskeletal disorders such as rheumatoid arthritis and fibromyalgia. Mentally, we now experience more anxiety, fear, depression, loneliness, isolation, and a loss of identity and purpose. Hunter-gatherers simply did not suffer from these diseases of modernity.

But the news isn't all bad. We are still natural, adaptable beings, and knowing where we came from can show us the way forward. If we trace our genetics and behaviors through the history of life—from prokaryotes, to mammals, to primates, to our own human lineage—and if we study how hunter-gatherers utilized their encoded genetics to live a good life, we will learn to live in accord with our biology. Then we can use our intellect and creativity to change our behavior and become physically and mentally healthier within our modern world. Understanding our evolution is a powerful tool to help us make more conscious lifestyle choices and close the gap between our artificial worlds and our natural selves.

We can embrace the modern advances in technology and medicine while choosing to live our lives more aligned with our evolved nature. That means shifting our sleep to match the cycle of day and night. It means eating natural food in balanced ratios of nutrients. It means rejecting the corporate rat race and our culture of constant overwork. And it means realizing we are one part of the natural world and thrive when we leave our four walls behind. Realigning our behavior with our evolution is essential to our welfare and even to our survival in the modern world.

Humans—individually, collectively, and through conscious effort—can return to a more instinctive and genetic way of existence. Did hunter-gatherers know the secret of achieving eudaemonia? Maybe not explicitly, but innately, they did. Our evolutionary past offers strategies we can use today to help us enhance our quality of life and return to a state of flourishing, to our origin of being. By embracing the essential role of evolution—and acting on it—we can rebuild our modern lives to achieve eudaemonia.

PART 1

SLEEP

Yesterdays and tomorrows may seem to stretch in an
unending line, but within each day is a cycle that is
echoed by the ebb and flow of our inner life.

—MICHAEL TERMAN

Before sunrise, a sunflower looks east in anticipation of the coming dawn. Then, the flower's face tracks the sun from east to west until it dips below the horizon. Overnight, the flower head slowly but deliberately orients back to the east to start again. How do sunflowers accomplish this solar tracking? During the day, one side of the stem grows, tilting the flower on its solar trajectory. At night, the other side of the stem elongates, angling the flower back to its starting position. This rhythm evolved because it provided growing flowers with maximal sun exposure, and the flowers warmed in the sun attracted more pollinators. Sunflowers responding to patterns of light and dark reveal the utility—and the power—of an organism syncing with the daily cycles of the Earth.

When we think of how life evolved on Earth, we usually only think about the three-dimensional environments that provided the selection pressure for the evolution of organisms. However, the recurring nature of day and night and the changing levels of light throughout the seasons were prominent features of our planet even before life arose, so organisms evolved in response to these temporal rhythms as well. For example, most plant species are diurnal. Their flowers bloom in the day and close at night, which makes sense because of photosynthesis. The flowers of nocturnal plants are closed in the day and bloom at night because they evolved to take advantage of nocturnal pollinators, such as moths and bats. The earliest mammals were nocturnal because that temporal niche initially enabled them to survive and thrive in the age of dinosaurs. Most current mammals are still nocturnal, but independent evolutionary transitions to a diurnal pattern have occurred. For example, the great apes evolved to be active during the day. Conversely, most species of birds are diurnal, although a few, such as owls, made the nocturnal evolutionary transition to take advantage of nighttime prey. Nocturnal or diurnal, all plants and animals evolved to fill all of nature's spatial and temporal niches.

All life has the internal ability to keep time because hidden inside every cell, a clock evolved to respond to the cycles of our planet (figure P1.1). We call these timekeepers circadian rhythms, named for the word *circadian*, which means "around the day."

These rhythms govern almost every aspect of an organism's life, including gene expression, hormone secretion, even patterns of activity and rest. These rhythms not only allow an organism to react to a stimulus, such as a sunflower following the light of the sun, but they also allow an organism to *anticipate* a change in the environment, such as a sunflower reorienting itself at night to be ready for the dawn.

Figure P1.1. Animals Fill All Temporal Niches "Around the Day"

Billions of years ago, when life first scrabbled out its existence in the primordial sea, cyanobacteria, one of the earliest cells recorded, evolved circadian rhythms to anticipate the solar cycle so they could avoid UV-sensitive DNA replication and cell division during the day. By undergoing this sensitive phase at night, these cells evaded DNA damage from solar irradiation and decreased the chance for mutations.[1] Later, eukaryotic phytoplankton algae evolved to migrate vertically over great depths in response to changes in light intensity. During the day, they formed swarms at the surface to undergo photosynthesis, whereas at night, they sank to take advantage of higher nutrient levels at depth, optimizing energy generation and consumption.[2] Since all life evolved from the first cells that appeared eons ago, circadian rhythms are one of the oldest features that every organism has in common.

However, the existence of circadian rhythms in humans was controversial even 50 years ago. Many thought humans had evolved beyond these ancient timing systems; the ebb and flow of cognitive, behavioral, and emotional processes were now determined socially and culturally. But our genetic circadian heritage says otherwise, and our internal clocks still determine the evolved timing of our processes just like every other organism.[3] The big problem is that we still determine our daily rhythms socially and culturally anyway.

One of the primary functions that circadian rhythms control is our patterns of sleeping and waking. Based on the fact that we spend tens of billions of dollars a year on prescription and over-the-counter sleep aids, specialized mattresses, gadgets, and smartphone apps, it is obvious that we are not sleeping well. Are we unintentionally ignoring and overriding our natural, evolved rhythms to the detriment of our health? The answer is a resounding yes. We stay up late, work through the night, sleep less, and require alarms to wake up and drag ourselves to work. This creates a society of sleep-deprived people who depend on stimulants, like caffeine, to function. Not adhering to our natural circadian rhythms alters our bodies' biochemistry, and this lack of proper sleep has profound consequences on our health. Cancer, cardiovascular disease, obesity, and diabetes are all linked to the disruption of circadian rhythms. There is also a relationship between distorted sleep and depression. Our sleeping habits do not fulfill the physical and mental health requirements for living a good life.

How do circadian rhythms work?

The Earth's rotation provides predictable rhythms of light, temperature, food availability, and predator activity. The circadian rhythms of all organisms are tuned to these environmental cues, so built-in internal processes are synchronized to their ecosystems. These external cues are called *zeitgebers* ("time-givers"). Light is the most important zeitgeber because it entrains, or modifies, the duration of the biological circadian cycle to match the Earth's cycles of light and dark.

Our brain's central circadian clock is called the *suprachiasmatic nucleus* (SCN), and it is located in the hypothalamus, where the optic nerves cross behind the eyes. When exposed to sunlight daily, specialized neurons in the eye not tied to the rods and cones of vision send signals to the SCN to synchronize it with the Earth's 24-hour rotation cycle. Melanopsin neurons are exquisitely reactive to blue light (459–485 nanometer wavelengths), due to the specific sensitivity of the melanopsin pigment. Interestingly, the power of blue light to reset circadian rhythms has nothing to do with color; photoreceptors could have evolved to respond to any wavelength of light. However, life began—and the first photoreceptors evolved—in the oceans. Our circadian rhythms synchronize best to blue light because its wavelength could penetrate the ocean surface more readily to reach those first inhabitants of Earth's prehistoric seas.[4]

Based on the light signals it receives, the SCN communicates with other parts of the brain that control things like core body temperature, alertness, or the production of hormones, such as cortisol and melatonin. The SCN also coordinates and synchronizes the peripheral biological clocks present in all cells. When clock functioning is smooth and entrained by sunlight, the organism functions in equilibrium, attuned to the environment.

Circadian clocks don't need light to function, but without the continuous, rhythmic exposure to daylight, a clock will desynchronize, and an organism's inherent, internal rhythms may no longer align with the cycle of day and night. In 1729, French astronomer Jean-Jacques d'Ortous de Mairan discovered this phenomenon in an experiment using *Mimosa pudica* plants. He noticed that the plants continued daily leaf openings and closings even in constant darkness. Left without input from sunlight oscillations for many days, the leaves started opening and closing on a shorter, 22-hour cycle.[5] This was the first observation that biological clocks function independently of light, that routines continue when external cues are removed, and that without these cues, the clocks may deviate from the 24-hour solar cycle.

If humans lived in isolation, completely cut off from any sort of external cue, each person's perception of time would be different because of genetic variation in circadian rhythms. Our rhythms would function independently of the 24-hour solar cycle, just like *Mimosa pudica* did in darkness. Some would have shorter internal clocks, and some would have longer. To stay entrained in a 24-hour schedule, everybody's clock must be wound by the sun. A person's clock genes determine their circadian phenotype, a fancy word to describe the observable characteristics that result from the interaction of genes and environment. A circadian phenotype is also called a *chronotype*.[6] Every person has a genetically determined chronotype, just like we all have a genetically determined height. This means that the natural sleeping/waking rhythm of a person's chronotype is unique and very hard to change.

One of the main ways circadian rhythms regulate patterns of sleeping and waking is by turning on or off the production of melatonin, a hormone that causes drowsiness and facilitates slumber. Core body temperature, cortisol secretion, and blood pressure also have daily highs and lows in response to this clock and affect our levels of energy and alertness over the course of the 24-hour solar cycle. The timing and intensity of light exposure have vastly different effects on the circadian rhythms of sleep. For example, a bright light in the morning will move the clock (and melatonin release) earlier so it is easier to fall asleep and wake up early the next day. A bright light after sundown will move the clock (and melatonin release) later so it is harder to fall asleep and wake at the same time the next day. In nature, most organisms get the right combination, compressing or stretching the cycle, to keep their clocks entrained with the external world, and therefore, get the sleep they require.[7]

SLEEP BIOLOGY

We sleep for about a third of our lives, but why do we need it? There is actually no consensus for the why and how of sleep, but the fact that sleep has survived millions of years of evolution offers proof of its importance. Sleep is a brain state, a collective behavior that everyone shares. Our bodies rely on entrained circadian rhythms to tell us when it's time to sleep so we can restore energy, immune and endocrine function, and metabolic balance. During sleep, our bodies and nervous systems recover after the cost of being awake.[8] Sleep also plays a role in neural development, cognitive functioning, and emotional processing and is critical for working memory, attention, decision-making, memory formation, brain plasticity, and visual/motor performance.[9] Although exactly why it does all these things is still under investigation, we do know a lot about *what* the brain does when we sleep.

While we sleep, our brains shift between qualitatively and quantitatively different but complementary states—REM (rapid eye movement) and non-REM. Information processing, synaptic plasticity, and cellular maintenance are thought to be performed in non-REM sleep, which is why it's considered the "recovery phase."[10] REM sleep is thought to be responsible for mental and emotional regeneration, and recent studies suggest it plays an important role in learning.[11] The specific timing and length of REM and non-REM sleep is called *sleep architecture*, and although most animals' sleep features similar sleep states, each has its own unique architecture.

For humans, non-REM sleep has two main stages: light and deep. In the light stage, we are easily aroused, but our brain waves slow. In the deep stage, we are hard to wake as we experience nothing but the slowest brain waves. When we transition into REM sleep, our brains exhibit wave activity similar to the waking brain. The REM stage of sleep is heavily shielded from external stimuli, so we are at our most vulnerable during this phase, especially since we experience sleep paralysis. The infographic in figure P1.2 summarizes these stages. Non-REM and REM stages cycle about every 90 minutes in humans, and this cycling over the course of a night ensures that functional, cognitive, and emotional demands are met.[12] REM sleep follows circadian rhythms and reaches its maximum potential late in the night and its minimum in the late afternoon.[13]

We do most of our dreaming in REM sleep, when physiological changes, such as increased heart rate, breathing, and blood pressure, take place.[14] But is dreaming important? A physiological theory is that we dream to exercise neural connections that influence learning. Psychologically, most theories hypothesize that dreaming allows us to sort through experiences and figure out problems.[15] REM sleep and dreaming help us process challenging or traumatic events in a way that allows us to revisit emotions without being overwhelmed, which is important for emotional regulation and cognition.[16]

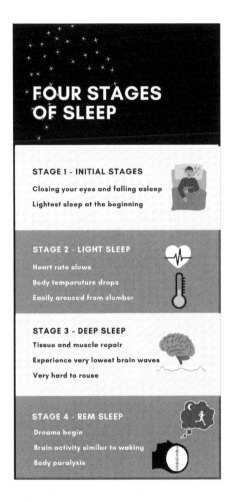

Figure P1.2. Four Stages of Sleep

DETACHED FROM OUR RHYTHMS

In spite of the circadian rhythms being around since early life on Earth, most modern humans are not in tune with them. This isn't because we've never heard of them but because we are detached from them. Our lives are so busy, we work so hard, and we are so stressed that we are no longer conscious of the signals our bodies naturally give us over the course of a day.

When we can't feel the sleep signals (or choose to ignore them), we don't follow them, and eventually, this disregard causes problems.

Fewer and fewer Americans, even children, get enough quality sleep. With over 70 million American adults suffering from sleep disorders, like insomnia, the Centers for Disease Control and Prevention (CDC) declared sleep deprivation a public health epidemic in 2014. If sleep is essential for our physical and emotional well-being, why are more and more modern humans falling short?

In our fast-paced world, we are isolated in countless ways from the proper triggers that set our circadian rhythms. For starters, we spend most of our time indoors and aren't exposed to enough natural sunlight, especially in the mornings. On the other side, we are subjected to enormous amounts of artificial light, especially at night, to keep us awake beyond normal bedtimes. We also stay up late to get work done or to be entertained and sleep way past sunrise to catch up. Alternatively, some people work at night, completely shifting into nocturnal behavior, an unnatural state for humans. How can we feel alive and vital if we are too tired to keep our eyes open? With a deep understanding of how circadian rhythms and sleep evolved and how hunter-gatherers respond to their rhythms, we can make conscious decisions to live (and sleep) more in sync with our nature and stop the cycle of bad health due to poor sleep.

CHAPTER 2

THE EVOLUTION OF SLEEP

Natural selection favored the human circadian clock system to promote energy intake and metabolism, physical activity, and cognition during the light portion of the day and to promote sleep and related functions during darkness at night.

—KENNETH WRIGHT

M ammals evolved during the Mesozoic era, the time of the dinosaurs. Initially, they were all nocturnal to avoid becoming lunch. However, following the extinction of the dinosaurs, some mammals began to emerge from the shadows, first into an intermediate stage before evolving to full daytime living, filling the temporal environmental niche left behind.

Protoprimates were nocturnal, but as they evolved, they split into two groups. The prosimians, such as lemurs, still tend to be nocturnal today. The ancestors of simians, who evolved into today's monkeys and great apes, were among the first mammals to exhibit strictly diurnal activity.[1] The transition to a daytime existence triggered evolutionary adaptations. Since diurnal primates relied more on their improved eyesight and color vision to forage and hunt, physiological changes to the skull, eyes, and brain occurred. Because they were more exposed to predators in the day-light, there is strong evidence that larger, more cohesive social networks coevolved with the diurnal transition to adapt to new survival challenges.[2]

Diurnal primates have rigid sleep and wake times tied to the sun, wak-ing when it rises and sleeping when it sets. Most primates do not seem to have different chronotypes, meaning there is not much variation in the clock genes within each species. Corresponding to the larger social net-works, primates sleep in groups. The average size of a great ape sleeping group is five, and mothers always sleep with their infants and children.[3] The length of primate sleep corresponds to many factors, such as body size and group number. The vast majority of primates sleep in the trees, and our small, monkey-like ancestors probably had a difficult time getting quality sleep on branches, where anything from the wind to a tree snake would rouse them.[4] But as primates evolved increased size, sleeping on mere branches became precarious.

The evolution of higher encephalization in great apes, meaning their brains increased in size and complexity relative to their body size, allowed them increased cognitive capacity. The arboreal great apes started building nests or sleeping platforms using tree branches and foliage to minimize the risk of falling and predation while they were sleeping. This adaptation led them to experience higher-quality and deeper sleep, which allowed for greater intelligence and cognition.[5] In fact, a study conducted on orangutans in captivity confirmed this correlation. The orangutans who were allowed to make their platforms with foam and other comfortable supplies had higher scores on cognition tests the fol-lowing day.[6] This positive feedback loop encouraged the tree-to-ground transition of our human ancestors.[7]

Although increased encephalization aided our move to the ground, sleep-ing there provided new challenges, which explains some of the adaptations seen in early hominins. How did they deal with the increased risk of preda-tion and the reduced thermoregulation caused by the ground conducting heat away from the body? Physiologically, early human ancestors began to exhibit variations in chronotype, so not everyone slept at the same time, and those who were awake could keep watch. *Homo erectus*, the first fully terrestrial, ground-sleeping hominin, had behavioral adaptations such as the use of beds and shelters, the controlled use of fire, and sleeping in large social groups, which offered protection from both predators and the elements, allowing for deep, efficient sleep.[8]

The possession of fire is viewed as essential for the full ground transition of *Homo erectus*. For the first time, we could cook food, which expanded the types of foods we could digest, unlocked nutrients otherwise unattainable, and decreased chewing time. Fire also illuminated the uninhabitable dark places and extended the day past sundown. Fire provided warmth, which enabled our migration into colder climates of the world. Sleeping around a fire in a large group warded off predators and insects, permitting our ancestors to increase their sleep quality yet again. The habit of gathering and sleeping around a fire also provided social connection and encouraged prosocial behavior. Recently, exposure to firelight was found to decrease blood pressure and stimulate relaxation, another way it may have induced cooperation and sociality in our hunter-gatherer forebears.[9] Firelight at night had a minimal effect on circadian rhythms because the burning of organic material produces a red-orange glow, with wavelengths at the opposite end of the visual spectrum from blue light;[10] therefore, it is not an efficient trigger of the SCN.

Early humans, inhabiting new, more dangerous terrestrial environments, needed to fulfill their sleeping needs in the shortest time possible. This selection pressure initiated the evolution of even deeper, more efficient, more REM-dominated sleep. In fact, humans evolved the highest REM-to-non-REM sleep ratio of all primates,[11] spending on average 22% of sleep in this phase.[12] More REM sleep meant more dreaming, which potentially benefited humans by priming sleepers to better deal with situations while they were awake. More REM produced intense and concentrated sleep, shortening our required time asleep. We now have the shortest sleep time of any primate, at only seven hours. This is a lot less than would be predicted based on the patterns found in other primates.

The short but deep pattern of sleep may have helped promote our extraordinary cognition.[13] University of Toronto primatologist David Samson says, "One of the reasons I think REM is linked with improved cognition and perhaps [with] improved fitness in early humans is because, as we became more social, we needed ways to cognitively cope with the new variables of a larger group size."[14] The increasing size and complexity of our social groups required us to read the thoughts and predict the moods and actions of group members using theory of mind, the sociocognitive ability to think about the mental states of ourselves and others.[15] By evolving compact, efficient sleep architecture, humans had more time to become more socially adept. Extended wakefulness allowed prolonged group interaction, which was important for bonding, transmitting cultural information, and social intelligence. We also had more time to innovate, acquire, and transmit new skills. Then, our evolved deeper sleep ensured that what we learned during the day was consolidated. The evolution of human sleep led to the enhanced social skills and cognitive abilities we experience today.[16]

The unique, marked variation in human chronotypes demonstrates the flexibility of human sleep. This was evolutionarily valuable.[17] Normal human circadian rhythms exist on a continuum of chronotypes, from morning people to night owls and everything in between. Having different chronotypes was a definitive survival advantage for our sleep security because humans shared the task of nighttime vigilance. Therefore, the natural outlier chronotypes in modern humans "represent a legacy of natural selection acting in the past to reduce the dangers of sleep," writes Samson.[18] Chronotype variation also increased the likelihood of the evolution of our intense sleep because we no longer needed to sleep lightly to make sure we could hear danger. We trusted others to do so. By the time behaviorally modern humans appeared in the Late Paleolithic, our human sleep characteristics were well established.

Hunter-gatherer sleep

We assume our modern-day sleeping habits are vastly different from those of our Paleolithic ancestors, but are they? We speculate that they got more sleep, that they slept whenever the sun was down, that they woke for extended periods at night, and that they took long naps. Sleep is obviously not something preserved in the archaeological record, so the only way to uncover the sleeping habits of our ancestors is to study modern hunter-gatherers. Remember, modern foragers are not ancestral humans; however, they still live a traditional lifestyle without electricity and depend on their own foraging and hunting for food.

From birth, hunter-gatherers are exposed to a continuous daily and seasonal variation in light and temperature. Their sunlight zeitgeber is constant and unavoidable, making entrainment of their circadian rhythms to the 24-hour day inevitable. Without electricity, their only light comes from firelight or the moon after the sun goes down. Under these primal conditions, when do hunter-gatherers fall asleep and wake up? Do they encounter sleep problems or physical and mental pathologies related to the disruption of sleep?

The evidence of hunter-gatherer sleep patterns comes from several research studies of indigenous populations. In the first, the sleeping patterns of people from the Kalahari San of Namibia, the Hadza of Tanzania, and the Tsimane of Bolivia were tracked using Actiwatch devices, which are similar to Fitbits but with different features. The analysis showed that, on average, these foragers were in bed from 6.9 to 8.5 hours and slept between 5.7 and 7.1 hours a night. Surprisingly, that is not very different from the average length of Western sleep and is, perhaps, even on the low end. The San and the Tsimane, who live far enough south to have substantial seasonal changes in daylight and temperature, slept an average of one hour longer in the winter because they went to bed earlier. All three groups used small fires in the evening, so nighttime light intensity was very dim, and went to bed around three hours after sunset. This comparative study showed most of the subjects to be continuous sleepers without long periods of waking in the night. In all three groups, individuals usually woke before sunrise. They were classified as infrequent nappers; however, they napped more in the summer to escape the heat. Insomnia seemed to be nonexistent, and none of the groups even had a word for it. Once insomnia was explained, only 1.5% to 2.5% of them said they experienced it more than once. This is compared with the 10% to 30% of people who report chronic insomnia in the Western world.[19] Since these three preindustrial societies all exhibited similar sleep characteristics, it is conceivable that these were also the characteristics of premodern-era *Homo sapiens*.

Another research study, led by David Samson, focused strictly on the Hadza of Tanzania and had slightly different findings. The time a Hadza individual fell asleep was relatively random, but everyone in the group woke within an hour of sunrise. According to their tracking devices, the Hadza seemed to have relatively short and poor sleep quality.[20] The National Foundation of Sleep Research recommends a sleep efficiency of 85%. The Hadza's was rated under this recommendation.[21] That being said, these individuals rarely classified their sleep as unsatisfactory: 95% of them considered their sleep to be "just enough," 92% claimed to fall asleep quickly, and 97% reported that they found their beds comfortable. Over the course of the study, none of the study participants complained of any sort of sleep problem.[22] Of this experience, Samson says, "Just to paint a picture here . . . their sleeping environment is extremely spartan. We're talking a hide and maybe a textile and 40% of the population using their arm as a pillow. They'll pile dirt under the textile or shove some dirt under their arm to make sure [their spines] are aligned (figure 2.1). Yet when

Chimpanzee   *Hunter-gatherer*   *Modern human*

Figure 2.1. The Evolution of Sleeping Conditions

Photography credit: David Samson for hunter-gatherer photo; Canva for chimpanzee and modern human photos.

they were asked the question, 'Are you happy with your sleep?,' literally everyone in the group said, 'Yes.'"[23]

Unlike the previous study, napping was found to play a more significant role for the Hadza. Individuals were found to nap almost half of the day, and the naps corresponded to bouts of wakefulness the previous night. This led the researchers to classify the Hadza as more segmented sleepers, although most still slept for at least one long phase at night.[24] Samson hypothesizes that this sleep segmentation was adaptive. Looking at the sleep of all the adults over a night, they only slept synchronously for 18 minutes. Samson says, "That, to me, is incredible, how little overlap there is in their sleep timing. Which shows how important sleeping in a group is, in a dynamic environment in the savanna, where you functionally have someone up at any given epoch of the night."[25] He concludes that sleep is flexible, and this plasticity in sleep-wake patterns has been a target of natural selection in human evolution.[26]

Many common trends emerged from these studies. Hunter-gatherers tended to rise from sleep at the same time each day, usually around sunrise, meaning they received maximum sunlight exposure in the mornings. On the other hand, the onset of sleep for each group was variable. When they went to sleep, sleep segmentation and how they used naps to supplement sleep were more culturally dependent.[27] Sleep onset was not determined by falling light; they all remained awake several hours after sunset, but sunset most likely triggered their initial melatonin production. They started to sleep when the night was cooling, so the falling temperature was important for its onset.

Although none of the groups experienced more sleep than we do in the modern world, with some having more sleep fragmentation, none of these traditional foragers seemed to have a problem with their sleep quality. Perhaps this is because they possess strong circadian rhythms and were completely entrained to their environment and in sync with the solar day. Conversely, they did not have any modern conveniences that would override their natural processes or mask the signals their bodies gave them. These similarities appeared even though the groups live in isolated parts of the world and have different cultures, suggesting that these patterns are representative of the core traits of human sleep in a natural environment very near to the latitudes where our species evolved.[28, 29]

Another common feature of hunter-gatherer sleep is how they sleep in communal groups, from an entire family to an entire tribe. Mothers and babies always sleep together, and no one in a tribe ever sleeps alone. Camps are small enough that if someone yelled, everyone would hear it. Samson looked at this natural protective environment to develop his social withdrawal hypothesis. Humans are unique because no matter where we go—and we went nearly everywhere on the planet—we were able to create these socially constructed, technologically buffered, protected, and safe sleep niches to withdraw into.[30] This feeling of safety in a communal group allows members to be vulnerable for a deep and satisfying sleep.

The final study we will discuss directly addressed the circadian mismatches that rapidly occur with modernization. This study compared two communities of indigenous Toba/Qom people in Argentina. Traditionally hunter-gatherers, the Toba/Qom now exhibit a spectrum of subsistence activities and lifestyles. One community in the study had access to electricity, was more settled, and participated less in foraging. The other relied on natural light and used more hunting, gathering, and fishing for their subsistence. This was a well-controlled study because the community with electricity had recently migrated from the other, giving them the same ethnic and sociocultural background. Although both groups slept longer in the winter, in all seasons, the community without electricity slept on average an hour longer than the community with artificial light. This difference was mainly due to earlier bedtimes.[31] In the short time since the first group gained access to electricity, they'd already stopped sleeping according to the circadian rhythms that were entrained by nature. Exposure to artificial light at night stretched their circadian clock, making bedtimes later and shortening sleep. The possession of televisions also acted as a stimulus to stay inside and awake during the evening for entertainment.

Strikingly, the community with access to electricity doesn't even come close to the level of light exposure in typical industrialized societies. They did not have smartphones or computers, nor did they have access to the abundant sources of mass media prevalent in the modern world. So, this study actually underestimates the effects of modernity on human sleep duration.[32]

These examinations of modern hunter-gatherer sleep reveal many differences from our initial perceptions. Instead of getting more sleep, the sleep duration of hunter-gatherers is more like our industrial society. However, being constantly in touch with their external environment, they are completely entrained to the Earth's rhythms of day and night, light and temperature, making their sleep characteristics have strong evolutionary origins. Their sleep is modulated by the season, and they sleep longer in the winter than in the summer. Hunter-gatherers don't go to sleep when the sun goes down; rather, they stay up for several hours into the night until consistent melatonin release and falling temperatures induce sleepiness. Without blue wavelengths of light, firelight does not delay the onset of sleep. Hunter-gatherers sleep in community and typically don't wake for long periods during the night. However, if sleep is more fragmented, their sleep deficit is replenished the next day with a nap, although napping is not a universal trait. More fragmented nighttime sleep is hypothesized to be a survival adaptation that ensured someone would be awake to be on watch and protect the group. A hallmark of hunter-gatherers is that individuals wake at the same time each day, usually before sunrise. Finally, the groups studied never complained about insomnia or their quality of sleep. Imagine going through your day without hearing ourselves or others complain about how tired we are!

The evolution of human sleep led to a concentrated, intense, more efficient, and REM-dominated but shorter period of sleep than any other primate. It also led to the variation of chronotypes and more segmented sleep, things that are not common among other primates, because of the required vigilance to protect those who were sleeping on the ground from danger. Modern hunter-gatherers sleep and wake in response to what is going on in the natural world around them. Chances are that our ancestors slept and woke according to their evolved circadian rhythms for tens of thousands of millennia before the modern world started altering the signals that are critical to entrain us to the rhythms of the Earth. How else has the modern world affected our sleep?

CHAPTER 3

MODERN SLEEP AND ITS CONSEQUENCES

Changes from our ancestral sleep ecology, where physiology
was in constant exposure to the environment, may have had
significant consequences for sleep-wake patterns . . . and
evolutionary mismatch may have occurred as Western populations
shifted to living in climate controlled, artificially extended
photoperiods, resulting in multiple negative health outcomes.

—DAVID SAMSON

I n the 1930s, electrical grids provided widespread electricity in North
America and Europe, and suddenly, electricity and artificial lighting
allowed us to be active, or even working, well into the night. Shiftwork
emerged to allow the industrial complex to run nonstop, and now, even
if we are not working, high-tech innovations keep us up to be entertained
well into the night. Our sleeping patterns shifted dramatically, not due to
some evolutionary pressure, but purely due to our cultural adaptations of
living in a world powered by electricity.

In the United States, the average total sleep duration has fallen from eight to nine hours per night in 1959, to seven to eight hours per night in 1980, and then to less than seven hours on workdays in 2013.[1] Nearly one-third of the US population, hundreds of millions of us, complain of some form of insomnia, trouble getting to sleep, staying asleep, or waking too early.[2] It feels like most of us can't get enough sleep. Is it a coincidence that our decreased sleep quality corresponds to the decline of our health and well-being? How did the rise of high-tech modernity affect our circadian rhythms?

Our patterns of light exposure have been radically altered. Not only did industrialization and technology start keeping us up past our bedtimes, but they also drove us indoors, where our light levels are a fraction of that of sunlight. Then, at night, we are bombarded with light pollution, again at levels that are only a fraction of the sun. Normally, our brains begin to secrete melatonin after dark; however, all the blue light emitted from our technology tricks them into thinking it is still daytime and suppresses its release. In fact, our exposure to blue light one hour before bed has been found to delay melatonin release—and, therefore, REM sleep—by 30 minutes.[3] Imagine the delays that occur when we look at screens until we finally close our eyes. Then we wonder why we have a hard time sleeping, a hard time waking up, and are tired all day. In their book *Chronotherapy*, Ian McMahan and Michael Terman write, "Most of us live a twilight existence."[4] Figure 3.1 compares the timing and intensity of light exposure for hunter-gatherers versus modern humans.[5]

Our "twilight existence" gives us consistent low levels of light throughout the day: too little in the morning and too much at night. Our circadian rhythms are erratic because we are both isolated from the natural external cues that entrain us and exposed to light at the wrong times. This altered circadian timing and decreased sleep quality and quantity cause acute and chronic health problems.[6] Chronobiology expert Abraham Haim goes so

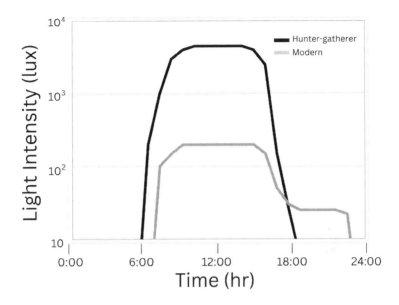

Figure 3.1. The Timing and Intensity of Light Exposure for Hunter-Gatherers and Modern Humans

Adapted from: Skeldon, A. Phillips, A. Dijk, D.J. 2017. "The effects of self-selected light-dark cycles and social constraints on human sleep and circadian timing: a modeling approach," Sci Rep 7: 45158.

far as to say, "Light at night is a carcinogenic environmental pollutant that will continue to negatively impact our health and well-being until the world recognizes its harmful effects and makes important changes to how and when we use light."[7]

Another source of circadian mismatch arose when the requirements of modern life forced our natural chronotypes into unnatural rhythms. On the spectrum of chronotypes, 15% of people are inherently early birds, those who easily wake before dawn and feel most alert at midday. However, since they go to bed early, they may miss social functions or have trouble working into the evening. Most people (55%) have a chronotype that easily operates on society's nine-to-five schedule and are most alert from midmorning into the early evening, when most work, business, and socialization occur. Night owls, the 15% of people who go to sleep late and rise late, are most alert from late afternoon into late evening and are highly productive at night but often have trouble waking, making it hard to report to work on time.[8]

The last 15% don't fit into any of these three categories and are the extreme early risers, who have an *advanced* sleep phase disorder, and the extreme late sleepers, who have *delayed* sleep phase disorder.[9] Both night owls and those with the more serious delayed sleep onset are the most likely to deal with chronic sleep deprivation because their clocks are not aligned with typical work or school schedules. These circadian rhythm differences and other rarer ones are commonly caused by the altered or disrupted sensitivity to zeitgebers and mistimed melatonin release. We have no control over our genetic chronotypes, and all have our peaks and valleys at different times of day. So the sweeping adages about how early birds catch worms or how night owls are cleverer and more creative are nonsense.

Modernity presents a multitude of challenges to our sleep and circadian rhythms. We are no longer entrained to the natural light-dark cycles of the Earth, and our timing and intensity of light exposure are all mixed up. Our modern job and school schedules often do not allow us to follow the rhythms of our own unique chronotype; we may be a night owl forced to get up at 6:00 a.m. every day, or even someone with a relatively common chronotype forced to work a night shift. In an extreme example, think of the astronauts working on the International Space Station. Every 24 hours, these astronauts witness 16 sunrises and 16 sunsets, which must completely confound their circadian clocks.

Not only is our sleep affected by our mixed-up light exposure, but a multitude of other physiological functions that rely on circadian rhythms become off kilter. The result? Our performance, health, and well-being are negatively affected.

Performance

Light affects performance. Bright light boosts our attention, cognition, reaction times, and mood during the day.[10] This is why offices have bright fluorescent lights and why taking a walk outside during a mid-morning work slump can improve attention. All light has these effects, but blue-wavelength light, in particular, is more efficient at elevating body temperature and heart rate and reducing sleepiness. Research subjects under blue light had faster reaction times and fewer lapses in attention.[11]

Performance is also dependent on our individual circadian rhythms, and levels of alertness vary as a function of the time of day. Generally, alertness levels gradually rise from waking to midday, then fall as we approach bedtime. The timing of peak alertness and performance depends on a person's chronotype. A decrease in alertness—which we perceive as sleepiness—is the signal we are ready for sleep. If we feel drowsy over the entire day, it is signaling we are not getting enough sleep or are not properly entrained.

When we are tired, our performance on cognitive, reflexive, and physical tasks is impaired. One night of total sleep deprivation has the largest negative effect on mood but also decreases cognitive function through a lack of creativity and adaptivity, cognitive slowing, and a loss of motivation.[12] Chronic partial sleep deprivation is more common than total sleep deprivation, causing habitual sleepiness. In one study, the irregular and inconsistent sleep-wake patterns in college students were found to cause poorer academic performance.[13] In another, a psychomotor vigilance test (a sustained-attention, reaction-time test) was used to measure levels of performance in a variety of sleep deprivation situations. When sleep was restricted to two-thirds of normal for a week, or to nine, seven, five, or three hours of time in bed, psychomotor performance worsened linearly as sleep loss accumulated. Performance after two weeks of chronic partial sleep deprivation mimicked performance after two nights of total sleep deprivation. These performance deficits are not surprising, but interestingly, the perception of sleepiness reached a steady state. After a certain point, the sleep-deprived people could no longer tell exactly how impaired they were.[14]

These results on performance are critical though. Falling asleep or having even a momentary loss of situational awareness can mean life or death in many tasks and professions. Sleep deprivation severely impairs driving performance,[15] which is why fatigue-related car crashes peak in the early-morning hours. It is scary to think that, on average, long-haul truck drivers only get five hours of sleep per night. Tired operators contributed to accidents such as the Three Mile Island partial nuclear reactor meltdown and the *Exxon Valdez* oil spill. Countless lives are lost due to human error in hospitals when sleepy doctors or nurses struggle to perform their duties.[16]

Even if your job will not result in life or death, sleep is required to maintain mood and emotional regulation. Sleep restriction causes a progressive increase in emotional disturbances, amplifying negative events and blunting positive ones.[17] Have you ever noticed that, when you're tired, you feel more overwhelmed at work and can't remember why you ever liked your job in the first place? Performance, safety, and feelings of well-being at work directly correspond to the amount of sleep obtained the night before.

Sleep deprivation also has a significant effect on aspects of physical performance as well. Without good sleep, muscles reach fatigue sooner, muscular strength and power may decrease, and the perception of effort increases. In addition, sleep deprivation leads to poorer moods, sleepiness, and increased confusion, all of which affect our physical abilities.[18] The susceptibility to impairment depends on the activity and the level of fine motor control demanded from it. For example, reaction time is reduced by partial sleep restrictions, so playing tennis or baseball is affected, whereas swimming is not. The cognitive effects of sleep deprivation on physical tasks also differ depending on the activity. The cognitive demands of being a quarterback are highly compromised, whereas a runner has a lower mental demand and is less affected. Sleep deprivation also blunts the ability of our muscles to fully restore themselves, which inhibits sustained physical effort.[19]

Cognitive and physical performance flexibility afforded by differing chronotypes may be a survival adaptation. If all hunters peaked in the morning hours, humans would miss out on prey available at other times of day. If a tribe consisted of people whose performances peaked throughout the day, more resources would be acquired for the group. In the modern world, regularly not getting enough sleep or timing an important task when it mismatches your chronotype will result in suboptimal performance. To ensure we are primed for both peak cognitive and physical performance, we must get enough sleep and be in sync with our circadian rhythms.

Health consequences

Staying alert and optimally performing tasks are important reasons to get enough sleep and follow our natural circadian rhythms, but there are even more serious motivations. When the 2017 Nobel Prize went to scientists for their work on circadian rhythms, the Nobel Committee recognized how these rhythms and our health are interconnected. They wrote, "Our well-being is affected when there is a temporary mismatch between our external environment and this internal biological clock—for example, when we travel across several time zones and experience 'jet lag.' There are also indications that chronic misalignment between our lifestyle and the rhythm dictated by our inner timekeeper is associated with increased risk for various diseases."[20] In other words, the disruptions to our natural timekeeping system can profoundly affect our health.

In addition to the people who often travel across time zones, some of us have chronotypes that don't fit into our required working hours. Shift workers bear the brunt of circadian misalignment due to the timing of their work. Their internal biological clocks and behavioral cycles of sleeping and waking are completely at odds. Around 10 million Americans, including police officers, firefighters, nurses, doctors, pilots, wait staff, convenience store clerks, and truck drivers—to name a few—perform shift work, making them even more at risk.

The misalignment of circadian rhythms could lead to disease because the proper timing of cellular processes is disrupted. In any tissue, up to 15% of the mRNA, the molecule that conveys genetic instructions from the DNA to the protein-making machinery of cells, is controlled by the circadian clock. This incorporates temporal information into many cellular processes such as hormone secretion, metabolic pathways, DNA damage response, and cell cycle progression.[21] This is why people with circadian mismatch have increased risks for cancer, cardiovascular disease, metabolic disorders, depression, and even Alzheimer's disease. In the words of Susheel Patil, director of sleep medicine for University Hospitals, "Sleep-deprived people tend not to live as long as their well-rested peers."[22]

The dysregulation of circadian rhythms is linked to cancer, so much so that the WHO now classifies shift work as a possible carcinogen. Multiple studies of shift workers found that they have an increased risk of breast cancer, prostate cancer, lung cancer, skin cancer, lymphoma, and other forms of the disease.[23] Other studies found that people who experience continuously disrupted, shortened, and poor-quality sleep may also have elevated risks for the development of several cancers, although these results were more varied.[24]

Circadian rhythms control cell division and the DNA damage response, and when these are dysregulated, cancer can develop and grow unchecked. Melatonin also has antitumor activity in many cancers; therefore, reduced melatonin production due to dysregulated light exposure may increase risk. The regulation of many endocrine and metabolic hormones, such as estrogen, androgen, and cortisol, are also controlled by daily rhythms. Breast and prostate cancers are driven by estrogen and androgen, respectively, and have a strong association with mismatched rhythms.[25] Cortisol, the "stress hormone," usually peaks at dawn and decreases throughout the day, but shift workers and people with poor sleep have elevated cortisol secretion, playing a role in the development and worsening of cancer.[26] Circadian rhythms are so strongly associated with cancer that, when chemotherapy administration was coordinated with these rhythms, it had more profound effects on tumor reduction.[27]

When circadian rhythms are disturbed, people also have elevated risks for the development of cardiovascular issues. For example, shift workers have a 40% higher risk of hypertension, inflammation, and cardiovascular disease. Exacerbating these risks are other lifestyle choices that some shift workers develop, which also elevate risks, such as a poor diet, a lack of exercise, and increased smoking. Even in test subjects who experienced circadian misalignment for only a brief time, increased blood pressure and inflammation were triggered.[28] People who experience long periods of chronic sleep deprivation also have a greater risk of developing or dying from cardiovascular disease, having a heart attack or stroke, and increased blood pressure leading to hypertension.[29] For example, a study found that people who sleep less than six hours a night have a 20% higher risk of heart attack compared to those who sleep six to nine hours.[30] Sleep deprivation affects the body's inflammatory response, lipid metabolism, oxidative stress, and endothelial function, all of which contribute to the development of these diseases.[31]

Scientific evidence points to a correlation between cardiovascular disease and circadian rhythms, but perhaps anecdotal evidence is even more striking. Hunter-gatherers simply do not die from cardiovascular disease.

In traditional societies, adults have much lower blood pressure, and atherosclerosis is very rare.[32] Their near absence of heart disease is due to many factors, but one may be because their circadian rhythms are exquisitely entrained to their environment.

We also have a higher risk for metabolic disorders, such as obesity and diabetes, when we get insufficient sleep and our rhythms are disrupted. Dysregulated metabolic hormones, reduced insulin sensitivity, and increased insulin resistance and glucose intolerance all occur with circadian mismatch.[33] Shift work once again increases the risk for obesity and diabetes due to our maladaptation to sleeping and eating at abnormal times of day.[34] For example, Japanese workers with 16-hour shifts had a 50% higher incidence of diabetes than day workers.[35] In another study, when test subjects had sustained sleep restriction, they had temporary decreases in resting metabolic rate, and their plasma glucose after meals increased due to inadequate insulin secretion.[36] After exposure to a recurring 28-hour day for 10 days, a simulation of shift work, study participants had decreased levels of leptin (which inhibits the hunger response), increased circulating glucose, and a reversed cortisol rhythm. Many exhibited glucose responses after meals typical of someone with prediabetes.[37]

For people with irregular sleep patterns, with every hour of variability in time to bed and time asleep, there is a 27% higher chance of having a metabolic disorder.[38] Remember that hunter-gatherers had regular sleep schedules. This, in addition to their diet and exercise regimes, is probably why obesity and diabetes are also completely absent in modern hunter-gatherer populations.[39]

A strong correlation between circadian rhythms and depression also exists. For example, changes in the intensity of depression symptoms follow daily patterns; symptoms worsen in the morning and ease in the evening. Depressive symptoms also follow annual patterns. Seasonal affective disorder is a recurring depression associated with dark winters that spontaneously remits in the spring. Evidence suggests that sleep disturbances once thought to be a symptom of depression are now considered independent risk factors for the development of depression.[40] For example, shift workers are more likely to suffer from depression than non–shift workers because the dysregulation of internal rhythms lowers serotonin levels, a neurotransmitter that plays a key role in regulating mood.[41]

The field of psychiatry has gravitated toward neurotransmitter and receptor theories of mental dysfunction because they can be corrected by drugs. However, investigating circadian clock and sleep issues offers a different way of approaching emotional and behavioral issues.[42] But sometimes medication will mask any circadian causes of depression. Bright light therapy has greatly improved depression in patients alone or in combination with medication.[43]

Finally, we know sleep deprivation can affect our cognitive performance, but it can also affect more serious neurocognitive disorders, like dementia and Alzheimer's disease. In one study, the loss of one night's worth of sleep increased the accumulation of β-amyloid, the main component of neural plaques in Alzheimer's, in the hippocampus and thalamus.[44] In another study, the effective treatment of sleep apnea and hypertension (which can be the result of poor sleep) in test subjects reversed the cognitive decline of neurocognitive disorders.[45]

Figure 3.2 illustrates the countless ways the dysregulation of sleep and circadian rhythms affects the performance and the health of our bodies and brains. Our modern existence does not automatically give us the opportunities to entrain our natural rhythms to our natural environment, nor does it allow us to easily follow our own unique circadian clocks. More and more of us are living (and sleeping) in a circadian mismatch. Mitch Leslie of *Science* magazine writes, "The demands and distractions of modern life are stealing our sleep and perhaps robbing us of our health."[46] By first discovering and then realigning the evolutionary mismatch we have with our sleep and our circadian rhythms, we can start to address all of its physical and mental consequences.

Figure 3.2. The Consequences of Dysregulated Sleep and Circadian Rhythms

CHAPTER 4

REALIGNING YOUR SLEEP

Do but consider what an excellent thing sleep is . . . that golden
chain that ties health and our bodies together.

–THOMAS DEKKER

W e are not ignorant of the problems with mismatched sleep; we
are bombarded with articles about the importance of sleep. We
all know the behaviors and habits we should have for good sleep
hygiene, such as avoiding caffeine late in the day, not eating large meals
before bed, not exercising close to bedtime, avoiding alcohol and nico-
tine before bed, using our beds for sleeping and sex only, etc. We may even
follow all of that advice, but we still feel like we don't get enough sleep.
Since many of us consistently live with fatigue, we have a long-standing
cultural fixation on how to sleep longer and better, and we obsessively
record and track how much and how well we sleep. We spend tens of billions of dollars each year on sleep-related products. Many assume sleeping
problems have an external cause, thinking that sleeping pills, a better mat-
tress, or the next fad for the ultimate night's sleep is the solution.[1] But the
root cause of our fatigue is the misalignment of our circadian rhythms.

The good news is that circadian misalignment is entirely reversible. In a study from the Rocky Mountains, participants were first monitored while they maintained their regular routines, artificial light exposure, and self-selected sleep schedules. During this period, melatonin secretion was found to start two hours before an average sleep onset of 12:30 a.m. In the mornings, the rapid decline in melatonin occurred about two hours after waking. Next, the participants took a weeklong excursion into the wilderness, where they were exposed only to natural sunlight and campfires. The average measured light intensity increased fourfold during the day and decreased by more than half after sundown. In this environment, all measured markers of internal circadian rhythms shifted two hours earlier; melatonin release began at sunset and promoted earlier bedtimes. The sharp decline of melatonin now occurred right after sunrise and before waking, which made waking up easier. Sleep and wake times shifted earlier by more than an hour, but surprisingly, sleep duration and efficiency were not significantly different between the two conditions. In just one week, the internal circadian rhythms of participants were tightly synchronized and entrained to the 24-hour Earth day.[2] Our circadian rhythm's ability to respond to and to be entrained by natural light to align with the world has not changed.

It is time to connect ourselves back to every human, hominid, primate, animal, plant, and cell that came before us and follow the beat of circadian rhythms. First, we must relearn how to listen to the signals our bodies give us. We must take responsibility for our sleep and make better decisions to go to bed when we become tired. We shouldn't ignore our body's needs in order to watch one more episode of that hit series, scroll through our social media feed, or work on our computers for just one more hour. Our desire to stay awake to be entertained, to ingest more and more information, or to appease our fear of missing out should never override our health. When we chronically disobey our internal clock's signals, more and more problems will arise.

We can bring hunter-gatherer sleep practices into modernity to get our circadian rhythms back on track, including getting up at the same time every day, being exposed to bright light in the morning, taking naps if a sleep deficit occurs, and decreasing light exposure in the evenings. A few other hunter-gatherer sleeping traits, like going to sleep with falling temperatures and sleeping with companionship, may help us better fulfill our sleep requirements. Knowing our chronotypes and arranging our lives to fit with our natural rhythms is another way to live more in accord with our biology. Finally, if we stop problematizing our sleep, we will sleep better.

A consistent wake-up time

Hunter-gatherers usually woke before the sun rose, but more importantly, they consistently woke at the same time every day. Samson says, "To maximize efficiency, consistency is king. . . . If you need to be cognitively effective at the same time every day, then there is no better way to prime your body and your mind than by getting up at the same time."[3] In fact, consistency was found to be just as or more important as the number of hours slept for measures of well-being.[4]

A regular routine will make it easier to fall asleep and wake up, and it makes us more productive while we're awake. There is no one-size-fits-all time to wake in the morning. We have to figure it out for ourselves by becoming aware of our body's needs and choosing a time that will let us get enough rest, suit our lifestyle, and fit our chronotype. If our internal clock's natural wake time differs from our work and life requirements, there are ways, such as light therapy, to make our required wake-up times easier.

Another way to improve morning waking and alertness is to go to bed at the right time. Non-REM and REM sleep cycle about every 90 minutes, and tools such as sleep calculators will suggest sleep times to ensure we don't awaken in the middle of a cycle. Waking up at the same time every day is a good place to start getting your rhythms back on track.

Bright light in the morning

Hunter-gatherers received intense sun exposure in the mornings, so the next step in re-creating our primal waking environment is to get sunlight after waking. It's time to stop living a twilight existence and go outside to let the sun do its job.

In the darker winter months, specialized lights like sun lamps can mimic the early sun. Seeking out bright light when we wake will help entrain our internal rhythms and improve our alertness in the morning by encouraging melatonin secretion to shut off before waking. Bright light helps us emerge faster from sleep inertia, the grogginess we feel upon waking that helps us fall back to sleep in the middle of the night. The prolonged sleep inertia and sleepiness that plague night owls in the morning may be because their melatonin production doesn't shut down until long after waking. In the study where participants camped for a week with only natural light exposure, even the night owl chronotypes' melatonin production began to shut off before waking, more closely mimicking the morning and normal types and causing less morning sleepiness.[5] Therefore, bright light in the morning both entrains and invigorates.

Take a nap

Although napping is not a universal trait of hunter-gatherers, some traditional foragers like the Hadza do use napping to counteract the negative consequences of sleep debt. The fact that a full day's sleep can be obtained routinely through napping demonstrates yet another example of the flexibility of human sleep.[6] In fact, evolution primed us for naps with an easy-to-enter window for midafternoon sleep: the circadian dip in alertness. When a nap coincides with this dip, it improves our recovery of alertness.

There is no reason we, as modern humans, can't use naps in the same way. In many cultures, afternoon napping is already driven by social behaviors. An afternoon nap is a common, long-standing habit in Mediterranean cultures, and in China, Taiwan, and Japan, napping has been instituted recently as a countermeasure to working excessive hours and the resulting sleep debt. Across cultures, even in the US, at least a third of people participate in some sort of napping behavior, although at varying frequencies.[7]

Naps can positively affect attention and alertness, mood, concentration, and reaction time and can restore cognitive impairments introduced by poor nighttime sleep. But not all naps are created equal. The length, timing relative to the person's internal rhythms, and sleep architecture determine a nap's success. Timing is important to avoid deleterious effects, such as sleep inertia and disrupted sleep onset, quality, and quantity of night sleep. Sleep inertia occurs when naps last longer than 20 minutes, and the napper has entered deep non-REM sleep. Early afternoon naps seem to be better than late afternoon naps for avoiding these effects and for optimizing the nap's recovery power.

Naps are a good way to counteract the detriments of sleep deprivation. However, before we slide under our desks for a surreptitious snooze every afternoon, we should take a hard look at our nighttime sleeping habits. Naps won't completely replace the hours of chronic sleep loss. Except for extenuating circumstances, there is no reason we can't get all the sleep we require at night. Shift workers, however, should use naps to make up for the missed sleep their schedules dictate. Many companies, such as Google and Nike, have nap rooms as a commitment to the health and wellness of their employees, but it is also to help increase productivity. Some companies provide such resources to encourage their workers to stay at work longer, which creates new problems. Napping should not be used as a sleep Band-Aid before underlying problems are addressed, but it is a good way to supplement our sleep when nighttime deficits occur.

Decrease nighttime light pollution

At night, after the sun went down, traditional foragers gathered around a fire to eat, to talk, to sing and dance, to tell stories, and to celebrate. Firelight and moonlight were their only sources of light, so their melatonin release happened right on schedule, causing them to feel sleepy a few hours after dark.

In the modern indoors, our nights are almost as bright as our days, and many of our evening hobbies involve gazing at illuminated displays. The first step in decreasing this light pollution is to turn off the bright overhead lights and use lamps. Dim the overall lighting in your house with low–blue light or use blue-blocking LED bulbs. There are even bulbs that mimic firelight.[8] As for our devices, companies make blue-light filters for electronic displays, like Amazon's BlueShade or Apple's Night Shift, to reduce blue-light exposure. Use a sepia background when reading eBooks or, at the very least, use the smallest screen possible. Avoid bright screens for a few hours before bed and use dim red lights for nightlights.[9] If bright light exposure is a necessary part of your evening, blue-blocking glasses are available to prevent your body's sleep-delay reaction due to the blue light. Circadian timing can be strengthened by both increasing blue light in the daytime and reducing it at night.

Turn down the temperature

Hunter-gatherers went to bed as the environmental temperature fell, and their concurrent falling body temperatures assisted the process of falling asleep. However, today the daily and seasonal temperature rhythms are removed by insulation and artificial heating and cooling.[10] We miss the temperature cues for a good night's sleep.

Our core body temperature rapidly decreases before sleep onset, so if our sleeping arrangements are too hot, sleep is delayed. Sleeping temperature is also the reason not to engage in high-intensity exercise close to bedtime. It takes around three hours for our core body temperature to decrease back to baseline after a workout. A long, hot bath right before bed may be relaxing, but it may also delay the onset of sleep.

The National Sleep Foundation recommends that the optimal temperature in your bedroom at night be between 60° and 67° Fahrenheit. Mimicking falling environmental temperatures in the home will help us fall asleep easier, so turn down the thermostat.

Sleep in community

Since we are most vulnerable when asleep, our hunter-gatherer ancestors slept communally for protection, never sleeping alone. Communal sleeping occurred for millennia after the Agricultural Revolution as well. Homes usually had only one room, and it was normal for entire families to gather in the same bed and bond before sleep. Sleeping in isolation only occurred in the last two hundred years, with a cultural shift toward privacy and propriety and the extreme value placed on individuality. Communal sleeping became so improper and immoral in the Victorian Age that even married couples slept in separate beds.[11]

Even though communal sleeping is no longer strictly required for survival, it can still have positive effects on our well-being. It fulfills the basic human need of being close to others. In some modern cultures, where cosleeping is still commonplace, it is considered integral to the emotional patterns, social structures, and foundational relationships of family life. In communities with cosleeping, sleep is more regular, compact, and undisturbed, and people have more feelings of belonging, identity, care, and intimacy.[12]

The idea of sleeping in a room full of others seems foreign. We think communal sleep would be too loud or too stimulating, but loneliness is actually a significant predictor of sleep disruption and fragmentation,[13] not the other way around. Many of us with partners believe we'd sleep better alone because bedtime behaviors like late-night Twitter viewing, snoring, or excessive movement cause lost sleep and can become a big relationship problem. As we've learned though, sleep problems due to poor sleep hygiene or health issues are not irreversible, and by fixing them, we can fix our relationships. Researchers believe that sharing the same bed may be one way couples in intimate relationships live longer and have better health. Sleeping close to someone, touching them, or cuddling increases feelings of security, which lowers stress and the production of cortisol and releases oxytocin (the "love hormone"), which has been shown to ease anxiety.

Behavioral sleep specialist Wendy Troxel asserts, "The psychological benefits we get having closeness at night trump the objective costs of sleeping with a partner."[14] If we do not have a partner to share a bed with, sleeping in the same room as someone else has similar benefits of stress reduction. So, when it comes to sleep, the more the merrier. Sleeping in community was an evolutionary adaptation that was maintained until very recently and helped us feel secure enough to sleep deeply.

Align with your natural rhythms

Hunter-gatherers listened to their bodies and lived in alignment with their circadian rhythms. If we know our natural chronotype, we can alter our sleep and activity patterns to fit our clocks and set up our lives to do tasks at times of day when we are most alert and productive. Tools and resources exist online or in books that help determine someone's chronotype, which will help us make better choices for our sleep patterns.[15] Our ideal work schedule should mirror our natural circadian rhythm preferences.

We are lucky that more and more options are available to us in the modern world. As work situations become more flexible and many jobs are done remotely, it is easier to live in accordance with our chronotype. Although this may not be possible in high school (although many are choosing to start later), college classes can be scheduled in the mornings for early birds or in the afternoons for night owls. If a job or school schedule is not flexible, there are ways to help entrain our chronotype to our expected workday. We can also change the rhythms of our internal clocks to fit the patterns required of us with sleep therapy. Chronotherapy uses light to entrain our natural rhythm to a desired external rhythm.

Shift work may be a permanent consequence of modernity, and the circadian misalignment it causes may be unavoidable, since it is required for many important careers. The negative data on shift work doesn't mean we should rush out and quit our jobs. However, it is important to know the possible health risks of shift work so we can take steps to minimize the risk. Putting a strong emphasis on good sleep hygiene, a healthy diet, and staying physically and mentally active are ways to minimize the risks.[16] Naps are also a critical tool for shift workers to use to fill up sleep debt and avoid its potential negative health impacts. Shift workers should know their family's history of type 2 diabetes, obesity, heart disease, cancer, and other diseases linked to shift work to better assess risk and keep on top of any early markers of disease with a doctor.[17] Some forms of sleep therapy may also help shift workers minimize their misalignment.

Don't problematize sleep

With our obsession with getting a good night's sleep and with lack of sleep being declared a public health epidemic, most of us consider sleep to be a huge problem. However, when Samson was asked the one sleeping habit of hunter-gatherers he would most recommend, he emphatically said, "Don't problematize your sleep!"[18]

He studied the Hadza, who have the least sleep of any other small-scale or modern society. They sleep on the ground with their arms as pillows and have highly fragmented sleep, but they never think they've slept poorly. If they get a bad night's sleep, they don't panic. They supplement with a nap if they can but don't worry if they can't. Samson says, "We have this sleep homeostatic drive that is perfectly well adapted so you get deep sleep when you go back to sleep again."[19]

He wants to challenge the concept of a modern-day sleep epidemic, since most insomnia is treatable with simple techniques, like basic improvements in sleep and light hygiene. Often, when clinicians actually explain the evolutionary origins and survival adaptations of insomnia, that it was ancestrally adaptive, people change their perspective. They no longer believe their sleep is a problem or that they are broken. Once they don't think of it as a problem anymore, their symptoms usually improve because they are not internalizing it. Samson wants us to realize and hold on to the modern gains we've made on sleep comfort and security that made our sleeping environments better than those of our ancestors, but he thinks we need to "double down on the science of circadian rhythms and start amplifying them."[20] Figure 4.1 summarizes these recommendations.

1	Have a consistent wake-up time
2	Get exposed to bright light in the morning
3	If you had a bad night's sleep, take a nap
4	Decrease nighttime light pollution
5	Turn down the temperature where you sleep
6	Sleep in community with someone
7	Try to align your activities with your natural rhythm
8	Don't problematize sleep

Figure 4.1. Closing the Gap on Sleep

Our Paleolithic ancestors had to be in their best health to survive. Physical or mental impairment could cost them their lives, so they relied upon responding to their bodies' needs, unconsciously trusting their own evolved natures. Whether or not we get enough sleep is no longer a daily matter of life and death, but lack of sleep degrades our quality of life and health. When we are tired, depressed, and feel ill, we cannot fully feel alive. We've stopped listening to our bodies, to our own evolved natures. We override our bodies' deep sleep signals for more late-night entertainment or work. We gaze at blue light–emitting screens and throw our bodies' natural bedtime rhythms off kilter. When we have trouble sleeping because we have poor sleep hygiene or circadian rhythm mismatch, we take sleeping aids and don't address the underlying issues.

But now we know why and how our circadian rhythms evolved, and how hunter-gatherer sleep and wake cycles are completely entrained to the Earth's rhythms. We are armed to recognize where we've allowed ourselves to drift away from our evolved rhythms and have some strategies to help us realign them, so we can be rested and healthy enough to live our best lives. If we can re-create aspects of our primal sleep and wake environments, our new sleeping habits will give us the health and vitality required to achieve eudaemonia.

PART 2

NUTRITION

In only thirty days of eating nothing but McDonald's, I gained twenty-four and a half pounds, my liver turned to fat, and my cholesterol shot up sixty-five points. My body fat percentage went from eleven to eighteen percent . . . I nearly doubled my risk of coronary heart disease . . . felt depressed and exhausted most of the time, my mood swung on a dime, and my sex life was nonexistent. I craved this food more and more when I ate it and got massive headaches when I didn't.

–MORGAN SPURLOCK

I n 2003, after being intrigued by a lawsuit brought against McDonald's on behalf of two women who allegedly became obese as a result of eating their food, filmmaker Morgan Spurlock set out to determine whether habitually eating McDonald's food was "unreasonably dangerous," as outlined by the lawsuit. For 30 days, he ate nothing but McDonald's for every meal or snack, agreeing to supersize any meal when it was offered to him. He only exercised by walking the distance the average American walked each day, two miles. Then he chronicled his experience in the documentary *Super Size Me*.

Over the course of the month, his body mass increased 13%, his cholesterol increased into dangerous territory, and he experienced mood swings, depression, lethargy, poor sleep, and headaches, all of which improved with another McDonald's meal. Before the experiment was over, he had to go to the hospital for chest pains, causing his physicians to urge him to stop. The deterioration of his body and mind in just 30 days was astounding.[1,2]

Critics of the documentary said that Morgan intentionally ate more calories and didn't exercise to exaggerate the effects of his experiment. However, countless people eat to excess and don't exercise on a regular basis. Morgan subjected himself to the process that millions of Americans are already undergoing with their unhealthy eating habits and lifestyles. After all, in a CDC survey conducted between 2013 and 2016, more than one in three American adults eat fast food at least one meal a day (figure P2.1).[3]

Figure P2.1. Thirty-Three Percent of Americans Eat Fast Food for at Least One Meal a Day

The processed, sugar-loaded, fat-laden meals served by fast-food restaurants, which often have more calories in one meal than is recommended for the entire day, are cheap and convenient. We don't have to expend an ounce of energy to obtain them. We only have to drive in, order, and then pick up our food at the drive-through window.

Spurlock's documentary not only served as a wake-up call from a health perspective but also revealed the inner workings of American economics, choice, education, advertising, and the abuses of corporate power.[4] Since the film premiered, the fast-food industry has made some changes to include a few healthier options and to put calorie labels on their menus. It was no coincidence that, six weeks after the movie premiered, McDonald's stopped offering to supersize your meal.

Unfortunately, nearly 20 years later, it seems the eating habits of most Americans haven't changed much at all. Chronic noncommunicable diseases linked to diet are still the single largest cause of illness and death, and the numbers are rising.[5] Over 70% of Americans are overweight, and over 40% are considered obese.[6] Nearly 1 in 10 Americans has type 2 diabetes.[7] Almost 100 million adults maintain elevated cholesterol levels, and 30 million are at high risk for heart disease and stroke.[8] Half of American adults have hypertension—high blood pressure.[9] One person dies every 36 seconds from cardiovascular disease, the leading cause of death in the United States.[10]

These noncommunicable diseases became common in the West only recently; they are the diseases of modernity. They develop slowly, and they persist for years. If they are not halted or cured, they are fatal. Some estimate that almost 90% of Americans, Europeans, and Japanese will die of a noncommunicable disease.[11] These diseases are the primary reason the quality of American life has plummeted. They are also why modern medicine has shifted from keeping us healthy to trying to keep people alive—or, at least, dying for longer.

Thirty-five years ago, a musculoskeletal disease specialist and a biological anthropologist—S. Boyd Eaton and Melvin Konner, respectively—published a review in the *New England Journal of Medicine* that explained their new theory. In the evolutionary discordance hypothesis, Eaton and Konner proposed that today's human nutritional needs evolved over a multimillion-year process. During the hunter-gatherer phase of our history, our species experienced its most definitive and foundational genetic changes, particularly in response to nutritional resource availability.[12] However, in the last 10,000 years, our genes have undergone only minor alterations, and we, as a species, have in no way been able to keep up with the profound cultural changes of modern life.

Eaton and Konner claim that the departure from the patterns of our ancestors has contributed in specific ways to the epidemic of those chronic diseases of modernity, which never or rarely afflicted our ancestors.[13, 14] These scientists are considered the original founders of the Paleo movement.

What we eat can have a positive, protective effect in the prevention and treatment of noncommunicable diseases, or our diet can be a negative, compounding risk factor for them.[15] This is because our nutrition interacts with genetic and environmental factors in complex ways,[16] and what we put into our bodies affects us on a cellular and molecular level.

Archaeological and anthropological evidence demonstrates that every step in the evolution of human anatomy and physiology coincided with the nutritional shifts that enabled them. In this way, "The story of human evolution is a nutritional story," writes anthropologist William Leonard.[17] Just like circadian rhythms, it begins with the original evolution of life on Earth and continues through to the modern day.

The building blocks of life

The story of nutrition starts with the Big Bang, about 14 billion years ago, and the genesis of the foundational units of life. Hydrogen formed the stars, and within them, other atoms emerged: carbon, oxygen, and nitrogen, as well as sulfur and phosphorous. These atoms settled onto Earth when it formed 4.5 billion years ago, and they bonded with each other to form the organic building blocks of life, including amino acids, fatty acids, and sugars. These molecules formed the larger molecules we call macronutrients: Amino acids formed proteins, fatty acids formed fats, and sugars formed carbohydrates.

Around one billion years after the formation of Earth, these macronutrients organized themselves in the primordial soup into protocells and then into the units of life: cells. First, prokaryotic cells emerged—primitive cells without a nucleus or organelles, like the bacteria that still exist today. Nearly two billion years later, the larger, more complex eukaryotes evolved—cells with a defined nucleus and numerous organelles that are now the cells of plants and animals. The same organic atoms and macronutrients that first emerged billions of years ago still form our cells, which demonstrates a larger pattern in biology: Once it has generated something that works, evolution reuses it for billions of years into the future, even while generating variations of it.

Cells are composed of macronutrients and are constantly using them, especially amino acids and fatty acids, to grow, divide, maintain, and rebuild themselves in anabolic (synthesizing) reactions. At the same time, cells are constantly breaking down macronutrients, especially fatty acids and sugars, to generate the molecular energy known as adenosine triphosphate, or ATP. Plant cells make all these nutrients using only sunlight, carbon dioxide, water, and some minerals from the soil. All other cells must replenish these macronutrients through their diet. Let's look at the three macronutrients in more detail.

PROTEINS

Since they are the major structural and functional components of every cell, proteins are the most abundant molecules in the human body besides water. Proteins consist of chains of amino acids that are folded into three-dimensional structures. Nature makes 20 amino acids common to all proteins and one more, called hydroxyproline, that is found in tissue such as collagen. With the number of amino acids and the variation in length and shape, there are millions of unique combinations—and so millions of types of proteins (figure P2.2); the human proteome, however, includes only around 20,000. Our proteins participate in nearly every cellular process imaginable, such as catalyzing metabolic reactions as enzymes, providing scaffolding for individual cells and tissues, responding to stimuli as signaling molecules, transporting molecules around cells, aiding mitosis, and providing immune defense, to name a few.

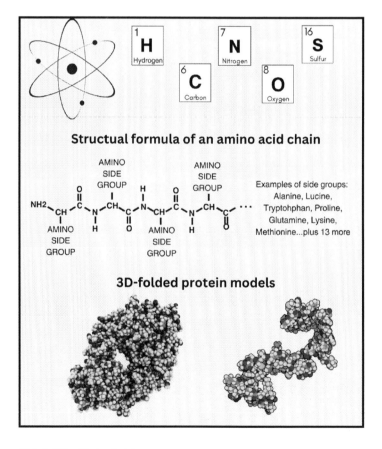

Figure P2.2. Building Blocks: Protein

Plants generate amino acids from glucose and nitrogen, which they gather from the soil. Generally, humans consume only trace amounts of protein from plants except for legumes, nuts, and grains—the seeds of the plant—where proteins are stored so that seedlings can use those amino acids when sprouting. When animals consume proteins, they digest them back into component amino acids that are transported in the blood to cells, where they are taken up and brought to ribosomes, the protein factories. Meanwhile, DNA sends templates called RNA to the ribosomes, which use the amino acids and the RNA templates to make the proteins needed by the cell.

Our bodies do not store or recirculate excess amino acids; rather they get rid of them through oxidizing them into glucose (glucogenesis) or ketones (ketogenesis), which are then used for fuel. Protein generates 4 calories of energy per gram, but this process produces a considerable amount of nitrogenous waste, like urea and ammonia, that are toxic to the body in higher amounts. On the other end, when not receiving enough protein in our diet, we break down protein in our muscles. If we can generate amino acids in our bodies, they are inessential. However, we cannot manufacture nine of them, so we must receive them in our diet. These are essential. Most proteins contain every single amino acid, so when eating any protein, we are acquiring both the essential and nonessential proteins.

Scientists generally rank proteins by their completeness or quality. Generally, animal proteins digest more completely than plant proteins do and contain better ratios of amino acids for use by the body. For this reason, they generally rank dairy and eggs at the top of their list—which makes sense given that these proteins were designed to optimize the growth of baby animals. Next in the ranking are muscle meats like steak, chicken breasts, and fish fillets, followed by soy, one of the few plant-based foods considered to be complete protein. Various plants like beans, nuts, and grains are at the bottom of the rankings; however, proteins from plant foods like these can be combined to generate a protein profile that is as or almost as complete as meat or soy. Collagenous proteins, once ranked at the bottom, have now been found to be beneficial, and when combined with these other quality proteins in the right amounts, they generate even more superior protein profiles.

FATS

About 50 fatty acids have been identified, but we consume only 15 to 20 of them regularly in our diet. Fatty acids are shaped kind of like snakes—with heads followed by long tails—and are categorized by their stiffness. Saturated fatty acids are stiffer at room temperature. Having no carbon-carbon double bonds, saturated fatty acids are straight and can pack together tightly. Monounsaturated fatty acids are more liquid at room temperature because with one (mono) carbon-carbon double bond, the molecules bend more easily and slide past each other. Polyunsaturated fatty acids have more than one carbon-carbon double bond and are even liquid in the freezer because these kinked molecules are much harder to freeze (figure P2.3). Fatty acids are further distinguished by the length of their tails, ranging from short-chain fatty acids (the ones our colon makes), to medium-chain fatty acids, which are all saturated (found predominantly in coconut oil), and long-chain fatty acids.

Polyunsaturated fats are further categorized into omega-3 and omega-6, which refer to their chemical properties. Humans cannot manufacture these polyunsaturated fatty acids, so they are called essential fatty acids, meaning they must be acquired through diet. However, we humans can make the inessential fatty acids—that is, all the saturated and monounsaturated fats—from precursors like glucose, glycerol, and component fatty acids.

Similar to amino acids and proteins, fatty acids form larger molecules called triglycerides and phospholipids. Triglycerides are three fatty acid molecules bound together by a glycerol molecule and are what make up the fatty tissue in animals. Phospholipids are a class of lipid molecules with

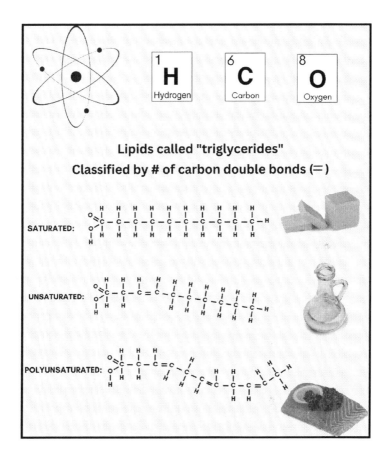

Figure P2.3. Building Blocks: Fat

a "head" containing a phosphate group and one or more "tails" derived from fatty acids that are used to make cell membranes.

We consume nearly all fatty acids from plants and animals as triglycerides and in smaller amounts as phospholipids, then digest all of them back into individual fatty acids. These are absorbed into cells along our intestines that reconstruct them back into triglycerides, which are then attached to lipoproteins—enormous molecules consisting of proteins as well as other fatty substances including cholesterol and fat-soluble vitamins—A, D, K, and E. All of these nutrients are transported through the blood using lipoproteins because fat and water do not mix, causing the fat to glob together, resulting in chaos and blockages—so we evolved to transport our fats on these rafts.

Once they arrive at the cells, these lipoproteins are deconstructed, and the fatty acids are taken up by the cell. Then nearly all of them are catabolized into ATP, and the longer the tail of the fatty acid, the more ATP they generate. So, the longer-chain fatty acids that predominate in our diet generate about 9 calories of energy per gram, which is over twice as much as other nutrients. Our brain, nervous tissue, and red blood cells will not use fatty acids for catabolism; however, most of the remainder of our tissues, such as muscles and organs, prefer fatty acids at normal levels of functioning.

When we are sated with fatty acids, triglycerides travel to our adipose tissues, which are used for cushioning, insulation, and fat storage. Interestingly, adipose fat across humans and primates is stored in the same ratios: 30% saturated, 30% monounsaturated, and the remainder as polyunsaturated. Humans store nearly all polyunsaturated fat as omega-6, linoleic acid. We also use fatty acids in our phospholipids in similar ratios, though it depends on the type of cells with nervous cells using much higher amounts of omega-3.

CARBOHYDRATES

Carbohydrates are composed of the three simple sugars—glucose, fructose, and galactose—connected in various ways (figure P2.4). In nearly all cases, plants make these simple sugars through photosynthesis and then combine them into carbohydrates. Fruit trees make glucose and then convert about half of that glucose into fructose. Then they combine those two sugars into sucrose, which they then put into the fruit—their offspring. The fruit needs to taste sweet and delicious so that animals will eat it, digest the fruit but not the seeds, and then scatter the seeds across the landscape to spread the plant's genes in a new plant. Grasses, like wheat, barley, and

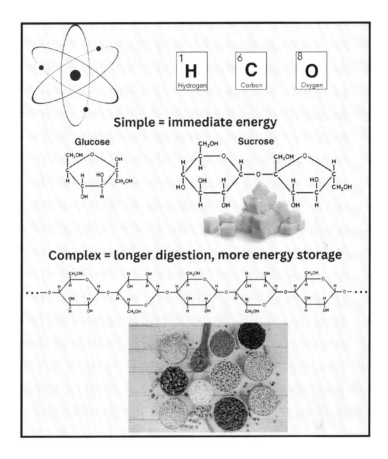

Figure P2.4. Building Blocks: Carbohydrates

oats, combine many molecules of glucose into various starches—called *complex carbohydrates*—to put in their seeds to use as energy before the new plant can access sunlight. Tubers do the same with glucose and then put that starch into their roots to use for energy when they cannot photosynthesize. All plants also combine enormous amounts of glucose into long, branched chains to create fiber—the skin and bones of their bodies. For millions of years, our ancestors specialized in eating plants that store large amounts of sugars, and modern humans still do.

After consuming carbs, we digest them down into their individual sugars. Glucose then goes directly to our cells to generate ATP; however, our bodies cannot use fructose and galactose, except in trace amounts. These sugars are converted into glucose in the liver because they are more unstable than glucose and prone to becoming damaged in our body, generating health problems. Most tissues will take up glucose for fuel, especially immediately after a meal. When our cells are sated with glucose, we store it as glycogen in our liver and muscles for later use. When that storage is full, glucose is converted into fatty acids, which are stored as body fat. So, in that way, eating too many carbs can make us fat.

At normal levels of exertion, only some tissues prefer glucose, including the brain and red blood cells. The rest of our tissues, including our muscles and nearly all our organs, prefer fatty acids. At higher levels of exertion, though, our muscles switch to preferring glucose. One gram of carbs generates 4 calories of energy.

We do not digest the fiber attached to whole plants, even though it is rich in glucose. Instead, the fiber passes through our digestive tract and then lands in our colon, where millions of microorganisms, including bacteria and yeast, break down the soluble fiber, which accounts for about half of the fiber in our diet, into glucose for their own use. In the process, these organisms liberate minerals, phytonutrients, and antioxidants from the fiber, as well as short-chain fatty acids. These nutrients pass from the colon into our blood for use by our bodies.

Humans, along with all other animals, can also make our own glucose through glucogenesis. When we don't eat enough carbs in our diet, we make our own glucose from specific amino acids, either from our diet or pulled from our muscles. We also make ketones from amino acids, which our brains can also use as fuel. Interestingly, many of our ancestors consumed diets that consisted almost entirely of animal foods, so to provide glucose for their brains, they lived in constant glucogenesis and ketogenesis.

To understand nutrition, think about the macronutrients on one side and then the two types of metabolism, catabolism and anabolism, on the other side.

We consume proteins and fats for anabolism throughout our cells—to make parts of ourselves. If we don't eat enough protein, we pull it from our muscles, and if we eat too much, we convert it into other nutrients— namely, glucose and ketones.

We also consume fats for anabolism, specifically for the various membranes throughout our cells, and for catabolism, specifically for energy generation. If we don't receive fat in our diet, we can use body fat for several days or weeks or make it from excess carbohydrates. When we consume too much fat, it recirculates back into our blood and is stored as body fat.

We consume carbohydrates for catabolism for our brain and red blood cells, as well as other tissues, but we consume more of them if we engage in moderate to intense levels of exercise. When we don't receive enough carbs in our diet, we start converting amino acids from dietary excesses or from our muscle tissues into glucose. When we consume too much glucose, we store it as fat. Generally, all animals are striving to consume all the nutrients they need in their proper amounts and ratios so that, under most circumstances, they do not need to store or convert any of them more than necessary.

The proverbial saying "you are what you eat" isn't just a metaphor. What we eat is used to provide for the energy for every cellular process and to build every cellular structure of the body required for life. Nutrition is integral to the growth, maintenance, reproduction, and health of an organism. Not only does what we eat directly affect our functioning and health, but it can also be the direct cause of many preventable diseases. Once we learn how we evolved to use the nutrition provided to us from nature and start changing our eating habits, we can avoid these diseases before they start, mitigate their effects, or reverse their course.

CHAPTER 5

THE EVOLUTION OF NUTRITION

Living organisms thrive best in the milieu and on the diet to which they were evolutionarily adopted; this is a fundamental axiom of biology.

—JAMES H. O'KEEFE

The single-cell prokaryotes emerged on Earth about 3.5 million years ago, when atmospheric oxygen was low. They were anaerobic, meaning they catabolized nutrients into ATP without using oxygen. Some of these prokaryotes evolved into the predecessors of plants and started to photosynthesize glucose while releasing enormous amounts of oxygen into the atmosphere over hundreds of millions of years. This oxygen was harmful to life because it could potentially damage other organic molecules through oxidation, so the prokaryotes evolved in two ways. Some hid away in places without much oxygen, like deep in the Earth or ocean. Many of these bacteria live in our colon and fermentation vats today. Others, who lived on the surface, evolved antioxidants to neutralize the damage from oxygen. Some of this group even evolved to use the electrons in oxygen in catabolism, allowing them to aerobically generate more ATP than their predecessors, which is why we are breathing today. Later, one of these prokaryotes engulfed another cell that became the mitochondria, the powerhouse, of the host. This gave rise to larger, more complex and energetic cells called *eukaryotes*, which inhabit all plants and animals alive today.

As they evolved, some eukaryotes were already like tiny animals in their *foodways*—in how they acquired food from their environment and used the underlying nutrients. Eukaryotes sense nutrients using proteins on their cell surface and respond in some way. Some cells wait for the nutrient to come to them, and their reaction is to absorb it when it approaches. Other cells move toward the nutrient via a variety of mechanisms, such as flagella, cilia, or pseudopods. Cells often move toward concentrations of nutrients, where the cell can passively absorb it through its cell membrane, actively transport it across its cell membrane with proteins, or extend pseudopods to surround, engulf, and then consume it in a process called *phagocytosis*.

Inside the cells, enzymes break down the nutrients into their base components. Eukaryotes then anabolize amino acids and fatty acids to make their bodies and use glucose and fatty acids, as well as other compounds, to make energy. Billions of years later, human hunter-gatherers used the same foodways—sensing, moving, capturing, ingesting, digesting, absorbing, and metabolizing food—showing once again how evolution tends to replicate the same working patterns (figure 5.1).

Soon, these eukaryotes combined with other cells to generate multicellular organisms. At first, these organisms were just collections of similar cells. However, in time, those cells differentiated from each other to make tissues to perform specialized roles within the larger organisms. This led to plants and animals. Animals, in particular, evolved collections of cells that served as eyes, legs, stomachs, intestines, vascular systems, and brains while still replicating the foodways of their predecessors.

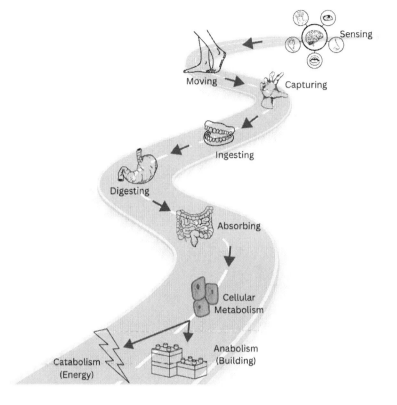

Figure 5.1. Foodways

Foodway adaptations

At any given moment, most animals are well adapted to their foodways because they have been living in the same reasonably stable environment for millions of years. However, animals will have to modify their food-ways if their ecosystem changes due to climate or geography shifts; if the flora, fauna, microorganisms, or even pathogens within their ecosystem undergo alterations; or if they migrate into a new ecosystem. After such an ecological change, foodways are usually disrupted: Their food changes, disappears, declines in quantity, or becomes harder to attain. When this happens, they may starve or even die. In order to survive, they must adapt.

The first way they can adapt is by changing their behavior. If a food source becomes scarce, animals have other foods they can turn to, even though they may be harder to obtain and less nutritious. For example, a primate who prefers fruit will start digging in the Earth for starchy roots when fruit is scarce.

When these behavioral changes do not work, they then may adapt through epigenetics—automatic processes that change the expression of their genes (but do not change the genes themselves). For example, some genes may turn on and off to varying degrees. However, scientists currently do not have tools to measure when epigenetics is happening.

However, with real and lasting changes to their environment, animals must adapt through evolution by natural selection. Genetic changes in offspring are generated by either random mutations or genetic shuffling during sexual reproduction. These genetic changes affect the function of a gene, and this functional change may be beneficial to the survival of offspring. If so, the organism is more likely to survive until it can pass its mutated genes to the next generation. In some cases, natural selection generates changes in existing species, but evolution is the accumulation of many favorable mutations over countless generations that may result in an entirely new species.

Primates

About two hundred million years ago, during the age of the dinosaurs, mammals evolved. They were small and nocturnal, limited in their evolution by the ravenous monsters that stomped around them. However, when the dinosaurs went extinct, these mammals soon evolved to become the largest, most dominant animals on Earth while radiating into nearly every ecosystem and adapting their foodways along the way. About 60 million years ago, some of them arrived in tropical rainforests and evolved into the first of our common primate ancestors: the tiny, nocturnal insectivore called the *purgatorious*. Anthropologist Katharine Milton writes, "The strategies early primates adopted to cope with the dietary challenges of the arboreal environment profoundly influenced the evolutionary trajectory of the primate order, particularly that of the anthropoids (monkeys, apes, and humans)."[1]

Over the next few tens of millions of years, primates radiated outward into various niches within rainforests, evolving their foodways while developing into new species. Some stayed small, nocturnal, and insectivorous, similar to tarsiers. Some became larger, diurnal, and folivorous (leaf eating), like the howler and colobus monkeys of today. Some, like the baboons, became larger, lived on the ground, and consumed omnivorous diets of grasses, roots, fruits, and animals.

Some primates became more and more like humans would eventually be. Generally, these primates tended toward a higher-quality diet, as well as greater intelligence and sociability. Many of these primates, like the nonhuman great apes (chimps, bonobos, gorillas, and orangutans), share a more recent common ancestor with us. Others diverged from our lineage before the great apes' common ancestor, including the capuchin, spider, and macaque monkeys. Some evolved in the Americas, separate from our own line of evolution. Even though they evolved separately from our ape ancestors, they evolved the same high intelligence when exposed to the same foodways as their distant cousins.

Remarkably, the foodways of the more human-like primates both allowed and required the evolution of larger brains. Bigger brains facilitated wit and behavioral skills, such as remembering the exact location of trees, how to get there, when these trees bear ripe fruit, and which foods to selectively eat. These skills enhanced their success in procuring that high-quality diet.[2]

We have an intense interest in the foodways and diet of chimpanzees for several reasons. First, chimpanzees (and bonobos) are the most like us of any species on Earth. They are not our direct ancestors; however, chimps, bonobos, and humans shared a common ancestor who lived five million to seven million years ago, from which all three species evolved. These three species share 98% of their DNA. Second, these two primates are the most similar to foraging humans in both their foodways and their social behaviors. Third, chimpanzees and especially bonobos highly resemble *Australopithecus*, one of the first species in the human lineage after it split from the common ancestor. They resemble those ancient prehumans in stature and in the size and complexity of the brain,[3] although *Australopithecus* walked upright. For all these reasons, chimpanzees are one of the closest models we have of the theoretical common ancestor of chimps, bonobos, and humans—the primate that launched our line of evolution toward human. Using chimps as a model of that ancestor will help tell the story of how human foodways evolved.

The chimpanzee diet

Chimpanzees consume a high-quality omnivorous diet. This means it contains all the nutrients they need so they don't have to convert many nutrients into other nutrients inside their body. Their diet is dense in macronutrients—primarily carbohydrates but also amino acids and fatty acids. Their foods are also easier to digest than those of other primates because they are lower (but still ample) in fiber and antinutrients (which block the absorption of nutrients) and toxins. Their dietary staple is fruit, one of the best carbs available in nature. Natural fruits contain less fructose than our modern domesticated fruits.[4] Chimps receive plenty of carbs to feed their larger brains; in fact, that abundance of carbs provided them the nutrients to evolve those larger brains in the first place.

Chimps also eat small amounts of tender leaves and some nuts, seeds, and piths. Although all these plants are low in protein, chimps eat them in considerable amounts and acquire most of their protein from them. However, plants, especially wild ones, are not the best sources of proteins.

They are difficult to digest and usually contain considerable amounts of antinutrients and toxins. To overcome this, chimps carefully select the plants they eat and sometimes eat only certain parts of a plant at certain times, such as young leaves and buds.[5] Chimps prefer these selections because they are the highest in protein, the lowest in toxins, and the lowest in fiber. In eating all these plants, they also consume enormous amounts of fiber, about 100 grams per day. The microorganisms in the chimpanzee gut ferment this fiber and generate many different nutrients used by the body.[6]

Chimps also eat animals but in small amounts, including ants, termites, and other insects. Male chimps hunt monkeys like the red colobus and bush babies and even small antelopes when fruit is unavailable.[7] They are more opportunistic hunters, not habitual ones, and usually hunt only when the barriers and costs are low.[8] Chimps spend less time hunting than gathering plant foods, but hunting requires much more time (approximately 30% of their time) and provides fewer calories (approximately 4% of their diet).[9] In short, chimps eat animals only in small amounts, but even those small amounts provide essential fatty acids or amino acids, micro and trace minerals, and even vitamins.[10] That limited quantity is important; chimps in captivity eat greater amounts of meat and develop hypercholesterolemia and vascular disease.[11]

Chimpanzees always consume all of their prey, including the muscle proteins, collagen proteins, and organs. They prefer the liver, which provides them with enormous amounts of preformed vitamins A and B12, and fattier tissues like the adipose, tongue, and brain, which are extremely high in cholesterol and the essential long-chain polyunsaturated fatty acids. Animal proteins are easier to digest than plant proteins and are devoid of toxins and antinutrients. Eating the whole animal combines the best ratios of amino acids and the best balance of micronutrients.

Overall, chimpanzees consume about 15% of their calories from protein, which comes from a mix of plants and animals. They get about 5% to

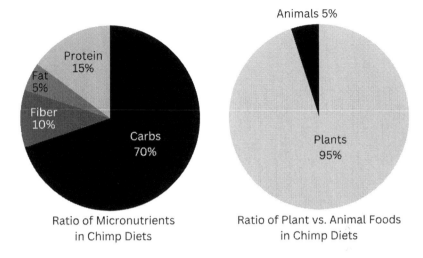

Figure 5.2. Macronutrient and Plant versus Animal Foods Ratios

10% of their calories from dietary fatty acids and about 10% from colonic fats that result from the fermentation of fiber. Those fats are likely somewhere around 30% to 50% polyunsaturated, predominantly from plants, at about two parts omega-6 to one part omega-3, and the remainder is split between saturated and monounsaturated fat, probably in somewhat equal ratios. The remaining 65% to 70% of their calories come from carbs (figure 5.2). They consume about 60% of those carbs as glucose and the remainder as fructose.

Chimpanzee foodways

Most mammals see, hear, and smell their food, but when they adapted to the daytime jungle, primates favored vision. In fact, both chimps and humans possess olfactory DNA that no longer functions.[12] They mostly use their ears for hearing other members of their troop and their noses tangentially for their foodways. Chimpanzees sense three colors and the combinations of them. This allows them to distinguish the various colors of fruit. Chimps are very good at differentiating red from green, so they can identify ripe fruit and flushed young red leaves that are high in protein.[13] They have excellent visual acuity, both close and far,[14] and their forward-set eyes allow stereoscopic vision for good depth perception.[15]

Primates evolved their tastes to identify the foods they want to eat and those they want to avoid. Chimpanzees have the same five tastes as humans—sweet, salty, sour, umami, and bitter—but with different levels of sensitivity. They are less sensitive to bitterness and astringency and can tolerate bitter plants more than we can, and they can also tolerate the toxins in these plants better.

Primates also move differently from the way most other mammals do. To live in the trees, they needed to climb and jump, and some also needed to move well over the ground. However, omnivorous primates, including chimpanzees, evolved locomotion superior to that of other folivorous and carnivorous primates. Chimps can climb well through the trees but can also move along the ground. This allows them to control larger vertical and horizontal territories to acquire their food. They can also travel farther over the course of one day, allowing them to collect their scattered and seasonal foods.

Omnivorous primates also tend to have better and more diverse ways of capturing food than other primates do. Chimpanzees may need to hang in more complex ways to grab their fruit. Thanks to their opposable thumbs, they can create and use tools: straws, sticks for dipping (for termites, ants, or honey), sponges, and rock hammers and anvils.[16, 17, 18] Male chimpanzees cooperate to hunt, using many of the same strategies that humans do, such as surrounding prey, corralling, and using crudely sharpened sticks to kill. Capturing the sheer variety of foods chimpanzees eat requires a broad range of innate and learned skills.

For ingestion, omnivorous primates tend to have smaller mouths, teeth, and jaws than folivores, but not insectivores, because they are consuming softer, easier-to-digest foods like fruits and insects. Chimpanzee teeth are larger than human teeth, but they have the same dentition pattern typical of all primates, including humans. They have 32 teeth—incisors, canines, premolars, and molars—in the same number and in the same order as our own. However, they have prominent spaces between the teeth and much larger canines than other species do.[19] These large canines allow chimps to kill prey with their teeth. Their jaw muscles are large and powerful because they spend a lot of time chewing plant material. In fact, they chew about five hours a day; we only have to chew about 30 minutes.

Chimpanzees evolved much smaller digestive systems than other primates did because their foods require less room and energy to digest. Fruits are richer in macronutrients and lower in fiber, allowing more to be absorbed in the small intestine. Chimps have huge colons that account for half of their gut volume and an overall larger gut size relative to their body mass than humans do. They eat enormous amounts of fiber compared to us, but chimps eat smaller amounts of fiber than folivores do, including gorillas, so they evolved much smaller colons than other primates did.[20]

In this case, we see some interesting, circular relationships between foodways. Chimpanzees eat higher-quality foods that require smaller digestive systems, so they carry less weight, which allows them superior locomotion, which, in turn, allows them to access more territory to acquire their higher-quality and scattered foods. These smaller guts also need fewer nutrients, which allows them to direct more nutrients to their brain— which then helps them acquire their higher-quality foods.

During digestion, chimpanzees use the sugars from fruit and other carbs to provide glucose for their brain. From their variety of plant foods, as well as insects, they provide themselves with amino and fatty acids for anabolism. And finally, they ferment much of the fiber in their gut into the three short-chain fatty acids, which then provide fuel for various cells throughout their body, including their brains.

Chimpanzee foodways can be a lot more challenging than what we've presented because of the obstacles they face. Chimps are at risk of predation themselves and of attacks from rival gangs. Their food is scattered, and acquiring it requires adept locomotion and ingenuity. They must compete for this food against other species, rival chimps, and even members of their own group. Finally, foods are defended. Animals do not want to be eaten, so they must be hunted through enormous effort. Plants also do not want to be eaten, except for their fruit, so they defend themselves with thorns, fuzzes, and chemical toxins and antinutrients. When adding these obstacles to their foodways, we see that the challenges increase considerably, and these challenges drive evolution.

Chimpanzee sociability and intelligence

Folivores live in small groups, and insectivores live alone, but omnivorous primates, including chimpanzees, are intensely social. Primates likely evolved to live in large groups to avoid predation. One primate can warn others about predators in their territory, increasing the chances of survival for every member of the group. However, chimpanzees are also better at foraging in groups, since their food is more widespread. They can spread out and travel through their territory to find food, vocalizing to alert the others when they find it. They can also hunt better in groups, often corralling animals by directing them toward others in their group. Chimpanzees share food with each other whenever one encounters more food than it can consume alone. Finally, it is easier for a group of chimps to protect their territory by acting together.

The omnivores also have the largest brains and highest level of cognition of all primates, with chimpanzees ranking highest of all. Chimpanzees have the highest encephalization quotient—the size and complexity of their brains relative to their body size—of all nonhuman primates. (See figure 5.3 for a comparison of encephalization quotients of many mammals.)[21] Initially, these primates became so smart because of their foodways, then became even smarter because of the size and complexity of their social groups.

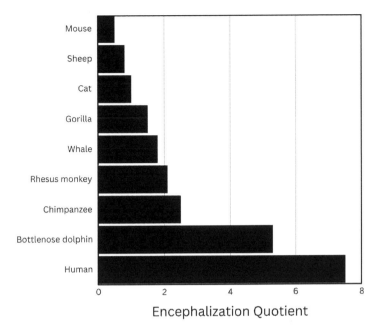

Figure 5.3. Comparing the Encephalization Quotient in Mammals

Source data: Roth, G. Dicke, U. 2005. "Evolution of the brain and intelligence." Trends in Cognitive Sciences 9 (5): 250–257.

Animals cannot evolve a new trait unless their nutrition supports that trait, and in the evolution of chimpanzees, foodways and intelligence are closely tied together. First, they consume a diverse and high-quality diet that provides them with the nutrients their brains most need: glucose for catabolism and cholesterol and long-chain polyunsaturated fatty acids for anabolism. With their larger brains, chimps can better navigate their large territories and understand the identities, attributes, qualities, and locations of so many plant and animal foods. They can solve problems in acquiring their food. They also developed the use of tools to make obtaining food easier, a behavioral trait enabled by their intelligence.

Chimpanzees need those large brains to live in large social groups because they need to identify the other members and to know how to both compete and cooperate with them. These social groups, in turn, help in the procurement of food. Obstacles to their foodways, including the risk of predation, competition, and animal and plant defenses, forced all the foodways that require intelligence to evolve even more. Brains are expensive; they require more calories relative to their mass than other organs do, so chimps have to eat more nutrients of higher quality, most of which are harder to acquire. To make that expense worthwhile, the brain had to provide greater value.

Chimpanzee foodways, highly varied diets, and the flexibility and adaptability to survive in many environments demonstrate how their intelligence affects their nutritional status—and the inverse: how their nutrition affected their intelligence. These same patterns in foodways continued into *Australopithecus,* into early *Homo* species, and even into humans. The foodways and diet of chimpanzees give us a good idea of the nutritional needs of our shared ancestor. Seven million years ago, that omnivorous ancestor was ready to embark on the journey to becoming human.

CHAPTER 6

THE HUMAN LINEAGE

Dietary needs apparently allowed for natural selection to favor increased brain size in the human lineage and the concomitant development of technological, social, and other abilities directed at securing these nutrients; in this sense, it can be said that diet influenced, indeed drove, human evolution.

–KATHARINE MILTON

For about 50 million years, primates lived throughout Africa in tropical rainforests—even as the continents farther north ranged from glacial maximums to retreats. Our common ancestor, living in similar ways to chimpanzees, inhabited East Africa about seven million years ago, marking the starting point of our evolution toward *Homo sapiens*. Around this time, the tectonic plates between East and West Africa collided and caused the formation of a mountain range and, soon after, the Great Rift that separated the east and west parts of the continent. West Africa remained mostly tropical rainforests, where most Old World primates now live.

However, on the other side of the mountains, East Africa's climate changed radically. Over millions of years, it became mostly hotter and drier. It also fluctuated back toward cooler and wetter periods at times too.[1] With this warming and drying trend, the region started losing its trees, replaced with areas of forests, shrubland, grasslands, and even deserts. As trees declined in number, the primates that inhabited this region, including our common ancestor, lost their principal foods of fruits and leaves, as well as many animal foods. Under this evolutionary pressure, the common ancestor split into two lines.

The one that would lead to chimpanzees and bonobos stayed in West Africa, whereas the more dynamic environment of East Africa stimulated the profound evolutionary changes in the human line: *Australopithecus* evolved more than four million years ago and was more like a chimpanzee who walked upright. *Homo erectus* ("upright man") evolved from *Australopithecus* around two million years ago and was more like a human (figure 6.1).

Australopithecus

Our East African ancestor was forced to adapt their foodways to this changing environment or perish, starting the long and arduous journey toward becoming human. They adapted in the usual ways, first by changing some behaviors, but behavioral adaptation only worked up to a point. Their

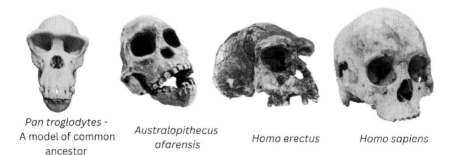

Pan troglodytes -
A model of common
ancestor

*Australopithecus
afarensis*

Homo erectus

Homo sapiens

Figure 6.1. The Skull Evolution of the Human Line

bodies also had to physiologically adapt their foodways to sense, move to, capture, ingest, and digest the new foods available in the changing ecosystem. This natural selection resulted in the creation of a new species, *Australopithecus afarensis*.

Australopithecus possessed many of the same traits as the common ancestor. For example, they retained their good color vision and depth perception. Eating fewer plant foods in favor of animals probably caused them to become more sensitive to the taste of bitter as their food became less toxic, however. They were about the same size and weight and consumed about the same number of calories, although *Australopithecus* guts are hypothesized to have become smaller. Considering their anatomy and comparing them with other primates, we suspect that *Australopithecus* also consumed diets like our other omnivorous primate ancestors. Some morphological evidence suggests that *Australopithecus* brains were slightly larger, and genetic evidence suggests greater intelligence. They probably had a social structure and group size equivalent to the common ancestor as well.

EVOLVING DIET AND FOODWAYS

East Africa still had trees, but they were fewer and farther apart. *Australopithecus* could still find their usual foods, such as fruit and tender leaves, in these trees, but they were more widely dispersed than the common ancestor's foods were,[2] so to find the same amount, they had to extend both their territories and daily ranges. Covering so much land required a more efficient type of locomotion. The types of food available to them changed, too, as more plant and animal ground foods became part of their diet. *Australopithecus* adapted its foodways through natural selection.

With food sources more scattered, *Australopithecus* evolved pelvic and foot structures that allowed the first bipedal locomotion, allowing them to cover a larger daily range.[3] It is more energetically efficient than knuckle-walking, so upright walking provided their bodies an energy savings.[4] However, *Australopithecus* hand morphology tells us that they could still climb trees and use arboreal locomotion.[5]

The new foods acquired by *Australopithecus* required different hunting and gathering practices as well. The availability of early animal foods, such as termites and smaller primates, would also have declined as the forest retreated. However, terrestrial animals, which were more plentiful in their new environment, replaced these foods. Their hunting was not unlike the common ancestor's, due to a similar level of encephalization. They got more protein and fat by expanding the types of animals they hunted, such as rodents, lizards, and shellfish—animals they could easily catch—and used crude tools to smash or kill the animals.

Like chimpanzees, *Australopithecus* ate all parts of the animals they hunted—brains, livers, muscles, and even connective tissue collagen protein. These animal products provided more refined protein and fat that were easier to digest, had less fiber, were free of toxins and antinutrients, and contained the best balance of both amino acids and fatty acids, including the cholesterol and long-chain polyunsaturated fat needed by the brain. They started the hominin evolutionary trend of eating more animal foods as they became available. However, hominins did not become exclusive carnivores, because of the limiting speed of their protein metabolism. The body cannot break down high levels of protein and excrete urea fast enough before toxic levels of ammonia buildup in the blood.[6]

Australopithecus still obtained most of their protein and fat macronutrients from plants, though. For example, seeds became nutritionally rich sources of proteins, fatty acids, starches, and micronutrients. However, they had to learn new methods to gather their new terrestrial plant foods, which are harder to obtain and to extract nutrients from and tougher to chew and digest. *Australopithecus* teeth became larger and flatter, their tooth enamel thickened, and their jaws became thicker and stronger.[7] With the consumption of increasingly starchy ground foods like tubers, piths, seeds, and grains, the genes for amylase, the enzyme that breaks down starch, started undergoing copy number expansion in *Australopithecus*.[8]

Australopithecus still relied on tree foods, such as fruits, as their main source of carbohydrates, glucose in particular. The roots, tubers, seeds, and berries they added to their diet would later become important sources of carbohydrates. By eating less fruit, they also reduced their consumption of fructose, which provided numerous benefits, since fructose requires conversion in our bodies to glucose and is less stable than glucose, and therefore, potentially damaging. Their diet also maintained a high proportion of fiber, thus gaining fuel from short-chain fatty acids.

The gut and especially the colon in *Australopithecus* may have been slightly smaller than their predecessors due to their changing diet and foodways, which was allowed by the higher-quality nutrition than the common ancestor. It was the continuation of the trend of evolution shrinking other energetically expensive organs to provide increased fuel for the ever-growing and metabolically costly brain. With slightly larger brains, the members of this genus would have increased their resting metabolic expenditure by a few percentage points (up to 11%) over nonhuman primates (8% to 10%).[9]

SOCIABILITY AND INTELLIGENCE

Australopithecus would have needed to maintain or increase their sociability and cognition to obtain new foods scattered in their new environments. The enhanced nutrition these foods provided, in turn, allowed them to evolve greater sociability and cognition. Levels of cognition are correlated with levels of encephalization, but *Australopithecus* only underwent a modest increase in brain size from our common ancestor's, from 400 to 500 cubic centimeters over two million years. However, in this time, *Australopithecus* laid the groundwork for the evolution of even larger brains in the *Homo* line.[10]

To provide fuel for the brain's higher metabolic requirements and the fatty acid building blocks for brain tissue, *Australopithecus* needed more carbohydrates and fats. Our genetic and behavioral preferences for sweet or fatty foods evolved to ensure enough brain food was consumed. Late *Australopithecus* was the first hominid to show a gene duplication event in the brain's SRGAP2 gene, which is involved in neuronal lengthening and branching, neuronal migration and differentiation, synaptic development, neuronal density, and increasing the number of cortical neurons.[11] This increased the brain's processing power.

Homo erectus

About two million years ago, as East Africa's climate continued becoming hotter and dryer but with more short periods of cooler and wetter climate, and as the trees continued to disappear, *Australopithecus* struggled to keep up. They could not walk long enough distances to feed themselves, and they were especially susceptible to predation on the open savannah. Their brains did not evolve enough for them to use intelligence to adapt to the constant environmental change.

Fortunately, before becoming extinct, *Australopithecus* evolved into *Homo habilis* and *Homo ergaster*, who then evolved into *Homo erectus*. Once *Homo erectus* evolved, *Australopithecus* disappeared, suggesting that *Homo erectus* started competing for the same foods with them—and wiped them out. *Homo erectus* then spread out of Africa.

The unrelenting decline of trees meant the continued loss of plant and animal foods in the jungle. *Homo erectus* adapted through natural selection, of course. However, in Africa, they inhabited ecosystems that were changing fast, and natural selection is often too slow to keep pace with rapid environmental changes. The much larger brain of *Homo erectus* enabled greater intelligence than *Australopithecus*, which led to social and technological innovations. That larger brain allowed *Homo erectus* to adapt to their environment more through cultural evolution than through natural selection, which, in turn, allowed for more rapid adaptation.

EVOLVING DIET AND FOODWAYS

Natural selection shaped *Homo erectus* foodways in response to their changing diet and means of retrieving it. *Homo erectus* vision adapted to better make sense of large and wide images in open terrain to spot scattered foods. To reach these foods, *Homo erectus* perfected bipedalism to move efficiently with walking, jogging, or running due to the evolution of large gluteus maximus muscles, more springy tendons in the leg and foot, and shoulder changes that allowed for better balance.[12] At this point, they looked like thinner and shorter versions of humans but with noticeably smaller skulls.

To feed their larger bodies and brains, the territory of a *Homo erectus* had to become ten times that of *Australopithecus*, which is one hypothesis for why *Homo erectus* had an abrupt expansion out of Africa; they were following the food.[13] The energy to cover such long distances required the new higher-quality foods as well.

With better locomotion and higher cognitive abilities, capturing food became easier. *Homo erectus* became more sophisticated hunters, using techniques such as persistence hunting (chasing an animal to exhaustion, then killing it with axes or spears)[14] or driving the animals off cliffs to hunt larger game animals. Some of the first stone tools, such as the sharpened stone hand axe, were used to kill and then process animal carcasses.[15] *Homo erectus* could bring down an antelope or a wild pig, which would have increased both the amount and the quality of their protein and fat intake. They, too, would eat the entire animal, from brains to tendons.

Homo erectus evolved smaller teeth as they started to process their foods before eating them. They used stone tools to grind their food into smaller particles; they also started to cook their food. With these techniques, *Homo erectus* essentially prechewed and partially predigested their food,[16] making it easier to digest so that larger teeth and jaws were no longer crucial. This increased the digestibility and energy availability of their new foods. They also evolved less specialized teeth, which could be used to consume a wider range of foods.[17]

Homo erectus easily fulfilled their anabolic needs with the surplus of protein and fat in their diet. These energy-dense nutrients would also help *Homo erectus* more easily meet their catabolic energy needs.[18] Also, because animal products provided more nutrition for its weight, *Homo erectus* could use more space in the gut for carbohydrate-rich plant foods, which fueled their increasingly larger brains.[19] Animal-based foods became more essential to fulfilling the nutritional requirements of this species, so they became a significant part of their diet.

In addition, animal fat provided the long-chain polyunsaturated fatty acids that are critical for brain development and function. Increased intake of these fats was key to encephalization, since hominins are poor converters of short-chain polyunsaturated fatty acids, found in plants, into the long-chain forms that are used for neural membrane synthesis and neural transmission and reception.[20] With increased consumption of animal tissue, the human lineage selected for meat-adaptive genes, such Apo3, a gene important for processing triglyceride-rich lipoproteins and mediating cholesterol metabolism. This allele is found in humans but not in chimpanzees and protects against cardiovascular disease, which is associated with eating meat and a diet higher in fat.[21]

Homo erectus had even less access to fruit, so starches from the ground became more and more critical. They used crude hoes and sickles to obtain starchy foods such as tubers and other roots, and they became even more dependent on these ground foods as fruit disappeared.[22] To digest more starches, *Homo erectus* also continued the gene expansion of the amylase enzyme to accommodate even more starchy foods. Today, the average human has three times more copies of the gene than chimpanzees and eight times as much amylase in their saliva.[23]

Starches are very dense sources of glucose and provide more glucose than fructose, which makes them a higher-quality macronutrient. More glucose meant more ATP production to better feed a growing brain. Consuming more animals, *Homo erectus* consumed a much less bulky and fibrous diet—although still vastly more than modern humans—but compensated for the loss of fuel from short-chain fatty acids by consuming more animal fat. The energy expenditure of *Homo erectus* was more than 80% greater than that of *Australopithecus*,[24] and the evolving diet of *Homo erectus* provided energy-dense fuel to meet this need.

The gut size of the human lineage continued to shrink, especially the colon. Their more energy-rich, higher-quality, and less bulky and fibrous diet made digestion easier, and preprocessing food outside the body also helped. However, as their overall gut length shrank, the small intestines lengthened to better absorb fats and proteins from animal foods.[25] Because the digestive tract requires a lot of energy, a smaller gut meant that the energy could be used elsewhere, like the brain. Finally, as the Homo line approached humans, more and more body fat was stored to cope with food shortages and the increasing energy needs of the brain.[26]

CULTURAL EVOLUTION

By the time we reached *Homo erectus*, the human line had started adapting to their environment more through culture than through physical changes. As some moved out of Africa, *Homo erectus* encountered rapidly changing ecosystems that natural selection was too slow to address. Genetic evolution fell out of step with the pace of cultural change.[27] Adaptations could now happen immediately or within a few generations through behavioral changes, rather than taking eons through genetic drift or mutation. These cultural adaptations were made possible by the continued evolution of larger brains and greater intelligence.

Such evolution affected the way they hunted and gathered. For example, when *Homo erectus* needed to hunt larger animals to attain their high-quality fat and protein, they didn't need to evolve faster legs or sharp fangs. They instead used their growing intellect to devise more cooperative and complex hunting strategies and to create spears and knives and then to perfect their use.[28] They used tools to gather plants, such as long poles to reach fruits, crude scythes to harvest grains, and hoes to unearth tubers.

Culture also affected the number and kinds of new foods *Homo erectus* consumed. They were now able to hunt larger animals and more of them. A rabbit would provide a meal for a small group, but an antelope would yield more than 30 times the amount of food while requiring only about 3 times more effort to capture and kill. Hunting herd animals also allowed *Homo erectus* to hunt and kill more than one animal at a time.

Food processing was another cultural evolution that radically changed foodways. Grinding their food dramatically decreased chewing time, which led to smaller teeth and jaws. *Homo erectus* may have also soaked or fermented their foods to make them softer and easier to chew. Importantly, *Homo erectus* was the first in the human lineage to use fire. Cooking meant less time was needed for processing and chewing foods. Cooking food predigested it, breaking down the food's cell walls, breaking chemical bonds, denaturing proteins, softening fibers, and even destroying toxins, making nutrient absorption easier and reducing the cost of digestion. Not only was more energy released from food, but the energy formerly used by the digestive tract was freed up. Primatologist Richard Wrangham hypothesizes that starting with *Homo erectus*, fire was a central force in human evolution—especially of our large brains.[29]

Nearly all animals eat food where they find it, but processing meant that *Homo erectus* would need to bring the food back to a central place to prepare and cook it. There, they would share the food with others, creating social bonds. This new foodway—sharing—helped the entire group better nourish themselves and prevent starvation while also increasing cooperation. Finally, *Homo erectus* likely began storing food, drying or smoking it, and storing it in animal skins or plant containers (such as gourds) in the ground to prevent theft.

SOCIABILITY AND INTELLIGENCE

Homo erectus were beginning to resemble humans more than other primates in their social behavior. The demands of such interpersonal and communal relationships were impossible without a bigger brain. The foods they ate provided the energy for those larger brains, and in turn, these larger brains helped them acquire increasingly challenging food.

Anthropologist William Leonard writes, "Diet and brain expansion probably interacted synergistically: Bigger brains produced more complex social behavior, which led to further shifts in foraging tactics and improved diet, which, in turn, fostered additional brain evolution."[30] The combination of nutritional, physiological, and genetic changes in the brain that began in *Australopithecus* continued in *Homo erectus*, whose brain size grew to be 900 cubic centimeters, more than double the size of the common ancestor's brain, and they would have consumed 17% of this species' resting energy.[31] Figure 6.2 is a graph that represents the trajectory of hominin brain growth.[32]

Millions of years after the East African geological shift, the newfound dietary diversity and flexibility—and those bigger brains—of *Homo erectus* allowed them to disperse out of Africa and into all the major biomes of Earth.[33] With these changes as a backdrop, *Homo erectus* marked the beginning of more adaptations coming via cultural evolution than via the rigid and slow biological evolution through natural selection. *Homo erectus* developed a strongly cooperative hunter-gatherer society, where game animals became important and resource sharing among the members of a group started to become commonplace.[34] Our bodies, brains, behaviors, and diet were ready to support the evolution of *Homo sapiens*.

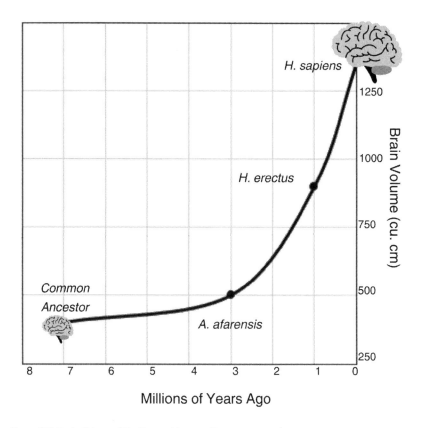

Figure 6.2. Brain Volume of the Human Line over Time

Source data: Carroll, S.B. 2003. "Genetics and the making of Homo sapiens." Nature 422 (6934): 849-857.

HUNTER-GATHERER NUTRITION

The characteristics that most distinguish humans from other primates are largely the results of natural selection acting to improve the quality of the human diet and the efficiency with which our ancestors obtained food.

–WILLIAM LEONARD

Some 300,000 years ago, the climate in East Africa continued to fluctuate, which generated considerable instability in the flora and fauna and the availability of food in the region. *Homo erectus* was not smart enough to adapt to these changes, so we evolved into another primate, *Homo sapiens*—us. Around 400,000 to 200,000 years ago, some version of *Homo sapiens* evolved in Ethiopia in arid terrains surrounded by lakes. From there, we migrated into South Africa, settling into caves along the coast. Once *Homo sapiens* appeared, *Homo erectus* disappeared, suggesting that the two species competed for the same foods and territories. Obviously, the more evolved species won.

Physiologically, *Homo sapiens* remained mostly the same as *Homo erectus*, with a few exceptions. First, we evolved smaller jaws and teeth—and probably slightly smaller guts as well because we consumed even more refined and predigested foods. We evolved the ability to store and mobilize large quantities of body fat[1] to buffer us from periods of food shortage and to keep our bodies going and brains nourished.[2] We also evolved slightly taller and more robust bodies, perhaps to protect against predators. But most importantly, our brains evolved to be about 30% to 40% larger, with most of that devoted to cognition. This increased brain power allowed us to become exponentially smarter, profoundly enhancing our adaptations through cultural evolution. We probably evolved these larger brains instead of other morphological changes because of the rapidity of changes to the environments that outpaced natural selection. We needed a faster and more efficient way to adapt.

Cultural adaptation

Seventy thousand years ago, cognitively modern *Homo sapiens* developed, and we used our superior brain power to behaviorally adapt with intelligence, technology, cultural innovation, and communication. Once the last ice age retreated at the start of the Holocene, about 10,000 years ago, we finally migrated into all regions of the Earth, including crossing the Bering Strait into the Americas, and radiated all over the world, eventually replacing all other hominin species (figure 7.1).

Our ancestors continued to adapt to these ecosystems through natural selection, with most of those adaptations related to their nutrition. The closer to the equator we lived, the more we evolved to have more pigment in our skin to protect us from the sun's UV rays; farther north, we had less pigmentation to allow for more sunlight to produce vitamin D. When less food was available, we developed a smaller stature, and with more, we became larger and more robust. When the climate was hot, we trended

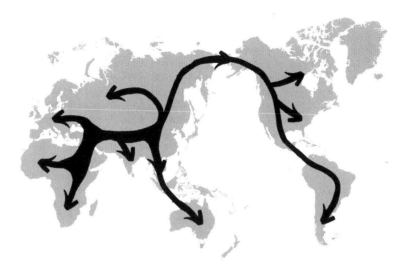

Figure 7.1. The Spread of Homo Sapiens All over the World

towards taller and thinner to better dissipate heat, and in cold climates, we trended towards shorter and stouter to keep warm. However, with our evolving larger brain, *Homo sapiens* mostly adapted to their foodways with cultural evolution.

Katharine Milton writes, "Expansion of the human brain and increasing dependence on cultural behaviors to obtain and prepare foods buffered human biology from many selective pressures related to diet the other animal species must resolve largely through genetic adaptations."[3] Through cultural evolution, humans enhanced the foodways of *Homo erectus*, showing improvements in using strategies and tools for hunting and gathering, processing (grinding, soaking, fermenting, cooking) food to "predigest" it, sharing food, and storing food.

We evolved these foodways in relation to the various ecosystems we inhabited. For example, in Eurasia, we evolved tools and strategies for hunting—in some cases, learning to drive enormous animals, like mammoths or herds of reindeer, off cliffs. We then learned ways to store the meat and fat of those animals for extended times. In the Levant, we hunted much smaller animals, including antelopes, deer, and likely rodents, reptiles, and other types of animals. Along the coastlines and lakes, we likely invented boats to help us acquire aquatic animals. Humans all over the world ate different ratios of plants to animals, of carbs to fats, as well as different sources of protein, fat, and carbohydrates.

The real Paleo diet

Homo sapiens continued the same trends as our ancestors, starting with omnivorous primates, towards consuming diets higher in quality—even as those diets varied considerably. Because human brain power accounts for 20% to 25% of an adult's energy needs—consuming 16 times the energy required of muscle tissue per unit weight[4]—we were required to, yet again, increase the amount, quality, and digestibility of the nutrients we ate to fuel the brain's high metabolic needs. We consumed more carbs and more starch relative to fruit, providing nutrients for our brains. We also continued the trend towards more animal foods—especially animal fat—into our diets, providing higher-quality and more-complete forms of amino and fatty acids.[5] While varying in our diet, humans also varied in their intake of macronutrients, especially their intakes of carbs and fats, depending on what they could acquire from their ecosystems. We also continued to consume considerable amounts of fiber but less fiber than our predecessors.

We see these trends in foragers alive today, ones that were observed and recorded in the recent past, as well as those we theorize about based on limited evidence from the distant past. We also see this same trend extending through much of agriculture, as well as our own age. This diet provides all the nutrients we need for our metabolism, anabolism, and catabolism, as well as for our various tissues while reducing unnecessary and likely detrimental forms of conversion and storage. It provides glucose for the brain, fat for muscles and organs, and the highest-quality proteins for anabolism throughout the body—as well as plenty of micronutrients.

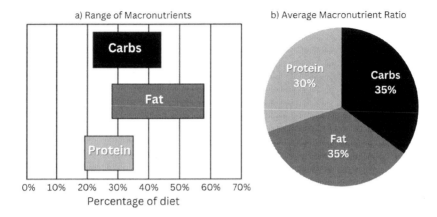

Figure 7.2. Ranges and Ratios of Macronutrients of Hunter-Gatherers

Source data: a) Connor, T. 2022. "Forget the Macronutrient Ratios. Here's Why." The Paleo Diet. Accessed April 7, 2022. thepaleodiet.com. b) Jamka, M. Kulczynski, B. Juruc, A. Gramza-Michałowska, A. Stokes, C.S. Walkowiak, J. 2020. "The Effect of the Paleolithic Diet vs. Healthy Diets on Glucose and Insulin Homeostasis: A Systematic Review and Meta-Analysis of Randomized Controlled Trials." J Clin Med 9 (2): 296-317.

This diet shows extreme ranges of nutrient ratios: These hunter-gatherer macronutrient ratios range from 22% to 44% carbs, from 28% to 58% fat, and from 19% to 35% protein (figure 7.2a).[6] The most recent calculations estimated for an average Paleolithic diet have maintained a roughly 35% carbohydrate, 35% fat, and 30% protein ratio.[7,8] Figure 7.2b shows these ratios.

To further complicate the matter, while humans trended towards the forager diet, they also varied their ratios of plant to animal foods. Some researchers calculated the plant-to-animal food ratio on average to be 65% plants to 35% animals,[9,10] while others calculated the ratio to be the exact opposite, 35% plant to 65% animal foods.[11] At the extreme, 95% of the Inuit diet comes from animals, while only 35% of the Ju/'hoansi diet comes from animals,[12] and the Hadza and Plains Indians obtain fairly equal amounts from both[13] (see figure 7.3).

In all ecosystems, humans acquired the bulk of protein we needed from animals[14] because we were apex hunters, able to kill the largest animals

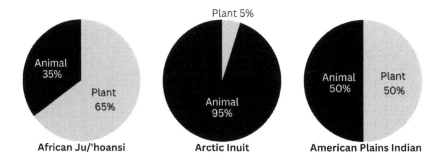

Figure 7.3. Comparisons of Plant versus Animal Food of Three Hunter-Gatherer Groups

Source data: Ulijaszek, S.J. Mann, N. Elton, S. 2012. "Evolving Human Nutrition: Implications for Public Health." New York: Cambridge University Press. & Crittenden, A.N. Schnorr, S.L. 2017. "Current views on hunter-gatherer nutrition and the evolution of the human diet." Am J Phys Anthropol 162 (S63): 84-109.

around, and then preserve them for extended periods of time through drying, smoking, and freezing in the permafrost. Even in the tropics, where animals tended to be small, we were good at collecting insects. Besides, we know that humans generally do not need more than 10% to 25% or so of their calories from protein.

However, we were not necessarily always able to acquire enough fats or carbs in every environment. When this happened, we consumed greater amounts of one or the other, some consuming diets higher in carbs while others consumed diets higher in fat. And in some cases, we consumed more protein than necessary for anabolism so we could make the glucose inside our bodies that we could not acquire in the environment.

Generally, in the colder climates of Eurasia, where plants were more scarce, *Homo sapiens* were not able to acquire enough carbs in their diet to satisfy their metabolic needs, which some speculate to be at least 50 grams of carbs per day (on average) to survive. However, in these same environments, animals carry more fat for storage and insulation through the long winters. So, to replace carbohydrates for catabolism, our ancestors consumed as much as 60% of their diet as fat. At the same time, they also consumed more protein than was needed for anabolism so they could convert those amino acids into glucose and ketones—both of which fed the brain. However, to avoid metabolic problems associated with the buildup of urea and ammonia in the blood—the waste products of conversion—these humans could only regularly consume 35% to 40% of their diet as protein, 55% at the very most if only for a short time. Groups that exclusively relied on hunted game in the winter evaded exceeding this upper limit by maximizing fat intake from blubber and organs.[15] During glacial maximums, and even in between, most of our ancestors in Eurasia consumed diets that specialized in mammoths as well as reindeer, aurochs, and bison. In more recent times, through direct observation, we know the Inuit consumed this diet, and to a lesser extent, the Plain Indians consumed mostly buffalo with small amounts of carbs.

However, in warmer climates, such as Africa and the Levant, where fatty animals are scarce, *Homo sapiens* were not able to acquire enough fat in their diet, especially from animals, so they consumed more carbs from tubers, grains, fruits, and honey. In tropical environments, fruit is more abundant, so these people consumed more fruit. In extreme cases, our ancestors may have converted those carbs into fat inside their bodies to compensate for a lack of animal fat in their diet. We also offset our need for animal fat by consuming more of our fat from plants, since our ecosystems held abundant fatty plants, such as palm fruit and nuts, other nuts, seeds, and fruits.[16] It was possible for us to consume a greater amount of protein from plants to survive, if we had dietary diversity that guaranteed quality and completeness of our amino acids.[17] We see these tendencies in extant cultures of the Hadza in Africa, the Aborigines in Australia, and many other hunter-gatherer cultures in warm parts of the world.

Humans not only varied greatly in the amount of fat we consumed but also in the ratios of fatty acids within those fats. The Inuit of the far north consumed mostly raw, fermented seal oil, which contained about equal amounts of all three classes of fatty acids—that is, saturated, monounsaturated, and polyunsaturated fats—mostly in the form of omega-3s. The Plain Indians consumed mostly buffalo tallow, which is about 45%

saturated and monounsaturated and the remainder polyunsaturated, at about four parts omega-6 to one part omega-3. Many cultures consumed enormous amounts of tallow like this, consumed fats from many different animals—showing a preference for certain fats over others, and consumed plant fats. Other hunter-gatherer cultures, while always consuming some animal fat, also consumed considerable amounts of plant fats—perhaps even more than animal fats, which increased the ratios of monounsaturated and polyunsaturated fats with various ratios of omega-6 to omega-3.

We also varied in the amounts of fiber we consumed. Overall, from *Homo erectus* to *Homo sapiens*, humans decreased fiber so they received more calories from dietary fats and less from colonic fats. Reducing fiber also increased both the speed of ingestion and digestion and helped us absorb nutrients faster. Humans varied greatly in their consumption of dietary fiber, ranging from zero fiber in their diet, as with the Inuit, to over 50 grams per day on average, which is still many times more than modern humans. The fiber intake of some hunter-gatherers may have been as high as 130 grams per day.[18] Wild fruit and vegetables have higher levels of fiber and protein than their domesticated counterparts, and we ate more of them.[19]

All of this is to say that prehistoric human nutrition was complicated. There is no real Paleo diet. Hunter-gatherers ate wildly different amounts and ratios of nutrients from a variety of sources, yet they managed to live healthy lives in the tundra, the desert, and everywhere in between. While humans adapted to all these variations in their diet, scientists do not really know whether these adaptations were due to natural selection or epigenetics—and to what extent. We also only have limited understanding of these adaptations and how they apply to modern humans. We moderns likely still possess many of these genes for particular adaptations, but we do not comprehend them. This may, in part, explain many of our struggles with nutrition and the correlation between nutrition and disease.

One thing we do know is that the frequency of environmental changes humans faced means we evolved to live with uncertainty, and our plasticity in response to the changing availability of food was a huge adaptation that allowed us to cope in vastly different scenarios.[20] Our primary coping mechanism was our evolving brain power and cultural adaptation, which gave us the key to survival by providing us the cognition and sociality to more easily adapt behaviorally to solve dietary problems.

Larger brains

Even though the picture of nutrition may be murky, it is clear that early humans used their nutrients for brain power. Remember, for organisms to evolve larger brains, they must have access to the nutrients to feed them. *Homo sapiens* evolved larger brains specifically because we could consume greater amounts of animal fats. Human brains require from 20% to 25% of an adult's calories for their energy needs. Even though they are less than 5% of our body weight, our brains consume 16 times the energy required of muscle tissue per unit weight.[21] We were required to, yet again, increase the amount, quality, and digestibility of the nutrients we ate to fuel its high metabolic needs. These energy-dense foods included the incorporation of even more animal products—especially animal fat—into our diets.[22] At the same time, humans evolved brains 30% to 40% larger than *Homo erectus* and three times larger than that of our common ancestor, as modeled by chimpanzees.[23] When all of this is considered, we radically increased our need for nutrients and, specifically, brain nutrients.

We might easily assume that we simply consumed more carbohydrates because brains consume glucose. While this is true, we do not really have much reason to believe that they could access many more carbohydrates than *Homo erectus* could. So, the most likely explanation is that we consumed more fat, specifically from large, fatty ruminants—even though this explanation may seem paradoxical, since we know our brains do not catabolize fatty acids.

Although our brains do not utilize fatty acids, they do acquire glucose from fats in two ways: First, the glycerol that is attached to all triglycerides is converted into glucose. When we eat more fat, we generate more glucose. Second, fatty acids provide enormous amounts of ATP for our muscles and organs, which allows more glucose from tissues—preferring to use fatty acids anyway—to be directed towards our brain. While our omnivorous primate cousins in the jungle, including chimps, generally consume about 5% to 10% of their calories from fat, humans consumed somewhere between 30% and 60%. We clearly evolved towards consuming more dietary fat as an adaptation to feed our brains.

Additionally, *Homo sapiens* emerged in areas that contained larger, fattier animals. In most of Africa, animals do not carry much fat for insulation or for storage because it's warm year-round. However, the areas close to lakes were full of hippos that needed lots of fat to float in the water, and coastlines were rife with fatty seals, whales, and fish. When migrating into Eurasia, *Homo sapiens* encountered much colder temperatures, where animals, especially larger ones, like mammoths, reindeer, and bison, carried enormous amounts of fat for insulation and storage, especially in the autumn. Humans were able to hunt these animals better than *Homo erectus* because of our increased size, but mostly because of our cultural evolution.

When locating in areas, like the Levant, that had fewer fatty animals, we likely consumed more plant fats that were abundant in the area—olives, pistachios, and walnuts. In arid regions of Africa, the seed from the baobab tree, which is rich in oil, is consumed to this day as one of the staples for one of the most ancient of people, the Hadza.

In addition to better tools for gathering and more deadly weapons for hunting, we invented boats to help us acquire aquatic animals. We decreased the considerable risk of hunting enormous and dangerous animals, such as hippos, mammoths, and bison, through our ability to cooperate. We learned ways of preserving food to consume when what nature provided us wasn't enough. We became members of bands where different people were responsible for different foods, and all food was shared. Our sociality and sharing radically enhanced the availability of nutrients to humans during times of scarcity. Also, imagine how much easier it was to obtain food and live in cooperative groups when we could communicate with language. All of these were made possible by our large brains and cognition.

Health

Generally, we study the health of hunter-gatherers by observing the ones still alive, the ones who were observed and recorded in the past, and by observing artifacts from long-lost cultures. Overall, hunter-gatherers were all healthier than modern humans, despite the enormous variation in their locations, their cultures, and their diets.

Hunter-gatherers have half the body fat of industrialized people, and their body fat actually decreases with age. Hunter-gatherers have low levels of insulin in their blood and excellent insulin sensitivity, both of which keep their risk of diabetes nearly zero.[24] This is because unrefined wild plant foods have low glycemic indices, a measure of how much a food raises blood glucose compared with glucose alone.[25] High blood pressure is unknown in their societies, with an average blood pressure of 105/80, which does not increase with age. They possess low levels of cholesterol in their blood, despite a higher intake of it due to the consumption of animals, and they hardly ever develop atherosclerosis or any form of cardiovascular disease. The high concentrations of soluble fiber in their diets favorably affect lipid metabolism.[26] They have a low incidence of cancer, and their high levels of fitness are maintained into old age.[27]

S. Boyd Eaton writes, "Individuals who continue the lifeways of our remote ancestors are largely immune to the chronic degenerative diseases which produce 'the greater part' of all mortality in affluent nations."[28] In other words, despite the enormous variation in their diet, humans were still healthy, obviously adapted to the range of diets they consumed. Since foragers ate varied diets and were healthy regardless of their nutrient ratios, we might assume that we modern humans can also consume any of these foraging diets to find our health. However, we should be careful of that assumption. The reduced quality and increased processing of nearly all modern foods complicate matters.

Activity levels and energy consumption

No matter where our hunter-gatherer ancestors got their nutrients and in what ratios, the nomadic lifestyles and physicality necessary to sustain their way of life required very high energy levels. For example, Ju/'hoansi women walk 2,400 kilometers every year while carrying equipment, gathered food, and children.[29] A hunter-gatherer's high muscular and aerobic fitness—and in colder climates, the need for increased thermoregulation—required more calorie consumption.[30] Their energy throughput was characterized by both greater caloric input and greater caloric output than most Westerners. For example, the Evenki of Siberia have a 15% higher resting metabolism rate than people in more temperate areas. A 125-pound Evenki male in Siberia needs to consume more than 3,000 calories, whereas a 160-pound American only needs 2,600 calories.[31]

The high energy expenditure and mobility of hunter-gatherer populations allowed them to follow the food, which was another way we overcame the seasonal resource fluctuations. In this way, a nomadic way of life was more compliant and famine resistant than more sedentary societies, which do experience greater seasonal nutritional stress.[32] Physical fitness is a hallmark of hunter-gatherers and another reason for the absence of non-communicable diseases.

Our hunter-gatherer ancestors were opportunistic, omnivorous foragers with tremendous dietary flexibility and plasticity who found and utilized the foods available in their ecosystem at any time of year.[33] Early *Homo sapiens* consumed higher-quality foods, better-quality carbs, and more animal foods, giving us higher-quality ratios of amino acids and fatty acids overall—even as our diets varied in so many ways. We primarily increased the quality of our diet compared to *Homo erectus* by consuming more energy-dense animal products like fat, which produces three times as much ATP as glucose, and we learned to process foods, which continued the trend of gaining as much nutrition, in as little volume, in as little time, and with as little effort as possible.[34] We also continued to improve our locomotion and shrank our teeth, jaws, and digestive system—allowing us even better locomotion and directing more nutrients to our demanding brains.

Through cultural evolution, we enhanced our hunting and gathering with tools and strategies, and we increased our food sharing and storage, too. Our dietary diversity and flexibility also helped moderate competition between group members and even between groups themselves, allowing humans to become more egalitarian than most other primates. Discovering efficient ways of finding and ingesting calories made time for more socialization, an important prerequisite to the high levels of cooperation our way of life demanded.

Even with all of the large-scale dietary changes in our history, our ancestors from the common ancestor all the way through the evolution of *Homo sapiens* followed the same patterns as all other omnivorous primates in our lineage. As we grew the most powerful brains on the planet and migrated to every corner of the Earth, we maintained our varied but nutritionally simple and balanced foodways. Slightly more than five hundred generations ago, all humans consumed only the wild and unprocessed food they could obtain from their environment.[35] But the relationship between humans and food was about to get a lot more complicated.

CHAPTER 8

THE AGRICULTURAL REVOLUTION

The origin of agriculture tends to be seen as the primary point at which dietary "adaptation" switches to "maladaptation" within humans.

—STANLEY ULIJASZEK

During the last ice age, around 40,000 years ago, some of us, as a group of human foragers, migrated from Africa into the Levant—also known as the Fertile Crescent—and began to forage and hunt food that would later be domesticated, including wheat, barley, and various legumes, as well as sheep and goats. During glacial maximums, we were still nomadic and moved with the seasons. But during one glacial retreat, we stayed in one place year-round. We built small villages and even started to practice rudimentary farming by sowing grains. But when another glacial maximum came, we returned to being foraging nomads again.

Around 10,000 BCE, a more permanent, stable, and warming climate trend developed, and our transient farming converted to agriculture full-time. At first, we farmed the same plants we foraged and herded the same animals we hunted. Agricultural settlements soon spread throughout the Levant and trickled into Europe during the next several thousand years. Agriculture spread slowly as farmers expanded their lands by displacing, absorbing, or defeating the natives living there by sheer numbers.[1] Foraging did persist in some areas, until the pressure to begin farming became too great and these groups were forced to adopt it full-time. Amazingly, although the new farmers were cultivating different plants and animals in different places, this Agricultural Revolution occurred independently in several places around the world, all about the same time.[2] Humans both developed and adapted to agriculture almost entirely through cultural evolution. The Paleolithic Age ended, and the Neolithic Age began.

Many assume that the transition to agriculture was an improvement. Yes, the domestication of plants and animals did create previously unheard-of food surpluses that allowed us to feed more people. But for a few thousand years, the world's population did not increase because the changes wrought by agriculture took their toll on human nutrition and health, caused disease, and promoted warfare.[3] How did our diet and foodways change? How did agriculture affect our way of life?

Foodway evolution

Those nomads and early agriculturalists consumed a diet likely similar to our predecessors because we supplemented it with foraging. We consumed animals, both domesticated and wild, and likely also ate oily seeds and nuts, including olives, almonds, pistachios, and walnuts. Grains, fruits, and berries continued to supply carbohydrates. The animal fat we consumed was lean, especially from sheep, so we possibly consumed more carbs to compensate.

However, after we had essentially captured our plant and animal food sources permanently, agricultural humans' diets and foodways started to transform radically through cultural evolution. We no longer needed to find food. Instead of gathering food daily, we had to plan months ahead to tend to what we planted and harvested at certain times of the year. Accordingly, our territories and day ranges shrank considerably. However, we continued the trend toward processing food more. For example, along with predigestion through soaking, grinding, or cooking, we learned how to ferment foods. We increasingly consumed less of the foods that we evolved with and more foods that we didn't. However, our means of converting those foods to energy—ingestion, digestion, metabolism—had not changed, and our bodies were faced with the challenge of using unfamiliar foods with nutrients in abnormal ratios.

The diet of agriculturalists

As agriculture continued to develop and spread, some populations continued to consume balanced diets, especially the more fortunate. These privileged groups, who would become the upper and ruling classes, had more access to animal proteins and fats. However, for most agriculturalists—the less fortunate ones—their dietary quality diminished over thousands of years as they crammed into smaller spaces, walled cities, and larger and oppressive civilizations. Protein and fat from meat were scarce, and they had to overeat carbohydrates for metabolic energy. They also did not have access to as much variety in plant foods; in many cases, they were limited to one or two, which robbed them of essential micronutrients. Notably, alcohol (beer and wine), eggs, and dairy were new foods that agriculture introduced into the human diet. And to preserve their food, these early farmers started consuming enormous amounts of salt.

More wealthy agriculturalists' anabolic protein needs were adequately met with complete nutrition from animal meat. They ate muscle and collagen proteins in broth, sausages, skins, and other such foods, attaining the proper ratios of amino acids this way. However, the laborers and lower classes were largely deprived of protein from animals, so their protein had to come from plants. They would have to eat the right plant food combinations or else develop amino acid deficiencies; if they are combined just right, grains, legumes, and nuts could generate complete and high-quality proteins. Some wild plants—nuts and seeds, like flax, chia, and sesame—were eaten to supplement the low levels of animal fat before the domestication of these plants occurred.

Soon, we discovered we could breed and raise animals to provide more fat at slaughter. Later, we also domesticated new animals that naturally had more fat, like pigs. Some animals provided protein and fat while they lived, such as milk from cows and eggs from chickens. Humans started to consume milk, one food we never previously consumed after weaning, for the first time about 8,000 years ago.

In many ways, dairy is different from other animal foods. It contains different types of proteins, such as casein and whey, and different ratios of amino acids. Dairy fat is also different from other forms of animal fats. It is much higher in saturated fats, as well as exceedingly low in monounsaturated and polyunsaturated fats. However, many of us consumed dairy and eggs as our premier proteins, and these sources were efficient to produce and provided high-quality proteins that were easy to digest. In general, there was no reason to overconsume protein to make glucose.

The fats from grain-based foods contained high levels of omega-6 polyunsaturated fatty acids. Oily flax, chia, and sesame seeds are high in both omega-6 and omega-3 polyunsaturated fat—high-quality fatty acids. Animal fat contains saturated fats, and turning animal products into cheese, butter, tallow, and preserved, salted fatty meats added concentrated sources of saturated fat to the diet. However, the polyunsaturated fatty acid profile of animal fat changed as farmers fed the animals domesticated plant foods year-round to prevent seasonal depletion of fat. This caused omega-6 polyunsaturated fatty acids to predominate over omega-3s.[4] The high levels of omega-6s in grains and the increased omega-6 in animal fat caused the beginnings of our modern omega-6 to omega-3 imbalance.

Agriculturalists received the most metabolic energy from carbohydrates, in the form of grains, tubers, and legumes, since fruit was not cultivated at first. We would consume wild fruits, such as berries, when available, which provided high levels of glucose and low levels of fructose. On average, we also started to consume a lot more carbohydrates than our hunting and gathering predecessors, which provided ample glucose for our brains and other tissues. One of the reasons we consumed so much was to compensate for the reduction of fat in our diet. Most of our carbohydrates were in the form of starch, so we received more glucose than fructose.

In some places, we had only limited access to plant foods, maybe just one kind of grain and one kind of legume, nut, or fatty seed. This is why people throughout agriculture have consumed enormous amounts of bread and porridge—things made only from wheat or limited amounts of other grains or legumes. We also ingested a lot of grains in the form of beer, which was made by fermenting surplus grain to preserve it. These were all single nutrients, greatly reducing digestive metabolism.

Milk also contains the sugar lactose, which is one glucose molecule combined with one galactose molecule. All humans consume lactose in breast milk as infants, but we used to stop making the enzyme needed to digest it, lactase. However, microevolution did occur in some pockets of humanity to cope with new foods such as cow's milk. The evolution of lactase enzyme persistence became selectively adaptive rather than neutral after the development of dairy farming.[5]

Farmers still consumed considerable amounts of fiber from grains and legumes, so we continued to produce lots of colonic fats. However, selective breeding techniques and new processing techniques that refined the "quality" of food gradually reduced humans' fiber consumption. We also continued the trend toward predigesting, or processing, food more, which started stripping fiber from our foods. Foods like sesame, flax, poppy seeds, grains, legumes, and nuts, which some agriculturalists ate more of, were high in antinutrients and toxins. However, we used many new methods to neutralize these compounds, including roasting, soaking, germinating, fermenting, filtering, and cooking in novel ways.

As agriculture progressed, the balance of macro- and micronutrients humans had previously consumed became permanently altered. Most agriculturalists, especially the lower class, survived on mostly bread and beer, frequently from the same grain, with only smatterings of legumes and animal foods. This created one of the poorest diets ever consumed by man.

Sociality

From omnivorous primates all the way through foraging humans, social structures and behaviors stayed relatively constant over the course of many millions of years, with larger groups and more cooperation as our brain size increased. However, the advent of agriculture irreversibly changed these social structures and behaviors. Early on, most agriculturalists lived in small villages, similar to our ancestors, but we became sedentary and moved into permanent shelters.

As food became centralized, we started living in larger and larger villages, where different forms of leadership and authority developed. Then, entire cities and civilizations evolved to have entrenched, hierarchical, and sometimes brutal authorities. Warfare occurred often since settlements, farmland, and surpluses had to be protected from others who desired to expand their territories.[6] Unlike nomadic foragers, we could not just move away from conflict; we had to stay and fight for our possessions and land.[7]

To govern so many people living within such confined spaces, governments, religions, and the like developed strict codes of morality that justified and promoted hierarchies and regulated sexuality, family behaviors, and business affairs, usually under threat of punishment and even death.

Health

The Agricultural Revolution made human nutrition less diverse and of lower quality. It often led to inferior nourishment, either by not providing enough or by not providing well-rounded macro- or micronutrients. Farmers planted foods for taste, size, and yield, not for nutritional content. This shaped wild foods into what human palates prefer: large, sweet, and easy to peel or chew.[8] Since many farming societies relied on only one or two crops or animals as staples, if these failed, we had nothing else to eat.[9]

The health impact of new foods, different foods, and differently processed foods and the imbalanced ratios of nutrients were long lasting and far reaching, and they still affect modern populations today. Neolithic people faced starvation, vitamin deficiencies, anemia, and mineral disorders, all of which caused them to live shorter, less healthy lives.[10]

Because of the close quarters people lived in with each other and animals, and because of our inadequate sanitation, huge swaths of the population were wiped out by infectious diseases that had never affected hunter-gatherers. We also began to suffer chronic, inflammatory, and degenerative diseases, such as obesity, arthritis, diabetes, and cardiovascular diseases from the changes in our food consumption. We started suffering from the diseases of civilization. We got shorter, our teeth and bones became weaker, and for the first time in our evolutionary journey, the size of our brains actually decreased. Early farmers were more likely to die from malnutrition, poor sanitation, disease, or violence than most hunter-gatherers were, and the average person died before the age of 20 during the transition from hunter-gatherer to agriculturalist.

Why farm?

After hunting and gathering had been a successful adaptation for so long, why would humans give it up if agriculture did not provide a survival advantage? As botanist Jack Harlan succinctly asked, "Why farm? Why give up the 20-hour work week and the fun of hunting in order to toil in the sun? Why work harder for food less nutritious and a supply more capricious? Why invite famine, plague, pestilence, and crowded living conditions?"[11] Agriculture may have persisted because we now had the power to override the forces of natural selection with our behavior. In the process of domesticating plants and animals, we domesticated ourselves. However, the overriding answer to Harlan's question is population growth.

The transition to farming began to incrementally increase fertility rates,[12] so even as infant mortality increased, people were having more children more frequently. Babies were breast-fed for shorter periods and weaned onto cereals and cow's milk so their mothers could have another baby.[13] Whereas hunter-gatherers had children every four to five years, agrarians were able to have children every one to two years, causing a dramatic upsurge in births.[14] As Yuval Noah Harari points out, evolution cares only about the sheer number of copies of DNA produced, not about a poor quality of life. Anything that causes more offspring is considered an evolutionary win.[15]

The Agricultural Revolution initiated the population explosion. Humans settled and centralized, propelling us toward modernization. However, it had serious nutritional consequences, including malnutrition and even starvation. Our foods, even completely unprocessed, bear little resemblance to the nutrient content of the wild foods of our ancestors.[16] The only way agriculture outcompeted hunting and gathering was through its ability to create food surplus, and with it, incremental population gain. Then, the cascade of population growth picked up speed exponentially and ultimately required agriculture to sustain it. We could not go back to the hunter-gatherer lifestyle.

Despite all of the disadvantages, agriculture started a vicious cycle from which there was no turning back. As Harari succinctly writes, "Population growth burned humanity's boats."[17] We were so far removed from our indigenous ecosystems, foodways, and lifestyles that we could never return to hunting and gathering (figure 8.1).

These profound changes to our diet occurred very recently on an evolutionary timescale and through cultural evolution rather than natural selection. The human genome did not have time to adjust to this new way of eating. Agricultural humans were still genetically adapted to the nutritious, minimally processed, wild plant and animal foods of our ancestors.[18] These nutritional maladaptations followed us into the modern world.

Figure 8.1. The Agricultural Revolution

CHAPTER 9

THE MODERN DIET AND ITS CONSEQUENCES

This discordance between ancient, genetically determined biology, and the nutritional, cultural, and activity patterns of contemporary Western populations are the root cause of the so-called diseases of civilization.

—LOREN CORDAIN

Agriculture drove our nutritional choices for thousands of years as our ancestors improved farming and herding, generated more abundant and diverse foods, and provided for more people. But in the last few hundred years, industrialization and modernity—and the lifestyle changes they wrought—have affected our diets the most. The Industrial Revolution brought about advanced technology, such as tractors and combines, and corporations formed to handle the massive yields this new tech produced. These enormous companies took over every aspect of growing, harvesting, processing, packaging, and then distributing food all over the world.[1] All of this mass-produced, processed food has allowed the world's ever-growing population to be fed cheaply and predictably, but the resulting abundance of these unhealthy, nutritionally unbalanced foods has damaged human health and shortened our life spans.

From our common ancestor through agricultural humans, our predecessors lived in small communities. However, with industrialization, our everyday lifestyles changed radically. Most people moved from farms and villages into large, crowded cities as most countries trended toward urbanization (figure 9.1).[2]

We went from interacting constantly with nature to being enclosed in offices and schools. This rapid cultural evolution is the driving force behind our evolutionary mismatch, and most if not all of these societal changes have affected how we approach our foodways.

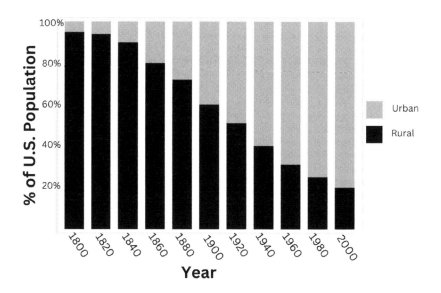

Figure 9.1. Changing Rural and Urban Demographics from 1800 to 2000

Source data: Greenfield, P. 2017. "Cultural Change over Time: Why Replicability Should Not Be the Gold Standard in Psychological Science." Perspect on Psychol Sci 12 (5): 762-771.

Modern foodways

The foodways of humans changed radically in the face of modernity. While we used to work to make our food, we now just work to pay for it. Most humans aren't connected to our foodways—sensing, moving to, capturing, processing, and sharing food—in any way. Most of us have never hunted, gathered, farmed, or herded in our lives. Those of us who do hunt and garden understand human foodways much better than most. However, the majority of hunters or gardeners do not necessarily procure their family's entire food supply but use these activities for sport or as a hobby.

We have also overcome nearly all obstacles to accessing our foodways. It's not scattered across territory or season but available in one location year-round. With plentiful and easy-to-attain food, we don't face competition in getting it. We've even outcompeted the microbes with preservatives. Most of us no longer share food with anyone outside of our immediate families except on special occasions, and even immediate families often don't eat together or are preoccupied with the distractions of modern life at dinnertime. We eat alone or in restaurants with strangers in plastic chairs, with fluorescent lights, and staring at large-screen televisions. Nutritional anthropologist Stanley Ulijaszek writes, "One of the things that industrial and, subsequently, postindustrial society has done in many places (especially in the United States) has been the displacement of foods with food products, food markets with supermarkets, and dining with feeding."[3]

Interestingly, we followed our evolved instincts to process and refine our foods to make them easier to digest and to reduce our digestive metabolism. We followed our instincts to reduce plant antinutrients and toxins. We followed our instincts to have our foods contain only macronutrients in their most pure and distilled forms. However, in following those instincts, we used tools and methods not found in our past, and the process came about too quickly for us to evolve biologically. Paradoxically, in following our evolutionary instincts, we got way ahead of ourselves and deviated from our evolutionarily effective diet.

Diet

As modern humans, we've drastically changed our diet in many ways. In the past, we consumed foods in accord with our biological evolution, but during modern times, we broke from those traditions. For example, our bodies now metabolize less, but we eat more. In the past, we moved, strategized, and toiled directly for our food. We also lived for many months out of the year in cold, ambient environments, causing our bodies to produce energy to keep us warm. Both processes kept our energetic equation—calories consumed equals calories burned—mostly in balance and prevented weight gain. Now, food is abundant, and we are constantly encouraged to eat as much of it as possible. As a result, we have altered our metabolic equilibrium—we undermetabolize calories while overconsuming them. The extra calories have to go somewhere, and our bodies instinctively store the excess for use when food is scarce. Only, for most of us, food is never scarce, so we become overweight.

Next, we followed the trend established in agriculture to increasingly consume foods we are not adapted for. The foods we stack in our refrigerators and pantries are less likely to be whole-plant or whole-animal foods; instead, they are products of industrial processing. Modern food-processing techniques led to ultraprocessing, which resulted in a large-scale increase in carbohydrate consumption.[4] Ready-to-eat products made from industrial ingredients (i.e., flour, sugar, and oils) are stripped of fiber and nutrients.[5] Most of what we put into our bodies today comes from these products we are not adapted to eat.

Over time, we've also disconnected from our ancestors' culinary practices of preparing and combining foods for optimal nutrition. In the past, we predigested and combined foods in specific ways to make them both nourishing and delicious. We soaked, sprouted, and fermented our grains and even most of our seeds, optimizing both flavor and nutrition while reducing toxins and antinutrients and preserving the fiber. Today, we usually remove these steps or just refine the grains. We've lost contact with these ancient traditions due to commercial expedience, while nameless people in corporations control how our food is prepared.

Not only did the way we prepare food change, but the motivation behind our foodways changed too. Traditionally, other members of our tribe or community, our families, our grandmothers, and our mothers managed our diet. They were motivated to provide nourishing and complete foods in their own community, to provide for their family and neighbors. We've lost contact with these ancient traditions. The goal of modern foodways is driven by food company profits, often achieved by manipulating our taste buds and marketing malnourished foods as if they were good for us. These novel practices born from capitalism were not designed to optimize our diet, only the bottom line.

With massive corporations providing our food and receiving government subsidies, we have nearly unlimited choices of what to eat, resulting in extreme variation in our diet—from one day to the next or even from one meal to the next. In the past, our ancestors repeatedly ate mostly the same foods, with some seasonal variation, in both the types of foods and the ratio of the nutrients in those foods. Today, we can consume Chinese food cooked in vegetable oil for lunch, then hamburgers consisting of ruminant fat and little or no fiber for dinner, and both are splashed down with soda made from high-fructose corn syrup and artificial colors and flavors. With all this variation, we cause our bodies to work hard to adjust to constant changes. In recent studies, increased dietary diversity is linked with poor eating patterns: high consumption of processed foods and sugar and lower intake of whole, minimally processed foods.[6]

Finally, we have become really confused about our diet. When we learned our diet was causing our declining health, we started asking, "What is healthy?" In an attempt to answer, we are bombarded by misleading, confusing, and contradictory information. Food companies encourage us to eat what makes them money, dietary gurus market trend diets with high promises but underdeveloped ideas, and the media

inundates us with information about the latest research, frequently mis-
interpreted and removed from context. Even when turning to science,
we may see confusing and conflicting information. Worst of all, despite
modern education, most of us do not even understand our own nutritional physiology—how nutrients function inside our bodies. So, we not
only fail to *eat* our optimum diets, but we don't even *know* what our
optimum diet is.

Macronutrients

The average macronutrient consumption ratios in the modern diet represent a huge disconnect between what we evolved to eat and what we eat
now. The average modern human eats 52% carbohydrates, 33% fat, and
15% protein in their diet. Figure 9.2 compares these modern ratios with
those of our hunter-gatherer ancestors. While we eat similar levels of fat,
we have increased our carbohydrate consumption by around 15%, and

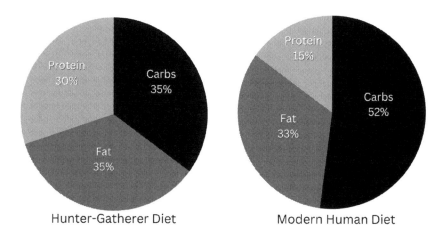

Hunter-Gatherer Diet   Modern Human Diet

Figure 9.2. Comparison of Macronutrient Ratios between Hunter-Gatherers and Modern Humans

Source data: Eaton, J.C. Iannotti, L.L. 2017. "Genome-Nutrition Divergence: Evolving Understanding of the Malnutrition
Spectrum." Nutr Rev 75 (11): 934-950.

our protein intake has dropped about 15%.[7] However, these ratios don't even begin to tell the story of modern nutrition. Where we get our macronutrients from, how they are processed, and the breakdown of amino acids, fatty acids, and sugar content make the modern story of nutrition complicated.

PROTEIN

As modern humans, we've altered our consumption of proteins. When working our muscles, humans need to consume more protein to replenish those tissues, and in the past, our ancestors—foragers and agriculturalists—consumed considerable amounts because they used their muscles every day for their foodways. These days, however, we still eat a lot of protein because it's available and inexpensive. However, we rarely need that much protein because we are more sedentary.

We need to consume only about 0.8 to 1.2 grams of protein per kilogram of weight daily, or somewhere between 8% and 15% of total calories. Remember, the more active we are, the more protein we will need. The caloric cost of digesting macronutrients from whole protein is three times that of carbs or fats, so when we eat more than we need, we devote a lot of energy to digestion. Protein will make us feel fuller longer,[8] which is why high-protein diets are thought to help with weight loss. A high-protein diet was shown to facilitate weight loss in obese people through increased satiety, increased thermic effect of digesting protein, slower gastric emptying, and better glucose regulation.[9] However, we must be cautious with these types of diets because the vast majority of people gain the weight back, and increased protein consumption beyond the recommended daily allowance can also have adverse effects on metabolic functions, including the increased risk of prediabetes and type 2 diabetes.[10] We also convert that extra protein into ketones and glucose while generating more waste products like urea, uric acid, and ammonia. Kidney function may worsen on a high-protein diet as well.[11]

We still get most of our protein from animals. However, while both hunter-gatherers and early farmers consumed the entire animal, we now mostly consume muscle—steaks, chicken breasts, and fish fillets. This meat is good for our muscles and most of our organs; however, we do not eat enough of the collagen proteins that are good for our skin, fascia, ligaments, and tendons, as well as part of our cardiovascular and nervous tissues. Over the years, we devalued and avoided other tissues, including organs and connective tissues, which has deprived us of vital nutrients. Organ meat provides a wider variety of essential vitamins and minerals. For example, the liver provides two vitamins—vitamin B12 and preformed vitamin A—that are difficult to obtain in sufficient amounts from other foods but provide us with enormous benefits. Only some humans can convert enough beta carotene into vitamin A, and we don't eat enough beta carotene in our diet, which leads to vitamin A deficiencies. Collagenous and elastic proteins, such as hydroxyproline, are only found in our connective tissues and provide more balanced amino acid ratios. Dairy products and eggs remain large components of our diet as they did after the Agricultural Evolution. However, these proteins are better and more complete than muscle proteins.

Many of our ancestors consumed most of their protein from plants, mostly legumes, nuts, and grains, and they carefully combined them to generate complete proteins. However, modern people receive most of their protein from meat—even as plant proteins are shown to provide many advantages, especially in counteracting the diseases of civilization. We still get some protein from plant foods, and supermarket shelves full of protein powders, like whey and soy—not even protein has escaped processing and refinement. We have never eaten proteins processed this way so are not clear how it will affect our health in the long run.

FAT

Modern humans consume enough fat to meet most of our fatty acid needs, and the percentage of fat in our modern diet is similar to that consumed by our ancestors. However, we now consume too much fat relative to our metabolic needs. Hunter-gatherers consumed considerable amounts of fat—between 30% and 60% of their calories—mostly from animals but combined with smaller amounts from plants. They used this fat for catabolism, for their resting metabolism, to keep themselves warm in colder temperatures, and most importantly, to provide energy for their everyday labor. Remember, our muscles prefer to catabolize fat into ATP, so the more we use our muscles, the more fat we need. Modern people consume enormous amounts of fat, yet we are sedentary and do not utilize this fat. It circulates around unused until it is stored, causing weight gain and contributing to disease.

We've also qualitatively changed our fat consumption by altering the types of fats we eat and skewing the ratios in which we eat them. In the past, we ate combinations of animal fat and plant fats—mostly from nuts and seeds, and very rarely small amounts of plant oil. This variety maintained a balanced fatty acid intake.

The fat profile in modern, domesticated animal meat has changed dramatically. Industrialization initiated the practice of feeding surplus grain to animals, whereas before, all domesticated cattle were free-range or pasture-fed and slaughtered in four or five years. Now, thousands of cattle are packed into a feedlot and continuously fed grain so they can be quickly fattened for slaughter in only 14 months. These obese cattle produce marbled meat with exceedingly high levels of saturated fatty acid and cholesterol, which wild or free-range animals rarely have. In addition, marbled meat has a high level of omega-6 polyunsaturated fatty acids and almost no omega-3s due to an all-grain diet. Strikingly, 99% of US beef is produced in this manner.[12] Countries that still pasture feed their domesticated animals produce leaner meat that contains less saturated fatty acids and omega-6s and more omega-3 polyunsaturated fatty acids, a fat profile that is closer to that of wild animals.[13]

We have also reduced our consumption of animal fats from fatty tissues in favor of enormous amounts of dairy—such as milk, cheese, and butter—combined with large amounts of plant oils, including safflower, canola, and corn oil. Milk and dairy products contain a lot of saturated fats but minimal mono- and polyunsaturated fats. Refined plant oils, which we never consumed before industrialization made extraction possible, have fatty acid ratios that are radically different from how we store and use them in our adipose tissue and phospholipids. These plant oils have low levels of saturated fats and extremely high levels of mono- and polyunsaturated fat—especially from the omega-6 family.[14] Add this consumption of vegetable oils to our mass consumption of grains that contain high levels of omega-6 and meats that now contain high levels of omega-6, and the ratio of essential polyunsaturated fatty acids in the modern diet becomes very skewed. Modern Americans have an estimated intake ratio of omega-6 to omega-3 of 10:1, which is 5 to 10 times higher than the ratio of hunter-gatherers.[15] In fact, omega-6 polyunsaturated fatty acids are predominantly available to most industrialized populations due to its prevalence in grains and plant oils, which are the main ingredients in industrial food products.

Finally, a new manufacturing technique, hydrogenation, enabled vegetable oils to be made solid at room temperature, adding new food products to the market. However, this process produced a completely novel class of fats, called *trans fats*, that the human race had never encountered before.[16] Trans fats, found in foods like shortening and margarine, were developed to replace animal fat and were initially thought to be healthy because they are unsaturated.[17] Nearly a tenth of all fatty acid intake by Americans comes from trans fats, primarily due to the high amounts present in ultra-processed packaged foods.

In the mid-twentieth century, scientists started to blame fat—specifically, saturated fat and cholesterol from animal products—for the frightening surge in cardiovascular disease. They recommended we reduce our overall consumption of animal fats and replace them with vegetable fats. People began to cut animal fat from their diets, and suddenly, vegetable fats containing high omega-6 to omega-3 ratios and trans fats became the fats of choice, replacing the "bad" animal fats.[18] For millions of years, the trend in the human line was to consume more animal products; now we were consuming less.

The popularity of low-fat diets also had the unintended consequence of people eating more refined carbohydrates and sugars, often added to make low-fat or no-fat foods taste better. Not only did heart disease not get better—it is still the number one cause of death in the world—but obesity accelerated. Much of the research was focused on the effects of a single nutrient, whereas our diets are much more complex and multifactorial.[19] Our periodic attempts to cut this product or that one from our collective diet have all failed to improve our health.

Around the same time fat became the villain, some researchers found a connection between excess sugar and heart disease, but for some reason, the scientific community focused on fat. The effects of sugar have been largely ignored until recently. Lately, the decades of emphasis on low-fat diets have been challenged when the benefits of diets rich in healthy fats, such as the Mediterranean diet, have been revealed.[20] The bottom line is that the absolute amount of fat is much less important than the types of fat we consume, and what we replace it with in a low-fat diet is crucial.

CARBOHYDRATES

The global increase in food production in the mid-twentieth century skewed our diets toward eating carbohydrates in ways in which we were not adapted. We eat more carbs, process our carbs until fiber is negligible, eat more fructose, and eat foods with high carbs and fats mixed together.

In general, the majority of our calories now come from carbohydrates: grains, starches, and sweeteners such as sugar and high-fructose corn syrup.[21] Three-quarters of the industrially produced packaged food products in American supermarkets have added sugar or other sweeteners.[22] Not only do we now eat far more carbohydrates than at any time in history (and prehistory), but we also eat different carbohydrates.[23] We eat tons of bread, cookies, cakes, and pastries, and replace water with sugary beverages. Dairy products, which give us lactose, make up around 10% of the calories consumed in the US diet.

Interestingly, until the fourth century CE, humans did not eat refined sugars, except for occasional honey. After the technology for sugar refinement was developed, it spread into the world to satisfy our insatiable appetite for sweet.[24] Industrialization made sugar cheaper and more accessible, and in the 1700s, the average sugar intake of one person in the United States was about four pounds per year. Three hundred years later, Americans consume a mind-boggling 150 pounds per year, with a quarter consuming more than 200 pounds each year.[25] This intake of concentrated, refined sugar has no precedent in any animal's evolutionary journey, and we are not genetically adapted to deal with it.

While our ancestors were driven to consume foods lower in fiber because they are faster and easier to digest, provide more macronutrients, and have fewer antinutrients and toxins, they never rid their carbohydrates of fiber and continued to receive its health benefits. Before the Industrial Revolution, we consumed our grains whole with fiber intact. However, we now use various technologies to refine grains and remove fiber, meaning we strip them of their husk and germ and leave only tiny amounts of endosperm. We now eat 85% of our grain this way.[26] Processed grains have four times less fiber than whole grains. Whole grains have an eighth of the fiber found in fruits and vegetables. And domesticated fruits and vegetables have less fiber than their wild equivalents.[27] We remove fiber from fruit to make juice, and we turn beets and sugar cane into pure sucrose. Our processing not only removes fiber from these foods but also many additional nutrients, including vitamins, minerals, phytonutrients, and essential fatty acids.

Without fiber, our carbs become denser, meaning we can then fit more sugar into our stomachs, causing us to overeat. Fiber helps us feel fuller longer and not overeat.[28] Fiber in the digestive tract also slows the absorption of sugars, but our highly processed carbs can be digested quickly and release glucose quickly. This causes an acute spike in blood glucose levels followed by an acute rise in insulin, which, over the long term, has severe health consequences. In the United States, nearly 40% of the energy consumed is from foods with processed grains and sugars with high glycemic indices.[29] Our glycemic loads are far in excess of anything experienced by hunter-gatherers or even early agriculturalists.

Finally, remember, the microbiome in our guts can ferment fiber to provide short-chain fatty acids. These serve as an energy substrate for host cells and the intestinal bacteria; they regulate glucose, lipid, and energy metabolism.[30] Substituting sugars for fiber favors certain gut bacterial species, which reduces ecosystem diversity and may be pathogenic.[31] In this way, fiber is required for the development and maintenance of a healthy gut biome and a healthy metabolism.

In the past, our ancestors evolved towards eating less fructose in their diet, but we started to reverse that trend. We cultivated our fruits to contain higher amounts of fructose to make them sweeter. In the last 50 years, sugar sweetener consumption in the United States has become increasingly fructose rich, thanks to the development of high-fructose corn syrup, a cheaper, sweeter alternative to cane or beet sugar,[32] but it is 50% fructose. These sweeteners were added to most of our foods, especially packaged foods and soft drinks, until fructose made up a third of all carbohydrate intake by US citizens. Unlike glucose, fructose does not cross into brain tissue, so it does not assuage hunger and causes increased and unneeded calorie intake later. Fructose additionally interferes with hormones that trigger our body to feel full, thus causing us to overeat.[33] Fructose also facilitates the production and deposition of fat better than glucose does, which is why hunter-gatherers preferred fruits and honey to better prepare for food shortages.[34]

Lastly, modern humans also combine our fats with high amounts of carbohydrates, so that we eat higher amounts of both. However, when our ancestors lived in colder environments, they ate lots of fat but not many carbs, and when living in hotter environments, they ate more carbs and less fat. So, we are perhaps adapted to one or the other, but we are not adapted to both. When we eat both fat and carbs together in high amounts, like in pizza, mac and cheese, ice cream, and fast foods, we are not helping our health. These processed foods may be "high quality" in the evolutionary sense, but they are actually very low quality. Since they are missing fiber and micronutrients,[35] they are nothing but empty calories.

Micronutrients: salt

The *only* micronutrient that hasn't decreased in the modern diet is salt. Until 5,000 years ago, the only salt in our diet occurred naturally. Once it was found to preserve food, however, it became one of the world's most valued commodities, and our use of salt only augmented our appetite for it.[36] Our physiological need for sodium drives our avidity for it, and because taste buds respond quickly and adjust to saltier tastes, our consumption has only increased.[37]

Now, only 10% of the salt in our diets occurs naturally in the food, whereas 75% is added to processed foods and 15% is added while cooking or before eating.[38] Salt is in everything, even in foods that don't taste salty, because it increases shelf life, makes cheap ingredients more palatable, and improves the texture and smell of processed food.[39] Modern Americans consume 10 grams of salt per day on average—200 times more than the Yanomamo tribe of the Amazon.[40] Our current salt intake has no precedent in evolutionary history either.

The consequences of modern nutrition

The nutrition of the modern Westernized world has done little to address the discordance that arose during the Agricultural Revolution, which is clearly evident in our health. Anne Wigmore, a wellness and natural living advocate, said it best: "The food you eat can be either the safest and most powerful form of medicine or the slowest form of poison."[41] In fewer than 10 generations, noncommunicable diseases linked to diet—such as obesity, type 2 diabetes, hypertension, cancer, and cardiovascular disease—are now the major causes of morbidity and mortality.[42] These diseases don't affect reproductive success, so there are no evolutionary consequences for our modern food habits. However, the consequences to our quality of life are immense.

OBESITY

Obesity is a complex disease caused by genetic and epigenetic factors, diet, lifestyle, and the chronic imbalance between energy consumed and spent.[43] The rise in carbohydrate consumption, especially of sugar and ultraprocessed foods, directly corresponds with the rise of obesity. Meals with high glycemic loads keep insulin elevated, which promotes fat storage, prevents fat usage, and increases appetite, all of which cause weight gain. The reduction of fiber in our diets reduces our feelings of satiety, so we tend to overconsume calories. Our high consumption of high-fructose corn syrup, due to aberrant and amplified leptin signaling, signals the brain that there is a negative energy balance, causing hunger and the promotion of more fat storage.[44]

The increased intake of fats contributes to obesity, but the omega-6 to omega-3 imbalance also stimulates the generation of more fat cells, especially in a diet high in carbohydrates.[45] The loss of short-chain fatty acids fermented from fiber in the gut also causes dysregulated glucose, lipid, and energy metabolism, which also leads to obesity. Being overweight or obese is a risk factor for nearly every other disease of modernity.

TYPE 2 DIABETES

In healthy individuals, rising blood glucose concentrations trigger the pancreas to release insulin, signaling cells to take in glucose, which halts and then reverses the rise of blood glucose. Diabetes begins when the body's cells develop resistance to insulin and can't take up glucose normally. The pancreas must work harder, but chronic insulin secretion exhausts the pancreas, so it cannot overcome resistance. Our modern food choices lead to high glucose and elevated insulin for most of the day.[46] Decreased fiber consumption doesn't help because the presence of dietary fiber improves insulin sensitivity,[47] and increased fructose consumption reduces our glycemic control and leads to insulin resistance.[48] The high glucose in the blood of diabetics can damage every organ system, making it a risk factor for blindness, extremity amputation, kidney failure, stroke, heart attack, vascular disease, and nerve degeneration.[49]

Striking evidence of the effects of the Western diet on diabetes comes from the Native American Pima society. Before colonization, the Pima people ate a traditional diet, and obesity and diabetes were nonexistent. Then their lands and livelihoods were taken from them, and their foodways were forcibly shifted. Now a devastating half of all Pima people over the age of 35 have the disease, and 70% develop it by the age of 64, the highest frequency of diabetes in the world.[50]

HYPERTENSION

Hypertension, or high blood pressure, is the major risk factor for the development of cardiovascular disease and kidney disease. Sodium is required for nerve and muscle function and helps maintain proper water and mineral balance in the body. But our high sodium intakes underlie chronic hypertension[51] because although our kidneys excrete some salt, anyone who eats more than half a gram a day has sodium buildup, which causes water retention. Some calculate that we are carrying up to a liter and a half of fluid in our bodies more than we would on a natural salt intake, and all that extra water raises the volume of blood inside the vessels and causes high blood pressure.[52]

CANCER

The American Cancer Society found that obesity is linked to an increased risk for 13 types of cancer. Body fat affects cancer risk through body inflammation, abnormal cell and blood vessel growth, a cell's ability to live longer than normal, and dysregulated hormone and cell growth factors.[53]

No studies show conclusively that any particular dietary component either causes or prevents cancer in humans, because of a complex interplay of factors. The results only show an increase or decrease in cancer *risk*.[54] For example, high levels of fat are correlated with an increased risk of colon cancer because excessive bile may transform metabolites into carcinogens.[55] High levels of salt also contribute to stomach cancer risk due to irritation and damage of gastric mucosa, making the stomach vulnerable.[56]

Conflicting studies claim that red meat either is or isn't a possible carcinogen, making a definitive conclusion impossible. These studies did consistently find a link between processed meats and cancer due to the carcinogenic effects of nitrates and nitrites, used as preservatives, however.[57] Charred meat can also contain carcinogens that increase the risk of gastrointestinal cancers.[58]

CARDIOVASCULAR DISEASE

Cardiovascular disease—heart disease, heart attack, stroke, congestive heart failure, and coronary artery disease—is the number one killer in America. Atherosclerosis, the buildup of cholesterol-containing plaques that harden and thicken inside artery walls and restrict blood flow, makes the heart work harder to pump blood. If a clot forms from a plaque and blocks blood flow completely, a heart attack or stroke can occur. Remember that LDL cholesterol and lipoprotein bundles stick to the inside of the vessels and cause arterial plaques, and HDL bundles guard against atherosclerosis.[59] Excess saturated fats in the diet elevate total and LDL cholesterol, whereas monounsaturated and polyunsaturated fats have only mild effects on LDL and HDL. However, the predominance of omega-6 polyunsaturated fatty acids favors vasoconstriction, platelet aggregation, hypertension, thrombosis, and inflammation. Trans fats increase the risk of cardiovascular disease more than any other macronutrient by being highly proatherogenic, elevating LDL while lowering HDL.[60]

Cardiovascular disease is not solely a lipid or cholesterol problem. Processed grains, sugar, and refined oil interact to contribute to its development as well.[61] High glycemic loads elevate triacylglycerols and LDLs in the blood while reducing HDLs.[62] The reduction of fiber in the diet diminishes fiber's ability to reduce total and LDL cholesterol and to help high blood pressure.[63] High fructose intake stimulates triacylglycerol production in the liver, which is associated with more atherogenic LDL particles.[64] Finally, our high salt intake leads to thickened and stiffened arteries, increased platelet aggregation, and increased mass of the left ventricle. All of these modern dietary factors predispose us to cardiovascular disease. Figure 9.3 summarizes the health effects of modern nutrition.

Ironically, we've reached the pinnacle of what every hominin in our evolutionary line struggled to attain. We now have at our fingertips large quantities of foods that are energy-dense, easy to digest, and easy to acquire. We have taken it too far, though, and the changes happened too rapidly.

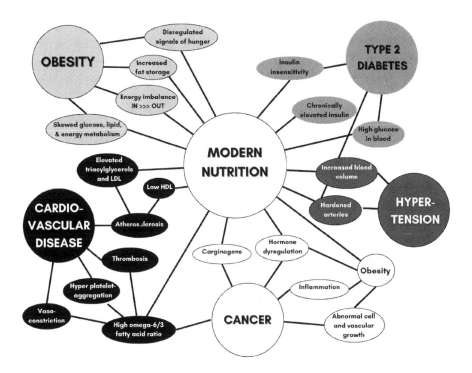

Figure 9.3. The Consequences of Modern Nutrition

We are no longer eating according to our biological evolution; rather, we consume foods generated from cultural evolution. The diseases of modernity can all be attributed to the ubiquitous and extensive consumption of our modern diet,[65] which deprives us of our most primal and biologically alive self.

CHAPTER 10

REALIGNING YOUR NUTRITION

The greater part of our ills is of our own making, and we might
have avoided them, nearly all, by adhering to that simple . . .
manner of life which nature prescribed.

–JEAN-JACQUES ROUSSEAU

N utritionally, humans no longer eat in the manner "which nature
prescribed." Our daily dietary decisions do not take into account
the millions of years of coevolution between our bodies and natural foods. Instead, our nutritional choices are driven by mass production,
consumerism, and convenience due to our cultural and technological push
toward excess, to the detriment of our health. However, we are now armed
with the knowledge to help us make new choices to close the gap between
our current nutrition and our evolutionary legacy. What have we learned
about how and what our hominin ancestors ate that will allow us to make
dietary decisions to promote health and prevent the diseases of civilization?

First, our dietary needs are not very different from those of our omnivorous primate ancestors. We all need protein and fat to anabolize the various

tissues in our body, we need fats and carbs to energize our bodies and feed our brains, and we need fiber to ferment into various nutrients and maintain a healthy gut. As we evolved toward human, our brains grew and our guts shrank, so we needed to consume foods that were easier to digest and that provided maximum macronutrients. We also trended toward eating more animal foods, which provided optimum ratios of amino acids and fatty acids.

As hunter-gatherers, we consumed some version of a universal human diet with balanced macronutrients, with a few exceptions. In places where we couldn't find a lot of carbs, we ate more protein and fat, and in areas without an abundance of fatty foods, we ate more carbs. We were adapted to eat the natural foods available to us. We thoroughly processed and cooked our food to release nutrients and to deactivate antinutrients and toxins, though we never removed the fiber. What we ate was in tune with our genetics, and we were fundamentally immune to the chronic degenerative diseases that now plague affluent nations.[1]

However, knowing the loose, universal patterns of our foraging ancestors doesn't necessarily mean we should eat exactly like them, since we don't live like they did. They needed more fat and protein because of their high levels of activity or due to living in colder environments. We are also genetically separated from them by 10,000 years, and some of us have evolved to adapt to the differences in our diets, like the consumption of dairy. But for the most part, as we moved into agriculture and especially into modernity, we ate more and more foods that we were not adapted to—imbalanced proteins, too much fat, the wrong types of fat, too many carbs stripped of fiber, and all sorts of artificial foods. How can we reshape our diet to improve our health and be more in tune with our evolved needs?

Closing the nutrient gap

To eat more like our ancestors, we must first learn to use our hunger as our guide—to eat when we're hungry and to not eat when we're not. Simple, right? The problem is we are still driven by our cravings to eat sugary and fatty foods. And we are psychologically and behaviorally programmed to overeat and store energy for times of food shortage that will never come. Neuropeptides that respond to the hedonistic pleasure of hyperpalatable food drive our overconsumption, much like the ways they drive addiction.[2] Our bodies prompt us to eat even though we don't need food and aren't hungry, so we get stuck in a refined carbohydrate loop, unwittingly eating more and more until we dull our response to feeling full. The easiest way to deal with this is to remove these foods from our diets, from our pantries, and even from sight to avoid the temptation.

We also tend to overeat when we don't eat a balanced diet. Amazingly, as it digests food, the gastrointestinal tract sends signals to the brain about the amount of food consumed, which organs it passes through, and how much of each nutrient it contains so the brain can adjust our behavior.[3] When eating an unbalanced meal, such as junk food that contains a lot of carbs and fat but little protein, our brain prompts us to consume more of that junk food to acquire enough protein. To avoid this, we must adjust our meals to have protein, fat, and carbohydrates in balanced proportions. The more balanced our diet, the fewer calories we will consume to attain the nutrients our bodies need. Meals consisting of balanced nutrients will also lower the glycemic and insulinemic response of carbs alone, and we will feel more satiated for longer.[4]

Macronutrients

The amounts of macronutrients available to hunter-gatherers at any given time fluctuated, so early human diets were not bound by eating precise ratios. Remember, the range of macronutrient ratios eaten by our foraging ancestors was wide: 22% to 44% carbs, 28% to 58% fat, and 19% to 35% protein (with averages of 35% carbs, 35% fat, and 30% protein).[5]

Compared with modern Western ratios (52% carbs, 33% fat, and 15%

protein),[6] our ancestors ate fewer carbohydrates, comparable amounts of fat, and more protein, but their diets are not considered low-carb or high-protein diets. They ate whatever their environment provided. In the modern world, our food choices are not limited to what nature provides, and not all proteins, fats, and carbohydrates are created equal. There are natural, healthy foods and unnatural, unhealthy foods in each category. However, the diets of all Paleolithic people had one thing in common: They were unaltered by modern agricultural methods, animal husbandry, or industrial processing.

PROTEIN

In determining how much protein we should eat, our sense of hunger should guide us. For example, meat may seem delicious to us one moment, then suddenly not. We should listen to our bodies and not continue to eat protein. If we need more guidance, we can calculate our theoretical protein needs. On average, a sedentary to moderately active modern human needs at least 0.8 grams of protein per kilogram of weight, while a moderately active one needs 1.3 grams per kilogram.[7] So, for a 150-pound person (68 kg), that range is around 50 to 80 grams of protein per day, or 200 to 320 calories from protein per day. If you are doing some serious resistance training or intense exercise, you may need more—upwards of 1.6 grams per kilogram.[8] Generally, the more you exercise and the more strenuous that exercise is, the more protein you need.

We should try to consume proteins that are considered complete, meaning all the essential amino acids are provided. At the top of this list are eggs, dairy, and soy, and then meat (muscle protein). We can get the equivalent of complete proteins from plants as well, if we combine grains with small amounts of legumes and nuts. However, since plant proteins do not digest as completely and easily as animal proteins, we must process these proteins well, through cooking, mashing, soaking, or sprouting.

Many studies show the benefits of plant proteins over animal proteins, especially in reducing the risk of the diseases of civilization, such as cardiovascular disease and type 2 diabetes.[9] As the world's population grows, increasing plant protein sources will be important and much more sustainable because they will have a lower environmental impact than increasing animal sources.

And finally, since collagen is the most abundant protein in our bodies, eating collagenous proteins provides distinct amino acids necessary for tissue building and repair, and we should add more of it into our diet. One of the better ways to consume it is through broth made from boiling down bones, skin, tendon, and ligaments in water for 4 to 24 hours (with a small amount of vinegar to help dissolve the tissues).[10] Bone broths are also available at grocery stores. Additionally, any form of skin we eat, whether from fish, chicken, or pork, is rich in collagen, as are some marine foods like sardines, shrimp, and calamari. Also when eating meats like chicken, we can try to eat more than the muscle meat—the skin, the tendons, and even the cartilage wrapped around the bones. One study reports that you can consume as much as 30% of your protein from collagen.[11] We can also take collagen supplements, although more independent research must be conducted to verify the beneficial claims.

FAT

In determining the amount and type of fat in your diet, our hunger is a less reliable guide than it is for protein because fat is so dense and easy to overeat. The average modern human consumes 33% of their daily calories from fats, which is within the 20% to 35% of total calories per day from fat recommended by the Academy of Nutrition and Dietetics, although it is on the high side, especially with our lack of activity.[12]

The types of fat and the ratios in which we eat them are as important as how much fat we eat, and most foods contain a combination of fats. It is important that we consume both omega-6 and omega-3 polyunsaturated fats because they are essential. We can only get them from external sources. Both are heart healthy, and we need somewhere between 10 and 20 grams of polyunsaturated fats per day to meet our requirements. However, as modern humans, we have a very skewed ratio of omega-6 to omega-3 fats. Our ancestors ate a ratio of nearly 1:1, but currently, the average ratio in modern diets is around 10:1 to 16:1. Our goal is to improve this ratio to 6:1 or even 4:1.[13,14] Obviously, we must decrease our consumption of omega-6 in favor of eating more omega-3 fats. Highly processed foods and oils, such as safflower, corn, and sesame, are high in omega-6. Lean red meat that was grass fed and wild poultry and fish provide more balanced fat profiles and have improved omega-6 to omega-3 ratios over those of meats from animals in feedlots. Fatty fish (like salmon), walnuts, ground flaxseed, and eggs from chickens with high omega-3 feed are good sources of omega-3 fats.

The Academy of Nutrition and Dietetics also suggests that we eat 10% or less of our daily calories from saturated fat, meaning one-third or less of our fat intake should be saturated. Foods higher in saturated fat and cholesterol include fatty domesticated meat and full-fat dairy products, and foods like lean red meat, poultry, and fish contain less saturated fat. The rest of the fat in our diets should be of the monounsaturated and polyunsaturated types. It is important to consume more monounsaturated—which we can get from nuts, avocados, peanut butter, and olive oil—than saturated fats.

Finally, we should also try to eliminate our consumption of the unnatural, man-made, hydrogenated trans fats. Because these fats were not around when we evolved, our bodies are completely unprepared to handle them. So we must reduce our consumption of foods like commercial baked goods (trans fats increase shelf life), fried foods, refrigerated dough, nondairy creamer, margarine, and shortening.[15]

We use some fat for anabolism, but most of it goes to generate energy for our cells and tissues during resting metabolism in between meals; it helps our hearts beat, our lungs breathe, and our livers cleanse, even as we sleep. Our muscles also use fat for low-level exercise, such as walking, and for mid-intensity exercise, like jogging.[16] Our ancestors did these types of activities all day long, so they steadily burned fat and needed more of it in their diet. But if we are sedentary and need fat only for resting metabolism, the percentage of fat we eat in our diet should be lower. Otherwise, our bodies just store it. However, the more activity we engage in, the more fat we'll need. If we are trying to lose fat stores, we should curtail the fat in our diet, maintain protein, and eat whole carbs to prevent sugars from being stored as fat, too. Finally, we should do as much low- to medium-level exercise as possible. We don't need to overexert to lose fat.

CARBOHYDRATES

Modern humans are obsessed with ultraprocessed carbohydrates. Donuts, bagels, cakes, cookies, soft drinks, and sugar-laden coffee drinks have become our staples at breakfast, lunch, and snack time. While most cells can take up and use carbs for energy, carbs are critical for the catabolic needs of our brains, nervous tissue, eye tissue, and red blood cells because they cannot use fat as fuel. Many other tissues will catabolize carbs when they are available in the blood after meals,[17] and our muscles will switch to using carbs as fuel during intense exercise, such as running or playing basketball or tennis. In general, though, we do not need as many carbohydrates as we think.

The amount of carbohydrates we should eat depends on age, sex, metabolism, activity levels, and overall health. A general guideline is for adults to eat 45 to 65 grams at each meal, which is a total of 3 to 4 servings. Snacks of 15 to 20 grams of carbohydrates should be consumed a few times a day. This amounts to around 150 to 250 grams of carbs per day.[18] As a reference, about six slices of whole wheat bread or six whole pieces of fruit equals 150 grams. Also when we consume too much carbohydrate, our bodies just convert the glucose into the saturated fatty acid palmitate and then convert that into other fatty acids and then store that as fat. It is believed that humans get fat from eating too much fat, but in reality, many modern humans get fat from eating too many carbs.

Just like with fats, the types of carbohydrates we eat are just as important as the amounts we eat. We should avoid highly processed grains and added sugars as much as possible to prevent spikes in our blood sugar and to keep our cells sensitive to the effects of insulin. In fact, eating refined sugar (or any other added sweeteners) is completely unnecessary in our diet. We lived without it for millions of years and can live without it now, though it will take time for our bodies to adjust and stop craving so much sugar. It may help to remember that our body's natural tendency to overeat the most sugary and fatty foods is a legacy left over from when we needed fat stores to survive the food fluctuations of seasons that we no longer face. Hopefully, it is helpful to understand the biological underpinnings of overconsumption and to realize it is not a moral failing. Those feelings only make us eat more. We can culturally adapt to resist eating too much.

Most of the carbohydrates in our diet should come from whole foods, such as whole grains, fruits and vegetables, and starches—potatoes, other root vegetables, peas, beans, and cereals. If we follow the trend of our ancestors, we should eat more starches than fruits to preferentially receive glucose instead of the more problematic fructose. However, fruits are wonderful and tasty, and if they are eaten in balance with other carbs, they provide additional nutrients like potassium, vitamin C, organic acids, and soluble fiber to our diet.

We must rid some of these whole foods of their toxins and antinutrients before consuming them, and many of these compounds are deactivated by cooking. Many processes our ancestors used, such as soaking grains, rice, and quinoa before cooking or fermenting flour before baking (sourdough anyone?), not only deactivated all harmful compounds but also made them highly digestible.

Our intake of fiber must increase. It needs to be at least three times higher than it is now, but if our main source of carbs is complete and whole foods, fruits, and vegetables and not processed foods stripped of fiber, our intake will naturally increase. With more fibrous bulk in our diet, we will feel more satiated after meals, reducing our chances of eating more than we need, keeping our gut biome healthy, and maintaining better metabolic control and improved insulin sensitivity.

Hunter-gatherers received enough fiber, vitamins, and minerals to meet their needs because their intrinsic diet of wild, native foods was dense with these nutrients. The only sodium available to them was whatever was in the foods they ate or the rare discovery of salty mineral deposits. With our new diet of whole grains, fruits, vegetables, and lean meats, our micro-nutrient intake will drastically improve. However, we must really work to decrease our sodium intake by at least five times what the average is now. This reduction will radically decrease our risk of hypertension and all of its complications. Raising potassium levels can also blunt the effect of salt on blood pressure.[19]

Input equals output

If we can make the connection between the foods we eat and how they fuel our bodies, it may be easier to balance our input with our output. Knowing that different fuels are used for different levels of activity will help us better choose which fuels we need and when. If we consume more calories than our bodies need, our output must increase so those extra calories aren't stored as fat. Before eating that extra donut sitting in the break room, it may be helpful to think, "If I eat that donut, I will have to run for 30 minutes to balance my input and output." The goal is for our bodies to be in equilibrium. We need to eat what is necessary to provide our bodies with enough building materials and fuel so we have neither nutritional deficits nor excesses. To do this, we don't need to restrict our calories or adhere to the newest fad diet; we simply surround ourselves with good, natural foods: whole grains, lean meats, beans, nuts, broth, fruits, and vegetables. Then we process our foods correctly—through preparation and fermentation—and eat our macronutrients in balance. Then, we must learn to listen to our body's needs and let them guide us.

The physical activity of the Paleolithic lifestyle factors heavily in the prevention of chronic disease. Hunter-gatherers, male and female alike, were like decathlon athletes and had tremendous strength and endurance. Most of us do not perform physical labor as a part of our jobs, so we must reintroduce some of the activities associated with our external foodways—locomotion, hunting, and gathering. To mimic their everyday active lifestyle, we must strength train to build muscle and lean body mass. This will increase our base metabolic rate and help us lose weight. Training for endurance will improve our cardiovascular and respiratory health.[20] Luckily, just as our bodies are still adapted to eat like our ancestors, our bodies are still genetically adapted to live highly physical and active lifestyles.[21]

The Paleo diet

In the early 2000s, nutritionist and exercise physiologist Loren Cordain wrote a book called *The Paleo Diet* based on his research on the discordance between the radical changes in our environment and the lack of time for our genome to adapt. His book launched this popular modern lifestyle trend. However, Cordain likes to emphasize that *he* didn't create the diet. Nature did. He just brought the Paleolithic diet to the attention of modern people, and in an atmosphere of rapid change and the alarming emergence of chronic diseases, it captured the public's imagination.

Contrary to popular belief, the Paleo diet is not based on meat consumption, nor is it vegetarian, although, by volume, it is heavily plant-based. We are not carnivores or herbivores but omnivores. Our bodies thrive on all of what nature provides us. Cordain basically recommended that if a food wasn't around 10,000 years ago, we should decrease or eliminate it from our diet, so the Paleo diet doesn't take into account recent human adaptations, like the ones allowing some people to effectively use dairy or grains with gluten. Other healthy and highly recommended diets, such as the Mediterranean diet, do include grains and dairy. It comes down to whether we can tolerate such foods and whether these foods are replacing other nutrient-dense foods. This may be a choice that is dictated by our DNA.[22]

Just like the present book's recommendations, the Paleo diet encourages us to add nutrient-rich foods such as fresh fruits, fresh vegetables, fish, shellfish, grass-fed meats, free-range poultry and eggs, seeds, nuts, and healthful seed or nut oils to our meals while eliminating industrially processed foods, grains, refined sugars, refined vegetable oils, trans fatty acids, legumes, dairy, salt, and artificial chemicals.[23]

The amount of research on this type of diet is increasing.[24] In the last 20 years, numerous scientific studies have investigated the efficacy and safety of the Paleo diet. Eating like our Paleolithic ancestors enhances satiety after meals, helps with weight loss, decreases waist circumference, lowers body mass index, lowers fasting leptin concentrations, lowers lipogenesis, improves glucose control and glucose tolerance, increases insulin sensitivity, improves blood lipid profiles (lower cholesterol, LDLs, and triglycerides and higher HDLs), improves blood pressure, reduces inflammation and oxidative stress, reduces mortality from cancer (especially colon cancer), and reduces all causes of mortality.[25,26] Eating like our ancestors vastly improves our health as we return to our evolutionary way of eating in accord with our biology (figure 10.1).

A wholesale and complete change to eating like our ancestors is not necessarily something we can do overnight. Rejecting all modern foods would only leave us with 30% of the foods we currently eat, and in many cases, processed and packaged foods are considerably cheaper than whole food alternatives. However, we can all begin sprinkling in more and more

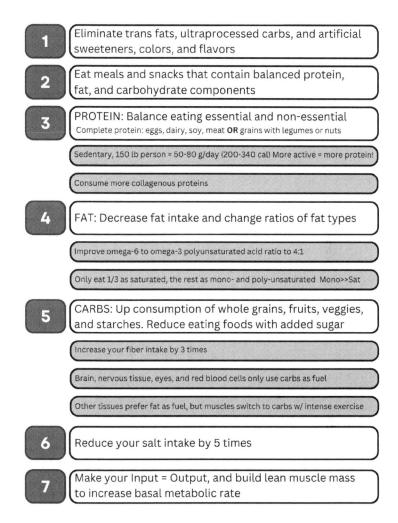

1 Eliminate trans fats, ultraprocessed carbs, and artificial sweeteners, colors, and flavors

2 Eat meals and snacks that contain balanced protein, fat, and carbohydrate components

3 PROTEIN: Balance eating essential and non-essential
Complete protein: eggs, dairy, soy, meat **OR** grains with legumes or nuts

Sedentary, 150 lb person = 50-80 g/day (200-340 cal) More active = more protein!

Consume more collagenous proteins

4 FAT: Decrease fat intake and change ratios of fat types

Improve omega-6 to omega-3 polyunsaturated acid ratio to 4:1

Only eat 1/3 as saturated, the rest as mono- and poly-unsaturated Mono>>Sat

5 CARBS: Up consumption of whole grains, fruits, veggies, and starches. Reduce eating foods with added sugar

Increase your fiber intake by 3 times

Brain, nervous tissue, eyes, and red blood cells only use carbs as fuel

Other tissues prefer fat as fuel, but muscles switch to carbs w/ intense exercise

6 Reduce your salt intake by 5 times

7 Make your Input = Output, and build lean muscle mass to increase basal metabolic rate

Figure 10.1. Closing the Gap on Nutrition

of these foods into a modern healthy diet. At first, it may be difficult to reduce the amount of processed foods, refined grains, refined sugars, refined oils, and salt from our diet and even harder to eliminate these foods completely. But the Paleo diet recommended by Cordain actually supports an 85/15 plan, where someone can receive health benefits without entirely cutting out non-Paleo foods, which can be eaten 15% of the time. This may help with sticking to the diet, especially initially. Then, the less we eat of these foods, the less we will crave them.

We can take back control of our nutrition if we choose to change our ingrained modern behaviors. Currently, many of our choices are controlled by corporations that care about the bottom line and not necessarily about the nutritional well-being of those who buy the food. The food industry is in control of our nutrition and manipulates us through advertising and by peddling extremely palatable (i.e., sugary, fatty, and salty) foods that have us craving more, so taking back our control may be tricky. We must divorce ourselves from all the noise about diet in our society: the endless temptation coming from marketing, one fad after another, and gurus trying to win your attention.

Imagine how alive we will feel when we finally surround ourselves with real, whole foods and then trust our bodies, at least in time, to find balance. When we eat the nutrients optimally suited to our evolved bodies in the ratios our ancestors ate them, we will thrive. Closing the gap between our genetics and our nutrition will vastly improve our health in so many ways and will take us one step closer to eudaemonia.

PART 3

WORK AND REST

Americans have a religion of work, a modern fetish,
work for more work, wealth for more wealth.

—BENJAMIN HUNNICUTT

An email lands in your inbox at midnight, and you are awoken half an hour later by a text demanding why you have not responded yet. You see your kids less and less as you are required to devote more and more of your time to the organization. Those in power encourage you to snitch on others if you consider their dedication not up to par. Your performance is intensely scrutinized after you battle cancer, lose a parent, or have a miscarriage, to make sure you are still focused on your tasks. You toil in atrocious conditions but are told not to worry because an ambulance is waiting if you collapse. Unfortunately, you don't find these things to be abnormal. Your insatiable need to please those in charge and to be successful has completely eroded your boundaries.[1]

If someone described these experiences out of context, they'd seem like outlandish stories from a cult. Sadly, they are real stories from employees at the commerce giant Amazon, and in 2015, The *New York Times* published an exposé about the company's high-pressure work culture. But despite knowing what potentially awaits them at Amazon, people still apply to work there in droves. Dina Vaccari, a former employee, may have an explanation. She said, "I was so addicted to wanting to be successful. For those of us who went to work there, it was like a drug that we could get self-worth from."[2] Many employees unquestionably accepted former CEO Jeff Bezos's intense work culture and use of fear to drive work ethic and innovative thinking. They've bought into the cult of work.

Americans have been conditioned by the idea that how much we work and how successful we are is a measure of our personal worth and identity. Columnist Derek Thompson of *The Atlantic* writes, "*Workism* is the belief that work is not only necessary to economic production but also the centerpiece of one's identity and life's purpose and the belief that any policy to promote human welfare must *always* encourage more work."[3]

This concept of work and achievement is integral to the ladder of success and deeply embedded in our culture. Look no further than the popular X (formerly known as Twitter) hashtags #nevernotworking,[4] #hustle, or

#grind.[5] These are meant to brag about your work ethic and to raise others' esteem of you. But isn't it strange that overwork, probable burnout, and such single-faceted lives are outwardly celebrated? This adoration and obsession with our ability to toil certainly has roots in our nation's Protestant background,[6] but in the last 50 years, we've even stopped taking sick days or paid vacations to spend more time at work. Our obsession with work is having an impact on our health and, paradoxically, on the economy itself.[7]

Modern work

The very seeds of this toxic overwork ethos took root thousands of years ago, when we first planted domesticated crops and transitioned from hunter-gatherers to farmers. Since then, work morphed rapidly, especially for the ones without power or wealth. For example, while serfs or laborers toiled every single day without a break, the landed gentry experienced weeks of leisure every year. A hundred years ago, "working bankers' hours" referred to the short hours enjoyed by bankers and other wealthy people, but this term is a relic of a time before the arms race of status and income in this country began.[8] In the last few decades, working extensive hours for the sake of work has become the norm. Now we see headlines about today's investment bankers such as "Deaths Draw Attention to Wall Street's Grueling Pace."[9] Even the wealthy are working themselves to death.

In the early twentieth century, some economists believed that, if workers were paid more, they would work fewer hours, and as technology advanced, work would become less and less significant in our lives. In 1930, economist John Keynes had a vision that the productivity and economic growth due to technology would allow a working paradise. He expected we would only work 15 hours a week to satisfy our needs and would then have time to enjoy the more profound pleasures of life, such as family, hobbies, music, art, philosophy, and faith.[10] As work became easier, these things would come to define our identities, not money.[11]

Unfortunately, only a part of his prediction came true. We have seen tremendous increases in human productivity, but the amount of time we spend at work has not fallen; it has soared. However, Keynes even anticipated this lag, suspecting that the biggest obstacle to overcome was our instinct to work hard and to create new wealth.[12] He was hopeful we would clear this hurdle, but 90 years later, we are still on the treadmill of work for more work and wealth for more wealth.[13] Will it ever be enough?

Today, there are no large countries with similar levels of productivity as the United States that average more hours of work per year.[14] Columnist Brigid Schulte writes, "In the United States, workers work among the longest, most extreme, and most irregular hours; have no guarantee to paid sick days, paid vacation, or paid family leave; and pay more for health insurance, yet are sicker and more stressed out than workers in other advanced economies."[15] Figure P3.1 is a table comparing the hours worked in the United States versus in other Western countries.[16]

	Hours worked in a year	40-hr weeks worked/year	Fewer weeks worked vs U.S.
United States	1811	45.3	–
Canada	1686	42.2	3.1
Spain	1644	41.1	4.2
Japan	1607	40.2	5.1
United Kingdom	1532	38.3	7.0
France	1511	37.8	7.5
Australia	1444	36.1	9.2
Netherlands	1427	35.7	9.6
Denmark	1372	34.3	11.0
Germany	1372	33.6	11.7

Figure P3.1. The Average Number of Hours Worked per Year in Several Western Countries

Data Source: The Organization for Economic Co-operation and Development (OECD), OECD. 2022. "Hours worked." Accessed July 8, 2023. https://data.oecd.org/emp/hours-worked.htm#indicator-chart.

It seems like Americans work more and get less. But the question is, *Has our biology been able to keep up with this obligation to work more?* Common headlines such as "The Way We Work Is Killing Us"[17] and "These Jobs Have the Highest Rate of Suicide"[18] demonstrate that it has not. Based on these headlines, our work culture is connected to poor quality of life.

Our health and well-being are suffering from the backlash of our modern work habits. We work ourselves beyond the point of exhaustion and tune out the body signals that indicate we need to stop. Did our bodies and minds evolve to toil this way, or is the way we work at odds with our natural, genetic programming?

The work of cells and organisms

All animals must do work to live, but analyzing the work habits of animals is tricky; only humans have a concept of work. Modern humans work so they can earn money to buy food, pay rent, and have health insurance, and they use their nonworking hours for "life." For animals, work *is* life. When they are hungry, they find food. When they need a refuge, they build it or find it. When they have offspring, they parent. When they are tired, they rest. When their physical needs are satisfied, they attend to other things that fulfill the social needs of their species, like play and grooming. Animals work and rest at the whim of their survival needs. They don't clock in and work for eight hours, waiting until they can go home to enjoy their life. Working or not working is all the same for them. It would be a gift to be able to integrate work and life that seamlessly.

As hard as it is to label work in animals, it is even harder to visualize more primitive lifeforms going to work. However, during the early stages of life on Earth, even single cells had to do work to live. If you think about it more deeply, cells are like miniature animals: They eat, produce energy, interact, move, reproduce, etc. Whether a cell is an individual, a eukaryote, or part of a multicellular organism, all cells have similar work outputs—cellular metabolism, locomotion, reproduction, growth, maintenance, and detecting and responding to its environment. At any given moment, any work being done by a cell is done by enzymes, powered by the energy and using the raw materials provided by cellular metabolism. The work of a cell is both energy generation and expenditure, and to achieve homeostasis, the energy in must equal the energy out.

In a multicellular organism, cells communicate with each other to divvy up the work and to share the fruits of their labor. These cells form tissues, tissues make up organs, and the organs work to keep the organism alive.[19] All cells serve the organism, but the opposite is also true; the organism serves the needs of its cells. For example, every organism must find and ingest the food needed for all cellular chemical reactions.

An organism must do the work to maintain the metabolic homeostasis of its cells—no more, no less. If it finds itself with an energy imbalance, an organism must either become less active (rest) or increase its efforts to find food (work). The survival of an organism is not possible unless it works to meet the needs of its cells, and animals evolved countless adaptations to fulfill their metabolic needs as efficiently as possible.

The work habits of chimpanzees

Just as with other organisms, it is hard to separate chimpanzee work from chimpanzee life. It is instructive, however, to trace the work of chimpanzees. Chimpanzees are active from dawn until dusk, usually about 14 hours per day. Their days can be broken down into the activities they choose to do, and we can look at how long they do them. These are not necessarily conscious decisions; rather, these strategies evolved over time. The instinctual actions that are the most efficient and optimized belong to the animals that are the most successful in the survival game.[20]

Chimpanzees spend their hours eating, traveling, resting, and socializing, but only the time they take to eat and travel are what scientists consider to be chimpanzee "work." In every habitat chimpanzees have adapted to, they must spend nearly the majority of their day obtaining food.[21] On average, chimpanzees spend one-third to one-half of their active time (about five to seven hours) eating, although the length of time largely depends on the type of food and how much processing it needs. Some foods require the use of tools to extract, and some foods necessitate lengthy chewing times.[22, 23] That being said, the lengthy time chimps spend finding, extracting, and consuming food is not a constant effort. Rest, socialization, and play are incorporated throughout the day.

Chimp troops have large territories and must travel around these areas daily to access food, to patrol, to mark territory, and to find mates. Within their range, chimps typically travel 2.5 kilometers per day, although every day varies significantly depending on the availability of food, the sex of the chimp, and the maternal status of the females. Chimpanzees usually spend between two and three hours a day traveling.[24] According to these measures, adding together the time chimpanzees feed and travel results in approximately 7 to 10 hours a day of work. That leaves at least four hours to devote to resting and socializing, which includes grooming, playing, and fighting.

To translate this chimpanzee data into human terms, chimps spend 50 to 70 hours working per week, or up to 70% of their waking time at work. That seems like a lot, even for modern human standards. However, chimps just don't see work as toil. The amount of time they spend doing work does not negatively affect their physical or mental health; it's just how long it takes.

When early hominids invented new tools and harnessed fire to cook food, the amount of time required to be spent on feeding decreased significantly. If species such as *Homo erectus* spent less time in the pursuit of food and less time chewing food, there was more time and energy for other human advancements and ventures. Did the trend of requiring less time to work, to track down and consume food, continue into the lives of our Paleolithic ancestors? How did evolution design humans to do work?

CHAPTER 11

THE HUNTER-GATHERER APPROACH TO WORK

A good case can be made that hunters and gatherers work less than we do, and that, rather than a continuous travail, the food quest is intermittent [and] leisure abundant.

—JAMES SUZMAN

For a long time, anthropologists assumed hunter-gatherers struggled for survival and existed on the verge of starvation. Anthropologist Richard Lee sums up this view: "Anthropologists have tended to view the hunters from a vantage point of the economics of scarcity."[1] It's no wonder. By the time scholars took an interest in extant hunter-gatherers, most groups had already been pushed to the most inhospitable and inaccessible fringes, which enabled the long-term preservation of their way of life. They lived in places where no agriculturalists were able or willing to displace them.[2] In the cold reaches of the Arctic Circle or in the hot climates of the African desert, we assumed all hunter-gatherers eked out a meager existence. Adding to the assumption of toil and hardship, those groups that did survive into the twentieth century seemed impoverished by modern standards. They possessed little; lived in temporary huts; slept on the ground; had no access to modern medicine, technology, or conveniences; and had to endure the whims of nature. Their lives appeared extremely difficult, and we assumed they toiled from dawn until dusk just to get by.

Frankly, some hunter-gatherers did lead an extremely difficult existence. Circumpolar peoples, such as the early Paleo-Eskimo, who inhabited the arctic regions as early as 6,500 years ago, faced extreme cold, hunted large and dangerous game, found little edible vegetation, competed intensely for scarce resources, and lived every winter with the threat of starvation. Since humanity has always had the potential to be dark and depraved, some hunter-gatherer groups had horrifying cultural practices that also made life brutal and challenging. At one time or another, every foraging band would have clashed in fierce warfare, suffered diseases and injuries that were death sentences, or starved when an occasional famine befell them. But those dangers were intermittent. We're interested in their baseline state, the average day-to-day life of the average hunter-gatherer.

A preferred way of life

Envision how the majority of our Paleolithic hunter-gatherer ancestors lived. They thrived in more temperate climates and in egalitarian bands, usually at peace. They inhabited the most fertile and abundant areas of the world, enjoying much more comfort than the ones living in fringe environments today. The huge swaths of land we now use for farming once teemed with animals and vegetation, and the entire human population was smaller than today's population of Cairo, Egypt.[3] In these conditions of abundance, hunting and gathering would have been anything but meager. Remember that hunting and gathering was an extraordinary evolutionary adaptation used for millions of years before the Agricultural Revolution; it wouldn't have lasted if they were all constantly on the verge of starvation.

Not only were they adapted to this way of life; it was their *preferred* way of life. Evidence appears in observational accounts from the Dutch colonization of Southern Africa. Although most white settlers felt the "savages" were not only beneath them but not even human, some marveled that, in spite of their apparent poverty, they were happy, smiling, and seemed to enjoy life without toil. Father Guy Tachard, a French Jesuit missionary, wrote in 1685 that "it was the Dutch settlers who were the slaves who cultivate the lands. The natives . . . disdain to plow the land. They maintain that this manner of life shows that they are the true owners of the land, and they are the happiest of men since they alone live in peace and freedom and in that, they say, their happiness consists."[4] Although most colonists perceived the indigenous peoples as lazy, Father Tachard understood they were just adhering to their long-held practices.

In account after account, if there was a choice, hunter-gatherers would always choose their own way of existence over that of the modern world. These hunter-gatherers were so difficult to coerce into working for them that the Dutch East India Company had to ship in slaves to provide agricultural labor in new colonies. As long as they could hunt and gather freely, the indigenous peoples survived and thrived outside of the colonial economy.[5] It was only after so much of their land was coopted to sustain agriculture that they had no choice but to give up their autonomy and become farm laborers. However, many would choose to return to their old hunting and gathering ways after a particularly good rainy season or when there was famine. Whenever hunting and gathering was more fruitful than working in the fields, they would sneak back to the bush.[6]

An early American farmer, Hector de Crèvecoeur, made observations that although thousands of Europeans chose to live as the indigenous Americans, not one Native American chose to live like a European.[7] Indigenous people who were "civilized" after being taken to modern cities and towns, where they learned English, wore English clothing, and even visited Britain, returned to their natural state of being as soon as they returned home. Hunter-gatherers did not abandon their traditional way of life because they thought the alternative was better. They were forced into agriculture because their land was taken, and there was nowhere left for them to hunt and gather.

Less work, few material wants, being in the present

Observations like these from all over the world did not convince people that hunter-gatherers had a good life, and efforts to civilize the "savages" were regarded as saving them from their life of hardship and godlessness—and also a good excuse to take their land. But at an anthropology conference in 1966, a groundbreaking new picture of hunter-gatherer life emerged. Even in what some considered "marginal" areas, most modern hunter-gatherers were discovered to have a routine and reliable nutrition base at worst and an abundant one at best. Plant resources were found to be far more important than game animals, once thought to be the main source of their nourishment. Their hunting efforts may not have been successful every day; however, the women never failed to gather vegetation.[8]

Surprising even to the anthropologists attending the conference, many of the hunter-gatherer communities studied thrived on only two to four hours of food-acquisition effort per day.[9] For example, the Kalahari San, who still live in the desert on the border of Namibia and Botswana, work at obtaining food about 2.5 days per week, and their average workday is around six hours. In spite of the harsh environment, food is abundant and easily obtained, and they only work 12 to 19 hours a week procuring food. Food is even available in the dry season, but they have to travel longer distances to get it. Their nomadic ways make it unwise to harvest more than can be consumed immediately, and their culture of sharing ensures that any surplus is eaten. They do not preserve or stockpile food. A sustained but low-level labor for food is required year-round, unlike in agriculture, where a season of heavy work is followed by a season of unemployment. The Kalahari San have an adequate diet, even though they live in what is considered a "marginal" environment, and the researchers did not encounter any malnutrition or nutritional diseases common in African agricultural societies.[10]

The Hadza of Tanzania is another group that was extensively studied. Even though they live in a desert climate, food is plentiful and varied with the seasons. Over the course of the year, the Hadza spend an average of less than two hours per day obtaining food, much less time and energy than the agricultural tribes neighboring their lands. They never preserve food but share all the food attained by hunting or gathering and eat it rapidly. They do not attempt to conserve plants or animals, but they only take what they need, living in balance with the environment. Remarkably, they do not coordinate food gathering with each other, and many men fail on hunts or don't hunt regularly. In fact, men and women are never forced to hunt or gather. It is a voluntary activity. Nevertheless, as a cooperative group, they obtain adequate food. Their nutritional status is good by tropical standards, and they are also better off nutritionally than their agricultural neighbors, who have a less diverse diet and are more liable to suffer from famine.[11] The Hadza were able to resist attempts to "civilize" them for such a long time because foraging was still a sustainable and viable option for them, and they didn't want or need to switch.[12]

It seems that many hunter-gatherer cultures had already achieved the 15-hours-per-week economic bliss John Keynes hoped for us. He would never have believed that the people who solved his "economic problem" had no interest in productivity, possessed limited technology, and did not accumulate capital.[13] At the 1966 conference, Marshall Sahlins introduced the concept that some hunter-gatherer groups were the "original affluent society."[14] It changed the way anthropologists perceived these "primitive" cultures. Figure 11.1 is a fictional calendar schedule that hypothetically demonstrates what two hunter-gatherer groups' work weeks look like compared to an American's week.

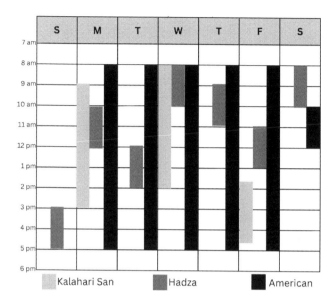

Figure 11.1. Comparing "Work Schedules" of the Kalahari San, the Hadza, and Americans

James Suzman, author of *Affluence without Abundance*, lived with and studied a group of Kalahari San called the Ju/'hoansi for many years. He observed that the Ju/'hoansi work to take care of only their immediate needs—to eat and share, no more. They do not work to amass wealth or things. Suzman witnessed that "avarice is no reigning passion among them, and all that come to want are immediately relieved by the rest."[15] There was also no value for a forager to possess material goods, and since all things must be carried to new camps, their belongings were few.[16] Because of these cultural norms, the Kalahari peoples do not measure success by the accumulation of wealth and possessions; rather, they are content with nutritional sufficiency and limited material culture. Their well-being is based on a few easily met wants, and because they do not desire more, more, more, they are not held hostage to their ambitions. This is a stark contrast to the "American dream." Suzman concluded that Keynes's prediction of man not being able to stop working to accumulate wealth was not in response to a permanent condition of humanity but a fairly recent phenomenon that emerged only after the Agricultural Revolution.[17] Without a material culture, these hunter-gatherers worked far less than we do.

Not only were hunter-gatherers reluctant to give up their way of life, but they were also not suited for wage labor and farming because those required an alteration of their worldview. Suzman observed, "The Bushman lives only for the day and the moment in which he finds himself."[18] Because hunter-gatherer work focused on meeting immediate needs, anthropologist James Woodburn coined the term *immediate-return economy* when he studied the Hadza. It is *immediate* because these hunter-gatherers used or ate what they obtained right away. Their labor was immediately rewarded, so they lived in the present. Obviously, since they didn't store food, small-band hunter-gatherers living in favorable climates did not plan for the future. Most hunter-gatherers lived and worked in the present moment.

In contrast, groups that lived in more difficult environments did have to plan for future-oriented survival concerns. The long, cold, and dark winter months were not survivable for the Inuit unless enough food was stored in the three or four months of warm weather. Plains Indians worked hard in summer to store food and prepare for the harsher winter months in the American Midwest. These groups approached foraging as more of a delayed-return economy long before agriculture forced that view.

Many hunter-gatherers have a cultural understanding of time that is very different from ours. To modern humans, time is linear, finite, and ever-changing, but hunter-gatherers see it as cyclical, rhythmic, and characterized by the predictability of the seasons and celestial movements. They believe they will always be provided for because they always have been, just as the sun always rises.[19] This approach may seem lazy or impractical, but in reality, it was our worldview for tens or even hundreds of thousands of years. However, this traditional perspective is changing in the face of their lands' forfeiture. This old way is dying. A Ju/'hoansi woman called //Eng now looks down at those in her group who still believe they will always be provided for. In Suzman's book, she says, "They do not yet know that to live you must now work hard. . . . This is what I learned from the whites."[20]

What about rest time? Hunter-gatherers may have had to work steadily, but they only acquired food for about 15 hours a week plus spending a few hours each day doing chores such as tool making, hut building, cooking, and fetching water. Hunter-gatherers' lives provided them plenty of leisure, and they took that time to relax. They would visit with others, entertain family and friends from their own group and those of other groups, or simply rest. They would talk, joke, sing, compose songs, play musical instruments, tell stories, make creative things, and play games. When they were not participating in hunting or gathering activities, dancing and rituals were another important pastime for them.[21] Our ancestors made the most of their idleness, so it is no wonder Father Tachard observed them to be relaxed and smiling all the time.[22]

Work in the realm of play

Not only did most hunter-gatherer groups work fewer hours than workers in industrialized societies, but they also had a completely different attitude toward work. Psychologist Peter Gray says, "Hunter-gatherers didn't really have a concept of work as we think of it. They obviously did things that were important, but they never called it work. There's nothing they did that they didn't *want* to do."[23]

Gray hypothesizes that, during our long existence as hunter-gatherers, we evolved the genetic desire to do the things we needed to do for survival. We evolved to enjoy work. Many present-day hunter-gatherers still have no concept of toil for themselves and only apply the term to the work of others.[24] For example, many of the Ju/'hoansi people view white men as being obsessed with work.[25] They are not wrong. Many in the modern world do equate work with toil, an unpleasant obligation to support themselves and their families. They wouldn't do that work if they didn't have to. Ironically, modern humans often recreate and vacation doing exactly the kind of things hunter-gatherers did regularly: hunting, fishing, hiking, camping, gardening, telling stories around a campfire, picnicking, and just enjoying nature.[26]

Gray has observed hunter-gatherer societies that maintained a spirit of play to accomplish their survival tasks. He's studied dozens of hunter-gatherer groups from all over the world, with different languages, religions, and foraging methods, but he found them to be remarkably similar in their social structure and attitudes, including being playful. Colonists often called indigenous peoples "childlike and playful," but they meant it as an insult. However, it was how these people sustained their pleasure in life and work.[27] This sense of playfulness also permitted the intense levels of cooperation required for their way of life. This attitude contributes to many vital aspects of hunter-gatherer life.

To hunter-gatherers, working and being productive are not arduous tasks. They do their work because they enjoy doing it.[28] It sustains life, and it is indistinguishable from life. In this way, hunter-gatherers resemble every other animal on the planet besides modern humans. Gray observed several aspects of hunter-gatherers' approach to work that kept it within the realm of play; their work is varied and challenging, social, and has freedom of choice.

Because hunter-gatherer work is varied and challenging, it requires an alert, active, and playful mind.[29] Both hunting and gathering require knowledge, intelligence, and physical skill. "The human collective knows far more today than did the ancient bands. But at the individual level, ancient foragers were the most knowledgeable and skillful people in history," writes Yuval Noah Harari in his book *Sapiens*.[30] Hunters must know the habits of the hundreds of animals they hunt and be able to identify their sounds, tracks, and scat. They use intelligence and technique because they cannot overpower an animal with speed or force. Tools of the hunt were invented, then carefully crafted, and the skills to use them are incredible.

Gatherers must know where to find nutrient-rich plant matter, how to extract it, and how to process it. Gathering food requires physical skill and the ability to remember, use, add to, and modify culturally shared verbal knowledge.[31] Gray claims, "There's nothing routine about hunting and gathering. You constantly have to learn and adapt to figure out what's the situation out there today and how you're going to handle it. That makes their work play."[32] In the 1990s, when James Suzman asked white farmers what they thought about the Kalahari San, they responded with terms like "technically gifted," "inventive," "intelligent," and "imaginative."[33] All of these qualities are developed through a lifetime of play.

Humans are social animals, and hunter-gatherers are no different. Most group activities are cooperative and done in a collective way. They hunt using teamwork, and they gather in groups. Their expeditions are happy events as they convert chores into social occasions with joking, singing, laughter, and good-natured attitudes. Both hunting and gathering are enjoyable because they get to do it with friends, and they get to share the fruits of their labor.[34] In other words, having fun while working with friends makes it more of a game and gives more enjoyment to the process of work, not just the end result.

Gray also observed that although "hunting and gathering are critical for survival, on any given day, for any given person, these activities are optional." Adults can choose when, how, and even whether to work. This choice is the crucial ingredient keeping hunter-gatherer work more like a game. They have an ethic of personal autonomy; no one tells anyone else how to behave. Hunting and gathering parties are only formed by those who want to go that day. The group decides where to go and how the job will be done. Anyone not happy with it can choose to form another party, go alone, or stay at camp. There is no retribution for taking a day off, and they will still receive their share of food. Long-term shirking is highly unusual because it is more fun to engage. Chronic slackers would be teased incessantly to change their behavior, and pathological freeloaders would be kicked out of the group.[35] However, anthropologists' accounts led Gray to conclude that as a hunter-gatherer "in the normal course of things, you had lots of time to play, and you could go for long periods of time not doing anything productive and still be supported by others." When work is optional and self-directed, it stays in the realm of play.[36]

Hunter-gatherer work is challenging and engaging, thoroughly social, and has some freedom of choice. In these ways, it can be approached with a playful spirit. Being a hunter-gatherer, even one of relative abundance, was not all fun and games. But, despite hardship, they still had this unique way of viewing the world. They did not seek to escape reality but to confront and cope with the dangers of a life that was not always easy.[37] Gray writes, "Hunter-gatherers simply trust that, as long as work is play and as long as people are treated well and are truly free to make their own decisions, the great majority of people will quite gladly contribute to the band in the ways they can."[38] Their ability to remain "child-like" in most aspects of their lifestyle, not just recreation, shapes their views about life and work, which are balanced and healthy.

Our distant relatives certainly worked hard, but now we know that many worked for shorter periods of time and had a very different view of work. Their work was incorporated into their lives in such a way that they didn't need to find a work-life balance. They already had it. Would our Paleolithic ancestors shake their heads and laugh at us, the fools who are slaves to work for our wealth and possessions or simply for work itself? Our concept of work has changed dramatically since our days as hunter-gatherers. The way of life of the hunter-gatherer is almost gone, but perhaps we can still learn from them.

CHAPTER 12

MODERN WORK CULTURE AND ITS CONSEQUENCES

Much of our contemporary economic and cultural behavior—including the conviction that work gives structure and meaning to our lives, defines who we are, and ultimately empowers us to master our own destinies—is a legacy from our transition from hunting and gathering to farming.

—JAMES SUZMAN

Our views about work fundamentally and irrevocably changed because of the Agricultural Revolution. In less than 10,000 years, most humans transitioned from hunting and gathering to farming after the social and population changes induced by agriculture made it so we could never go back.[1] This shift to agriculture spurred the accumulation of wealth, the development of a future-oriented mindset, and made work monotonous, individual, and compulsory.

As more and more people practiced agriculture, the ownership and protection of land became important. With farming, work must be invested over long periods of time before a yield is produced. It wouldn't make sense to plow, plant, weed, and water over an entire season only to let someone else come along to reap the harvest. They had to establish land ownership, build permanent dwellings, and drive others away. Land quickly accumulated into the hands of the few, and the many became dependent on and eventually subjects of the landowner.

The ruling elite gained material wealth from the storage and hoarding of goods but realized they could amass even more wealth if they used the labor of nonlandowners. A new system of masters and slaves or lords and serfs—bosses and employees—was created, concepts that were foreign to small-band hunter-gatherers. Wealth was passed down as inheritance, ensuring it would always stay in the hands of the few. Now that farmers had to stay in one place and work the land, they had permanent dwellings, and even they began to accumulate belongings. They may have been poor, but a single farmer may have had more possessions than an entire hunter-gatherer tribe.[2] The Agricultural Revolution commenced the accumulation of stuff at all levels.

Agriculture also changed our temporal outlook on life. The delay between the work investment of farming and the consumption of its products is called a *delayed-return economy*. In farming, and most of our modern contemporary occupations, the effort put in now is rewarded later with either a harvest or a paycheck.[3] This made us future oriented. We stopped living in the present and stopped trusting the land would provide. We made darn sure it did with backbreaking, hard work that also squashed any chance of a playful approach to our labors. Farming is tedious, routine, and monotonous. Every day, work was the same, and little skill was required to perform it. Unlike hunting, anyone can hoe or weed a field.[4]

Farming did not require cooperation the way hunting and gathering did and could be done in the absence of a social group. Food sharing with people other than immediate family ceased because they didn't share in the work. Individuals and families became more isolated.

Finally, most agriculturalists never had a choice to work or not. Work was compulsory, either because if the work wasn't done, the crops would fail, or because workers would be punished by their leader if they did not work. No wonder work became toil as we worried about the future and performed mind-numbing, solitary, and obligatory physical labor all day long. The transition to agriculture planted the seeds of our future working habits and triggered the adverse effects of overwork.

Modern work

Do you believe that a 40-hour workweek is the gold standard of a balanced life? In reality, the entrenched, 8-hour workday is an arbitrary convention based on a relic from the Industrial Revolution. Typical factory workers used to work an unsustainable 10 to 16 hours a day. In the nineteenth century, social reformists campaigned to end these grueling hours in favor of an 8-hour workday, not because of scientific reasoning, but because it was more reasonable. After the Ford Motor Company instigated these hours and started paying their employees double in 1914, this 8-hour workday became popular. In the next two years, Ford's productivity and profits skyrocketed. Other companies, eager to mimic Ford's success, followed suit.[5] Our schedule of 8 hours a day and 40 hours a week evolved from the success of a car manufacturer, not from the evolved needs of our bodies.

Today, we aren't even sticking to this artificial standard anymore. Here are some gloomy statistics about work in modern America. Adults who work full-time average 47 hours of work per week. Represented in figure 12.1, half of these full-time workers reported working more than 40 hours, 39% reported working 50 or more hours, and 18% worked over 60 hours.[6]

If all categories are included, which counts part-time and seasonal workers, the average work week is still 35 hours,[7] and annually, American work hours surpass most Western European countries and Japan.[8]

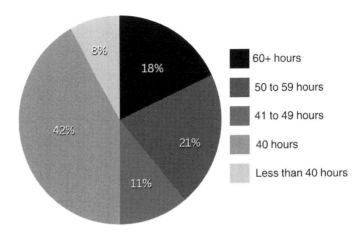

Figure 12.1. Number of Hours Full-Time Employees Work per Week in the United States

Source data: Saad, L. 2014. "The '40-Hour' Workweek Is Actually Longer—by Seven Hours." Accessed December 14, 2019. http://news.gallup.com/poll/175286/hour-workweek-actually-longer-seven-hours.aspx.

We now spend nearly 400 more hours at work a year today than we did 30 years ago—10 additional weeks of work![9] Many factors caused this escalation: uncertain economic times, the rise of a global economy, and the increase in economic inequality. Many people work long hours simply to make ends meet, whereas others do so to prove their self-worth.

Ironically, the increased hours we spend at work are not helping the economy. A linear negative relationship exists: The more hours a country works, the lower its productivity.[10] Instead, these increased hours are making workers physically and mentally ill.[11] The health of both workers and the economy are affected when people overwork.

Work is central to the American dream. The term was first popularized by James Truslow Adams in his 1931 book, *The Epic of America*. Adams "dream[ed] of a land in which life should be better and richer and fuller for everyone, with opportunity for each according to ability or achievement." He wrote, "It is not a dream of motor cars and high wages merely, but a dream of social order in which each man and each woman shall be able to attain to the fullest stature of which they are innately capable, and be recognized by others for what they are, regardless of the fortuitous circumstances of birth or position."[12]

The American dream used to mean freedom, mutual respect, and an equal opportunity to achieve prosperity through hard work. Unfortunately, working hard for the American dream has a very different connotation today. In the 1970s and '80s, the term lost its association with freedom and equality, as it began to be used in advertisements to make capitalism and consumerism seem patriotic. The dream came to mean home ownership, business ownership, and wealth. The morality of the dream morphed to mean material success.[13] This culture of materialism is a breeding ground for overwork. We had to work harder and harder to attain the things this new American dream now stood for, and somewhere along the way, work fused with our sense of worth. Americans focus on their material and social status as measures of success.

At 47 hours per week, the average full-time American worker works a full 32 hours more than Keynes's predicted 15-hour workweek paradise. What's even worse, we've stopped taking the breaks we've earned, the breaks written into our contracts, and often, the breaks required by law. Many workers will not take breaks unless they are mandated by their employers. Others tend to work beyond fatigue where performance already has declined to the point that a break will not be effective.[14] Millions of hours of our hard-earned vacation time are left in the bank every year. We even go to work sick, which not only risks exposing others but also lengthens our recovery time. We think getting our work done is more important than taking care of ourselves. The decline of rest in the workplace also has serious consequences on our health and economic productivity.

The consequences of overwork

Jeffrey Pfeffer, professor at Stanford Graduate School of Business, investigated the health effects of different workplace issues, such as economic insecurity, work-family conflict, long work hours, and the absence of job control. In his book *Dying for a Paycheck*, he found that these factors "account for about 120,000 excess deaths a year in the United States, which would make the workplace the fifth leading cause of death, and costs about $190 billion in excess health costs a year." This makes some work practices as harmful to health as secondhand smoke.[15] The scientific community is well aware of this, and since the 1990s, the number of scientific articles examining how work can take its toll on our physical and mental health, our safety, and our productivity has increased more than tenfold: a perfect reflection of our increased time spent at work.

PHYSICAL HEALTH CONSEQUENCES

Work's toll on our bodies is first extracted when we engage in poor health behaviors such as unhealthy eating, increased smoking or drinking, or reduced exercise when we are stressed. These behaviors and our physiological responses to stress activate autonomic, neuroendocrine, immune, and inflammatory responses that affect the body and ultimately cause disease.[16] A comprehensive report from the CDC published in 2004 showed that working overtime was associated with poor health, more illness, and increased mortality. In other words, overwork can backfire.[17]

If you knew that working crushing hours could trigger hypertension, fatigue, musculoskeletal disorders, and chronic infections, or that it increased your risk of stroke, diabetes, cancer, cardiovascular disease, and arthritis threefold, would you have stopped working 70 hours a week?[18,19,20] Maybe not. The ingrained cultural conditioning tells us we must do whatever it takes to succeed and gain personal worth, including ignoring our health. But eventually, our bodies will retaliate. Illness or disease will stop us in our tracks and force us to stop working.

MENTAL HEALTH CONSEQUENCES

The impact on our mental health is also clear. Employees who work 11 or more hours each day have double the risk of major depressive episodes compared to employees who only work 7 or 8 hours a day. And depressive symptoms increase or decrease depending on whether overtime is worked or not.[21]

Declining mental health in the workplace is a pressing concern. Pfeffer cites a report from the United Kingdom's equivalent to OSHA—the US Occupational Safety and Health Administration, which regulates workplace safety—that demonstrated in 2016 and 2017 that 12.5 million days of work were lost due to workplace stress, anxiety, and depression.[22]

Many countries are experiencing a precipitous rise in work-related suicides. Recently in France, a suicide epidemic at a telecom company reached such alarming numbers that the former CEO and other managers were investigated and went to trial for the extreme work pressure and deteriorating work conditions their workers faced. In Japan, there is even a word for suicide by overwork: *karōjisatsu*. Karōjisatsu is considered an urgent healthcare issue and is being actively addressed by the Japanese government.[23]

INJURIES

Not only do job-related illnesses and depression sideline employees, but 23,000 injuries occur at work every day in the United States. That's a monstrous 8.5 million workplace injuries per year.[24]

Here are more sobering statistics about injuries. Working a job with an overtime schedule has a 61% higher risk of injury than a job without overtime. Working more than 12 hours in one day has a 37% increased hazard rate, and working over 60 hours per week has a 23% increased rate. When we are overworked, we are stressed, and since we aren't taking care of ourselves, we are drowsy, fatigued, and more likely to make mistakes and misjudgments.[25]

The combined medical and indirect costs of these work-induced physical illnesses, mental illnesses, and injuries were $250 billion in 2007 alone.[26]

THE ECONOMIC AND SOCIAL CONSEQUENCES OF OVERWORK

Overwork is not just a personal problem; it is a socioeconomic one. Overwork-related illnesses and injuries cause millions of days of missed work, costing our economy billions of dollars. The cost to treat the health effects of overwork is also astronomical. The financial consequences to the bottom line are obvious and overt. But what about the more hidden consequences? For example, when extraordinarily long hours are required for a job, the pool of workers available for that job is squeezed. Many women or others with caregiving responsibilities are forced out of contention because the kind of hours the job entails are simply impossible.

Caregivers face a tough dilemma. Childcare is so expensive that many families can't afford to pay for it, meaning one of the incomes disappears (usually the woman's) in order to provide it cost-free. Is it really free? Women miss months or years of working and earning while caring for children. When they return, if they're able to find a job, they have to start over or take a job beneath their training and ability, which significantly affects lifelong earnings for the women and their families. Unfortunately, dual incomes are necessary for the economic well-being of most middle-class families in America. The absolute need for dual incomes to keep their heads above water hurts families.[27]

In many cases, the best and most talented person for a job may not be hired. Women now graduate in larger numbers from college and graduate school, and in this way, overwork is also affecting the gender pay gap. Overwork lowers the number of jobs available because it lowers the demand to hire more workers.[28] A company may resist hiring two people for a job because they perceive that it will cost less to employ just one person but make them work longer hours. But with the drop in productivity and the potentially lost workdays due to injury, illness, or burnout, wouldn't it have been more profitable to have employed two people in the first place?

Although some are spending too much time at work, others have trouble finding enough work to get by.[29] Rising economic inequity is a cause of long hours because of financial insecurity. When the Great Recession began in 2007, massive layoffs caused larger workloads to burden the employees that escaped being cut.[30] Business consultant Clay Parker Jones said, "Organizations are turning up the dial, pushing their teams to do more for less money, either to keep up with the competition or just stay ahead of the executioner's blade."[31] Many have no choice but to work mandatory overtime or simply work tirelessly to prove themselves when cuts make job security precarious.

Modern work is changing due to the economic globalization of labor markets. This has caused more job competition as companies face mergers, downsizing, outsourcing, or redundancy.[32] Precarious employment also has a detrimental effect on the health of workers, causing acute stress, anxiety, sleep disorders, burnout, and suicide.[33] The globalized workplace has also transformed the conditions of work. For many, employment is no longer stable, income is not enough, working conditions are deteriorating, and worker protection is eroding. Although our work has intensified, workers' rights have eroded.[34]

A growing number of people feel constantly overwhelmed as they try to succeed at a demanding job with long hours and little flexibility while attempting to manage personal demands such as children, aging parents, health, school, and community obligations.[35] This continuous feeling of overwhelm negatively impacts their health.

But overwork itself isn't the only cause of workplace-related illness. When a person is tasked with a job that requires high effort or high risk without a proper reward, not only does their motivation for the work diminish, but also their probability of developing cardiovascular disease or depression increases by 50%. This imbalance between effort and reward

Figure 12.2. The Consequences of Overwork

amplifies stress, which may lead to illness.[36] In this way, the big-picture economic and social consequences of overwork also cause physical and mental illness. Figure 12.2 is a summary of the consequences of overwork.

THE DECLINE OF WORK BREAKS

Not only are we working harder and longer than ever before, but we are working through lunch and skipping breaks. On average, less than half of all employees take a lunch break away from their desks. Twenty percent eat at their desks, and 13% don't take the time to eat at all.[37]

In a report from the National Institute for Occupational Safety and Health, 40% of Americans report their jobs as very or extremely stressful, but they do not use vacation days their company provides.[38] Millions upon millions of hours of vacation time are squandered each year, sacrificed on the altar of work. Why aren't we taking the time off we worked so hard to earn?

Social psychologist Jennifer Berdahl says, "A lot of companies might have great work-life balance policies, but people aren't using them because of the stigma associated with doing so." She has found that employees are unwilling to take leave for their families because they fear being thought of as not committed to their jobs or, even worse, may experience career retribution.[39]

This guilt and fear were found to be the primary reasons people skipped breaks and vacations. But over time, employees who do not recover their resources for work during breaks, evenings, weekends, and vacations have an increased risk for depression, fatigue, loss of energy, and cardiovascular disease.[40] People also tend to believe that, if we don't stop working to take a break or a vacation, we'll be more productive, more successful, and more respected.[41] However, focus is necessary for productivity, and breaks are necessary to regain our focus. Everyone suffers from decreased attentional capacity even after only 20 to 30 minutes of doing the same task.[42]

The American government isn't any help. There is no law in the United States that requires employers to provide paid sick leave. Many companies do provide this time, but 26% of workers, especially hourly workers, do not get paid sick leave.[43] The United States is also the only industrialized country that does not have *mandated* annual leave, much less paid annual leave.[44] Figure 12.3 compares the same countries as previous figures for the number of mandated paid vacation and holidays.[45]

The United States doesn't even provide a national paid parental leave benefit to new parents. In other industrialized countries, the average is 12 weeks of paid parental leave, and in Europe, the average is 20 weeks of paid parental leave.[46] The message this sends is, "You will work no matter what, or potentially lose your job."

This notion that if we work longer, we will get more done is misguided. In reality, the longer we work, the less efficient we become. For example,

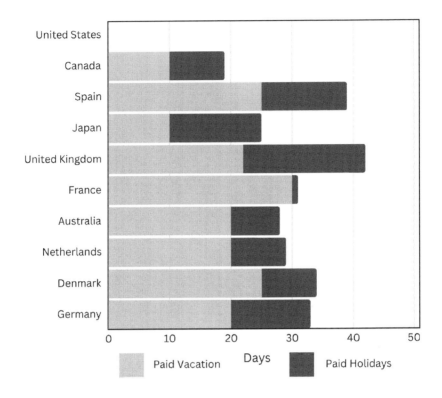

Figure 12.3. Average Number of Days of Mandated Paid Vacation in Several Western Countries

Data source: Maye, A. 2019. "No-Vacation Nation, Revised." Accessed July 18, 2023. Center for Economic and Policy Research (CEPR) https://cepr.net/report/no-vacation-nation-revised/.

productivity drops steeply after working 50 hours a week. Reducing the number of hours worked per week from 55 to 50 only has a minimal effect on our output. Even more striking, if we work 70 hours a week, we will get no more done than if we consistently worked 56 hours on a weekly basis.[47]

When productivity is reduced, so is profitability. However, in a bid to remain competitive and at the cutting edge, companies provide employees with incentives to remain at work far above the typical 8-hour-day, 40-hour-week schedule. Lavish amenities like free all-you-can-eat buffets, nap pods, and doctors' offices on-site all motivate employees to stay at work.[48]

Not only do all of those conveniences cost companies money, but the costs may be wasted. Does requiring employees to work longer hours improve the bottom line if they are less productive during the overtime? Long hours also result in poorer neuropsychological performance across the board. The longer someone works without a break, the more the overall quantity *and* quality of their work suffers.[49]

OUR FOCUS ON MATERIAL AND SOCIAL SUCCESS

We no longer work only to satisfy our basic needs, but we work for the sake of material possessions. When we have those things, we feel we must work longer and harder to attain more things, then we must pay for their upkeep or storage. This requires more money and more work. Our homes will simply not contain all of our stuff anymore, even though in the last 60 years, the average size of a new home has grown an astonishing 1,500 square feet. On top of this, fewer people now live in each home. We fill up all that extra space with stuff and then have to start storing stuff outside of our homes.[50] When you are driving around, notice the number of self-storage buildings popping up on every corner. The self-storage business has become a $38 billion industry in this country. About 1 in 10 Americans pay at least $100 a month to store their material overflow.[51]

Laura Ingalls Wilder, author of *Little House on the Prairie*, perfectly described the consequences of this avalanche of belongings: "We are so overwhelmed with things these days that our lives are all, more or less, cluttered. I believe it is this, rather than a shortness of time, that gives us that feeling of hurry and almost of helplessness in the face of them."[52] The crazy thing is, she wrote that in 1924. What would she think of us today?

But possessions may actually make us less satisfied with our lives. American consumerism has risen sharply in the last 70 years, but our happiness has gone down.[53] Research has shown that materialistic individuals are actually experiencing social disengagement and decreased well-being.[54] Consumerism is hurting the environment, too, because most of what we consume ends up in the garbage.[55]

On the flip side of material success is social success. We work for recognition and advancement. In other words, we work for the sake of our work. Since performance and achievement are now measures of self-worth, those who make a lot of money are viewed as not only having more net worth but also more personal worth.

Conversely, those who are poor are considered to have less personal worth because it is incorrectly assumed that if they just worked harder, they would not be poor. Many people in the lower socioeconomic classes work two, three, or more jobs just to get by. That is working hard.

By constantly being bombarded by these expectations or needs, overwork has become part of our psyche. We are in a constant struggle to become more efficient and more productive and to achieve work advancement so we can make more money and garner more recognition. It's no wonder we are continually stressed and overwhelmed. Overwork breeds overwork, and for many, a realistic work-life balance has become so unattainable it is almost mythical.

The purpose of pointing out these detriments of overwork in our modern culture is not to demonize hard work or make people who work long hours feel bad about their choices. Hard work is an admirable quality, and some have no other choice available. But there is a difference between working hard and working constantly—at the expense of your life. Rather, we wanted to uncover why modern humans have developed such extreme imbalances in their lives and how our unhealthy relationship with work can hurt us as individuals and as a society.

The negative consequences can be attributed to how we now work in ways and conditions we are not evolved for. However, we can look far into our past for solutions. What can we learn from our ancestors to help us tackle our problem of overwork?

CHAPTER 13

REALIGNING YOUR WORK

One solution to this epidemic . . . would be to make
work less awful. But maybe the better prescription is to
make work less central.

—DEREK THOMPSON

The discrepancies between how work used to be woven into our lives
and how we approach it today are dramatic. In evolutionary time, it
has not taken us long to move from one to the other. We have not
had time to biologically adapt to modern working conditions and are still
running our hunter-gatherer programming, so we have a jarring disconnect. This disconnect may be the cause of many pathologies of overwork.

We can't just suddenly give up our careers and return to a hunter-
gatherer's way of life to be more attuned with our biology, though. Our
survival in the modern world requires a paycheck. However, we can be
aware of how work and workplace culture negatively affect us and apply
the parts and pieces of a hunter-gatherer's outlook that resonate with us.

There are at least four things we can learn from our ancestors: to live
with less so we can work less, to live in the present and be mindful of our

needs, to take breaks and put work aside for leisure and recovery, and to infuse a playful spirit into our work.

Live with less. Work less.

Our modern culture of consumption is consuming us. With messages telling us that it's what we own that will give us joy, we drown ourselves in stuff and then have to work ceaselessly to pay off debt. But it wasn't always this way. Our hunter-gatherer ancestors could carry their few personal possessions on their backs, but they still lived happy and meaningful lives.

We have to reevaluate the meaning possessions have for us. Are they symbols of success? Are they emotional bandages to fill a void? Don't relationships and experiences fill our lives with more meaning than our possessions?[1] They do, which is why a social movement called minimalism is gathering momentum. *Minimalism* is a lifestyle choice where people possess only things that add value to their lives. Minimalists Joshua Millburn and Ryan Nicodemus claim, "By clearing the clutter from life's path, we can all make room for the most important aspects of life: health, relationships, passion, growth, and contribution."[2] In many respects, hunter-gatherers were unconsciously the original minimalists.

The motivations for someone choosing a simpler life range from environmental to economic to spiritual. But common to every story is the belief that, for everything that is given up, something far better will be gained in return. When entrepreneur Graham Hill moved from a four-story, 3,600-square-foot home into a 420-square-foot studio, he realized of his former life that "after a certain point, material objects have a tendency to crowd out the emotional needs they are meant to support. . . My house and my things were my new employers for a job I had never applied for." Paring back may seem like a step back—less success and opportunity—but most find they have more than they ever did.[3] Hill adds, "I have less and enjoy more. My space is small. My life is big."[4]

Millburn and Nicodemus also write that minimalism is "freedom from fear. Freedom from worry. Freedom from overwhelm. Freedom from guilt. Freedom from depression. Freedom from the trappings of the consumer culture we've built our lives around. Real freedom."[5] Minimalism is a tool anyone can use to assist in finding the kind of freedom that comes with being able to put your meaningful possessions on your back (or in your car) and make a change. This is one way we can listen to our inner hunter-gatherer.

If we have less and need less, we can work less. How do we next stop working for work's sake, for validation, for self-worth? First, we must decondition ourselves from believing that our work is the only measure of our worth. Work is only a fraction of our whole body of worth—maybe a pinkie toe. We are parents, spouses, partners, children, siblings, and friends. Our relationships are a large part of our worth. By spending time with those we love, pursuing hobbies we are passionate about, and experiencing the joys life has to offer, we can learn to celebrate and collect self-worth from the parts of life that have nothing to do with work. We do not have to be #nevernotworking to be successful.

For us to achieve the work-life integration of our Paleolithic ancestors, American workplace culture must also change. With all of the emerging research about overwork, health, and productivity, some employers have tried shorter work weeks to help their employees establish better work-life balance. It's been a resounding success. The shorter week makes the remaining days of work more efficient. If employees have more time off and autonomy of when to work, they are happier and more productive. With improved morale, they are more dedicated to work.[6]

When a company in New Zealand gave their workers an extra day off per week, the workers reported feeling less stressed, more satisfied, and more capable of managing a work-life balance. Not only that, but they were more engaged, committed, and stimulated at work. They were less compelled to check social media and were less distracted by nonwork projects. CEO Andrew Barnes says, "I have ended up with statistics that indicate my staff are fiercely proud of the company they work for because it gives a damn."[7] In Sweden, some large mainstream companies reduced the work week from 40 to 30 hours per week and reported their workers were also less fatigued, more efficient, and happier.[8] This concept is just beginning to take off in the United States. We still have to change our perception that more work is better.

Since many of our hunter-gatherer ancestors probably only worked acquiring food for about 15 hours a week, it is clear that we did not evolve to work the grueling hours we currently devote to work. We are certainly not evolved to work sitting at a desk, crouched over a keyboard for eight or more hours a day. The first step off the work treadmill that is making us physically and mentally ill is to make some conscious observations about our relationship with our jobs and our relationship with our things. We must give ourselves permission to bow out of what columnist Melissa Balmain describes as "this consumer-driven rat race of always needing more and wanting more and trying to earn more to buy more." If we are not busy all the time, we can find more life satisfaction.[9]

Live and work in the present

Hunter-gatherers worked to fulfill their immediate needs and were attuned to these needs in an organic way: by being connected to the present moment. Being conscious of the present needs of an individual or group dictated what work was done and for how long. Did they need to hunt for more meat, build a shelter, or process roots to eat? Once they worked to satisfy the need, they stopped. Obviously, we can't stop working in the middle of our shift or during a meeting when we feel like our needs are met. However, being mindful of the present moment will help us tremendously in the workplace.

Mindfulness is a mental state of focusing our awareness on the present moment while calmly acknowledging and accepting our thoughts and emotions without judgment. Our ancestors were always aware of the present; they did not dwell on the past or worry about the future. As a future-oriented society practicing a delayed-return economy, we find this difficult. Our modern concept of time "deludes us into concerning ourselves with its passing and [its] impeding arrival," writes mindfulness expert Alfred James.[10]

It seems we are seldom in the moment in which we find ourselves. This affects how we perceive our lives and how we experience our work. For example, we may be so worried about a future deadline or performance review that we cannot enjoy the task, and anxiety thwarts our best performance. We may miss the new career opportunities offered to us because we are too hung up on regret from a past job. And we may be so anxious about returning to work on Monday that the weekend time spent with family or friends is ruined.[11]

Both meditation and mindfulness can teach us how to remain anchored in the moment. However, in the workplace, mindfulness has a direct effect on lowering stress by decoupling work from the future, by centering our attention to the problem or issue at hand, and by changing our perceptions of the scope of professional demands placed on us.[12] With an ability to focus on the task at hand, we are not overwhelmed by looking at everything we must do at once. Being mindful at work will help us make better decisions, communicate more effectively, be more engaged, demonstrate resilience, and exhibit more creativity at work.[13]

If we can approach work in the present moment the way hunter-gatherers innately did, we can find a work-life balance more easily. Also, by being mindful of our bodies' needs, such as rest, nourishment, and exercise, we will be better able to maintain our health and will, therefore, be more productive at work and be able to spend less time there. Being present will also allow us to work fewer hours because we will realize which tasks are the most important and be less distracted while doing them. Mindfulness will streamline our efforts, as we spend less time in the limbos of the past or the future.

Take breaks and enjoy our leisure time

A demanding and stressful work environment may be unavoidable. However, scientific evidence proves that taking a break at work to breathe, take a walk, and be in touch with our bodies and immediate surroundings will reduce stress, and taking a vacation from work actually makes us happier and more effective. However, breaks and vacations remain low on our priority lists.

It was not always this way. If a gatherer was tired of digging for roots, she'd stop and recover before returning to her task. If a hunter was ill, he would skip joining a hunting party until he was well. With the mindset of a hunter-gatherer, we can be more receptive to the benefits of breaks and vacations.

As economist and philosopher David Hume wrote in the 1700s, "The mind requires some relaxation and cannot always support its bent to care and industry."[14] Regular rest breaks during the workday are necessary for maintaining performance, managing fatigue, and reducing the risk of injury. These breaks give the brain time to recover and refocus, to subconsciously think about a task, to simulate new ideas, and to make the task seem less tedious.[15] Breaks also facilitate work engagement and reduce boredom. Since we spend almost a third of our adult lives at work, it would be nice to enjoy it, have enthusiasm for it, and find meaning in it.[16]

The standard practice of one 10- to 15-minute break in the morning and one in the afternoon, along with a half hour to an hour for lunch, is being challenged. More frequent breaks were actually found to increase productivity. For example, in a factory setting, a 10-minute break every hour proved more productive than the standard break schedule. For computer programming work, short, hourly, or even half-hourly breaks resulted in fewer errors, reduced eyestrain and discomfort, and had no impact on productivity.[17]

The CDC now recommends incorporating a five-minute break every hour, including some sort of movement to increase circulation and prevent physical discomfort. It may sound counterintuitive, but taking more breaks can help eliminate distractions and increase focus because the knowledge a break is coming will give our work more urgency and intensity. We will be more efficient, make fewer mistakes, and be more engaged in our work.[18]

The activity performed during a break has an effect on the extent of recovery that can take place. Breaks should allow someone to shift their attention away from work stress, whether it's a break at work or an evening, weekend, or vacation.[19] Taking a walk, going outside into nature, reading a nonwork book, eating a healthy snack, getting a coffee, doodling, listening to music, exercising, being social with coworkers and friends, meditating, and daydreaming are all break-time activities that boost at-work recovery.[20] They all give our brains a break from the focused attention required of us.

This diffuse or daydreaming mode actually exhibits amplified brain activity. In a diffuse brain state, breakthroughs sometimes seem to come out of nowhere; our neurons are able to hook up, and associations can be made.[21] The same kind of brain state can be achieved through mindfulness as well. Hunter-gatherers, whose survival depended on multifaceted observations and tasks requiring problem-solving, did not spend their days focused on just one task. By focusing, resting, and changing tasks, they activated their diffuse attention that enabled them to have the creative insights that made them successful. A wandering mind is not necessarily a waste of time.

Evenings, weekends, and vacations are also crucial breaks. Being able to unwind and recover when not at work is a vital component of a healthy work-life balance. When compared with a baseline just before a vacation, the well-being and performance capacity of workers increase after they return. This effect may seem short-lived, but not taking vacation is associated with long-term health problems.[22]

Just like with work breaks, what we experience during a weekend or vacation can either help or hinder the recovery process. A relaxing experience reduces emotional drain and contributes to more effective work on our return. Having an experience that challenges us or broadens our horizons while on vacation also contributes to less exhaustion when we get back. If we have positive thoughts about work while on vacation, our recovery is improved, but negative work reflection contributes to greater burnout, more health complaints, and lower performance on our return. If we only deal with hassles over a weekend or on vacation, we will be more tired later at work. And finally, dealing with a high workload upon the return to work will mitigate the positive effects from an extended break.[23]

Columnist Tim Kreider writes, "Idleness is not just a vacation, an indulgence, or a vice; it is as indispensable to the brain as vitamin D is to the body, and deprived of it, we suffer a mental affliction as disfiguring as rickets. The space and quiet that idleness provides is a necessary condition for standing back from life and seeing it whole, for making unexpected connections and waiting for the wild summer lightning strikes of inspiration; it is, paradoxically, necessary to getting any work done."[24]

Don't work yourself to exhaustion. Give yourself breaks. Give yourself permission to leave work at work and relax your mind and your body. Give yourself permission to go on vacation and not think about work while on it. By not overworking and by taking breaks while you work, you will be healthier, happier, and able to perform your tasks more effectively when you return.

Infuse work with a playful spirit

Hunter-gatherers did not view work as toil; rather, it was how they sustained life. They worked because they wanted to help their group survive and thrive. And because their work provided them with intellectual and physical challenges, a great deal of social interaction, and an element of free choice, it was possible for them to approach it with playfulness. It's time to try and change our perception of work as toil and to infuse a playful spirit into it. How can aspects of hunter-gatherer work help us sprinkle this spirit into ours?

To survive in the modern world, humans no longer need to possess many skills. Most of our jobs are highly specialized, even in professions like medicine or engineering, so as individuals, we no longer have the broad and varied knowledge of hunter-gatherers. There is even evidence that our brains have decreased in size since the Paleolithic.[25] It is enjoyable and satisfying to learn and be challenged. Peter Gray says, "The more skill and intelligence is involved in any kind of a task, the more playful it seems to people. People today who regard their job as play are in jobs that involve some creativity and figuring things out; they're not in jobs that involve doing the same routine thing over and over again."[26] Mind-numbing tasks lead to monotony and boredom.

We may no longer have to bring down a mammoth to feed our families, but a challenge in the workplace such as a presentation, a complicated project, or mastering a new skill gives us the same sense of accomplishment and aliveness.[27] By stretching and engaging, our minds will become more alert, active, and creative. Work will become more fun.

Making connections with coworkers will also make work more fun and dynamic. Interacting with others during the workday—helping, sharing, and laughing—makes going to work more enjoyable. Conversely, feeling isolated and uninvolved at work will lead to discouragement and stress. In addition to having meaningful work interactions with others throughout the day, it is important to have social interactions during breaks. The sense of camaraderie we generate with coworkers makes arduous tasks more doable, like in group hunting or gathering excursions. Great relationships with people at work give us a greater sense of empowerment and personal achievement. When we are connected with the people around us at work, we feel less anxious, depressed, and lonely.[28] The network of relationships we create helps us succeed in our professional and personal lives, and we'll get to have a little fun along the way.

In work that is self-chosen, a playful attitude about work can be maintained. Psychologist Reed Larson conducted a study that followed married men and women who had jobs outside the home. The women reported being happier and more satisfied than the men at their jobs, whereas the men were happier than the women when at home. This reflects an element of choice. With the gender stereotyping we still have today, women feel they *must* work in the home but choose to work outside the home. Men feel they *must* go to work but can choose what they do at home.

Granted, not many of us have the luxury to choose our work. We can't just take a day off whenever we want, or we may always have to do what our boss tells us to do. However, finding ways within our jobs to give ourselves choices may be one way to make work more fun. Self-directed and creative work or work in which you have decision-making autonomy can be more enjoyable.[29] Gray writes, "Play's distinguishing characteristics lie not in the overt form of the activity but in the motivation and mental attitude that the person brings to it. Two people might be throwing a ball or building a house or doing almost anything, and one may be playing while the other is not."[30]

Jobs that are complex and varied instead of simple and routine, social rather than isolating, and autonomous rather than closely supervised by others are highly desired, playful job characteristics.[31] Activities undertaken for play and pleasure have the potential to fuel innovation and discovery because during play, we can ignore rules and conventions and have nothing to lose.[32] If we can find playful qualities at work, we may cultivate qualities like "technically gifted," "inventive," "intelligent," and "imaginative" in ourselves.[33]

For the sake of our individual and collective health and wellness, we must change our work habits so they are more suited to our biology. Hunter-gatherers viewed work as integral to life, but it wasn't the point of life. They worked to meet their needs in a pleasurable environment, then delighted in living. Today, work has generally become a drudgery that has commandeered our lives. How hard we work and how successful we are individually has become a moral quality, and as a result, overwork has become an ailment.

To overcome our glaring mismatch and reduce our stress, we must work less and own less, guard our breaks and leisure time fiercely, and have more enjoyment of work. We must live in the present moment and be more aware of our immediate work needs instead of always dwelling on the past or worrying about the future. To live a more balanced life, we shouldn't take our jobs so seriously; work hard, do what we have to do, but realize it is a means to an end, and that end is life (figure 13.1). We are more than our jobs, more than our success, and more than our possessions.

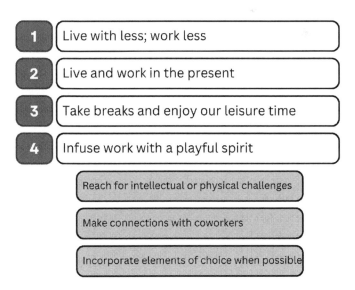

Figure 13.1. Closing the Gap on Work and Rest

Of all our ancestors' lessons about work, there is one lesson that stands out as the most vital. We must work to live, not live to work. Work, after all, is only one part of being. Balanced with the rest of life, work can be a part of the pursuit of eudaemonia.

PART 4

THE NATURAL WORLD

The universe is so unhuman, that is, it goes its way with so little thought of man. He is but an incident, not an end. We must adjust our notions to the discovery that things are not shaped to him, but that he is shaped to them. The air was not made for his lungs, but he has lungs because there is air; the light was not created for his eye, but he has eyes because there is light. All the forces of nature are going their own way; man avails himself of them or catches a ride as best he can. If he keeps his seat, he prospers; if he misses his hold and falls, he is crushed.

–JOHN BURROUGHS

Modern humans are the only species on Earth without a natural habitat. We dwell and work in artificial structures made of concrete, drywall, carpet, and glass, and we only view nature through windows. Our contact with the natural world diminished little by little as we left our nomadic ways and migrated into villages and towns. It happened so gradually that we were barely aware of it. However, now is the time to take notice as our modern culture accelerates our disengagement even further. If it weren't for our extraordinary brains and adaptability, the loss of our natural habitat would have surely caused our extinction, just as it has for countless other species. We may have survived, but our health and vitality have suffered.

"Inside" seems to be our new habitat. It is possible to exist without ever stepping foot outside, although what a deprived life it would be. At the same time, our old natural environments are shrinking through deforestation and the construction of asphalt jungles. They are also "shrinking in our collective imagination and cultural conversations," according to siblings Selin and Pelin Kesebir. In an analysis of millions of books, songs, movies, and documentaries, they found that nature has slowly dwindled from our popular culture since the 1950s. Since then, urbanization and massive technological changes have also altered *how* we entertain ourselves. Television, smartphones, streaming media, video games, and the internet have claimed more and more of the time we used to reserve for outdoor activities.[1]

On average, children spend three times as many hours on screens as they do playing outside, and the majority of adults spend five hours or less outside each week. Amazingly, they claim to be satisfied by this paltry amount of time.[2]

Nevertheless, we evolved to become human beings in nature, where our ancestors trusted that everything they needed would be provided and where the significance of the sky and the birds and the trees was elevated above the importance of humans. Now, the loud and relentless blitz of modernity can drown out any desire to be out in our natural habitat, and the magnetic attraction of modern culture tugs us back inside.

Unfortunately, we are pulling away from our Earth just as it needs us more than ever. This distance makes it hard for people to understand what today's wide-ranging losses of habitat and extinctions mean for humans. As conservationist and writer Robert Pyle wrote, "What is the extinction of the condor to a child who has never seen a wren?"[3] The futures of the condors and wrens of the world are in our hands. Rachel Carson, in an interview about her book *Silent Spring*, said, "Man's attitude toward nature is today critically important simply because we have now acquired a fateful power to alter and destroy nature. But man is a part of nature, and his war against nature is inevitably a war against himself."[4] Fifty years later, if Carson were still alive, she would see Earth in more of an environmental crisis than ever before. We now live in a new epoch because of our war on nature.

For 12,000 years since the Agricultural Revolution, we lived in the Holocene epoch, in which all advanced human civilization developed. However, since the 1950s, carbon dioxide emissions have risen exponentially, climate change has accelerated, sea levels are rising, the world's forests are being massively depleted, and what scientists are calling the sixth great extinction is underway. The Holocene epoch has ended, and we are in the Anthropocene, where humans' impact on the Earth is more profound than any other force. Geologists agree that the Anthropocene began when the first nuclear bombs were detonated, when we proved that our collective human activities dominate the planetary machinery.[5] (See figure P4.1.)[6]

Yet, nature provides our most concrete physical needs, such as food, water, material for building shelters, and resources for our technology. It is also critical for our well-being, and as we've headed inside, the health of our bodies and minds has deteriorated. Obesity, high blood pressure, diabetes, anxiety, and depression are just a few of the diseases that have become pervasive in our modern world.

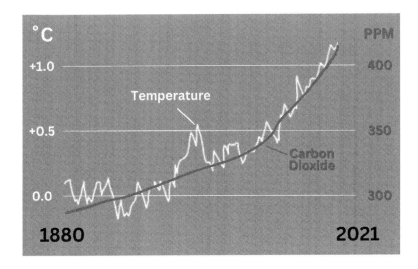

Figure P4.1. Global Temperature versus Atmospheric Carbon Dioxide

Adapted from: Keeling, R. Tans, P. Shindell, D. 2022. "Peak CO2 & Heat-trapping Emissions." Accessed December 16, 2023. https://www.climatecentral.org/climate-matters/peak-co2-heat-trapping-emissions.

Of course, the deterioration of our health is affected by the sedentary and indoor lifestyle we've adopted, but until recently, the health effects triggered by the separation from nature in our day-to-day lives were only thought to have a weak causal relationship. Now, science is accumulating evidence of nature's positive impact on our health, and recognizing the physical and mental disorders that plague urban societies may be alleviated by connection with nature.

Nature fulfills certain physiological, psychological, emotional, and spiritual needs that can't be fulfilled in other ways, and modern people are suffering a kind of spiritual famine due to the loss of our contact with it.[7] We may not even realize that some of the emptiness and alienation we feel is due to our separation from nature. We need nature as much as it needs us. Can we make our way back to our natural environment and solve our mismatch?

Primates and other animals

It is difficult to describe how an animal's relationship with nature evolved because it was seamlessly integrated into their daily lives since the dawn of life. Animals live with a constant connection to their surroundings, aware of where to get a meal, what predators to look out for, and where to find shelter if that storm breaks over the dark horizon. They are part of the natural world, and the natural world provides them with their physical needs. Animals live in equilibrium with the environment and take only what is required for survival. A species thrives when their habitat thrives. When animals are separated from their natural habitats, they usually do not thrive unless they develop behavioral or physical adaptations to help them in their new location. In other words, unless a species can evolve mechanisms to persist in a new environment, it will become extinct. Humans can use culture to bypass the necessity of evolution to survive, which is how we can live in 100-story apartment buildings. But are we thriving at the top?

Since we can't ask them, we may never understand how animals feel about nature psychologically and emotionally, but we can describe what happens to wild animals when they are removed from their natural habitats and confined in small or unstimulating environments. These animals get stressed and cope with *stereotypic behavior*, a repetitive behavior that serves no obvious purpose: the tiger at the zoo who paces back and forth until a deep trail is worn in the dirt; the monkey who compulsively returns to touch a wall in the exact same spot so often there is a dark mark on the concrete; or the rhino who has worn off a patch of its skin on a post. Gus, a polar bear at the Central Park Zoo, swims figure eights in his pool for hours at a time. These behaviors are extremely rare in the wild but are so common at zoos that they are called *zoochosis*.[8]

What the public doesn't know is that many animals on display are given pharmaceuticals such as antidepressants or participate in enrichment programs to help their mental health.[9] Animals in artificial habitats are surviving but do not necessarily thrive, even though their physical needs are completely taken care of, they don't have to worry about predators, and they have a large staff of veterinarians to make sure they are healthy. By inference, we can conclude that nature provides for an animal's psychological needs in addition to their physical ones; when it is taken away, the animals do not maintain the same vitality.

The natural world supports animals physiologically and psychologically; however, so much of this world is being destroyed. We are currently in the midst of a sixth great extinction; this time, species are dying out as a result of human activity, not due to unavoidable natural circumstances or the process of natural selection. An analysis of both common and rare species found that billions of regional or local populations have been lost in the last 50 years; 50% of individual animals are gone.

Since its passing in 1973, the Endangered Species Act has listed 2,375 worldwide species as endangered or threatened. In the United States alone, 1,678 species are listed as such.[10] Habitat destruction, overhunting, toxic pollution, invasion by alien species, and climate change have all contributed to these species dying out, but the primary causes of these events are human population growth, overpopulation, and overconsumption.[11]

Jane Goodall says, "Chimpanzees, gorillas, and orangutans have been living for hundreds of thousands of years in their forest, living fantastic lives, never overpopulating, never destroying the forest. I would say that they have been, in a way, more successful than us as far as being in harmony with the environment."[12] Everything from single-celled eukaryotes to insects, snakes, bears, whales, and primates not only need nature, they are nature. Together with the plants of the world, animals made up and populated vast and varied habitats of the world well before humans came along. They include the complex natural network of give-and-take, the interdependent web of life in which humans are only a gossamer thread. We've seen what happens when animals are removed from nature's web. We are now cutting the strands and removing *ourselves* from the web. Are we suffering from our own form of zoochosis in the modern world? Have we always held ourselves separate from nature?

Biophilia

In his 1984 book, an ant biologist named E. O. Wilson created the term *biophilia* (meaning "the love of life") to describe our innate and instinctive urge to seek connections with our natural environments and other organisms. He proposed that this affiliation had deep and complicated roots in our mental development. Wilson believes that since our very existence depended on this tendency, humans evolved such a connection to nature by natural selection. The hunter-gatherers who were the most tuned to nature had an evolutionary advantage and were the most successful, thus passing their genes on. This awareness of our surroundings was second nature for our survival. However, biophilia is for more than survival. Wilson writes, "Our spirit is woven from it, hope rises on its currents."[13] So in addition to increasing our chances of survival, our biophilia also increased our ability to achieve meaning and personal fulfillment and gives us many reasons to have a self-interested basis to care about and conserve nature.[14]

Wilson's biophilia hypothesis originated from his observations of biophilia in daily life, in the patterns of our childhood and culture, in the literature of anthropology, and in the awe and veneration given to nature.[15] For example, in a cross-cultural study that asked participants from Senegal, Ireland, and the United States to identify their favorite place and why, 61% of adults chose an element of a natural environment as their favorite place to be for relaxation, recharging, safety, or ecological reasons.[16] In another study, 96% of urban school children drew pictures of the outdoors when asked to make a map or drawing of their favorite place.[17]

Wilson also argued that since biophobia (the opposite of biophilia) evolved by natural selection, biophilia must have, too. Snake aversion is a biophobic trait that has a hereditary origin. Never having seen a snake, chimpanzees in captivity respond to them with fear because snakes were present in their evolutionary environment, and an instinctual fear of them is a survival adaptation. Conversely, lemur primates, who evolved on Madagascar in the absence of poisonous snakes, possess no such innate snake aversion. Humans maintain repulsion from snakes, a trait left over from our evolution, even though we do not face poisonous snakes in our modern cities. Wilson wrote, "The brain appears to have kept its old capacities, its channeled quickness. We stay alert and alive in the vanished forests of the world."[18] Our biophilia is still present, only in the modern world, we've forced it into dormancy.

When people are asked what their ideal setting would be, they are more likely to point to open, tree-studded land overlooking water than any other environment. This type of setting describes the vast grasslands of the savannah, the prevailing original habitat in which our brains evolved, and Wilson suggests we are predisposed to this habitat because of evolution. The savannah, dotted by groves and scattered trees, offered an abundance of food, water to drink, shelter, clear views by which to see predators or prey, and a natural perimeter of defense. Choosing such a habitat would be ideal for survival.[19] As modern humans, we prefer such a beautiful setting because our brains tell us it's where the best resources—and comfort—are located. This explains why children are inherently attracted to nature without being taught and why we prefer plants and views to be part of our living and work-spaces. However, our attraction to nature isn't only for our survival but also for our well-being.[20] (See figure P4.2.)

The fundamental rupture of the human relationship with the natural world is evident not only in our modern environmental crisis[21] but also in the decline of our collective physical, mental, and social health. New scientific evidence supports this, but first, we will delve deeper into what we know about hunter-gatherers' relationship with nature.

Figure P4.2. What Is Your Ideal Environment?

Photography credit: Canva

CHAPTER 14

HUNTER-GATHERERS AND NATURE

The old Lakota was wise. He knew that a man's heart away from nature becomes hard.

–LUTHER STANDING BEAR

We will never know for certain how our Paleolithic ancestors felt about nature, but it is reasonable to claim that hunter-gatherers were never separate from it. They were as much a part of nature as a blue jay or a grizzly bear is. They probably didn't even have a word for nature the way we do. They lived in the wide, open spaces of the world, where they were attuned to the daily cycles of life and to the life cycles of animals and plants. They slept in shelters made of grass, mud, skins, or snow in touch with the ground while all the sounds and smells of their surroundings filled their senses.

Not only did they depend on the land to survive, but they had a special connection with nature and respected its importance in their lives. They possessed sophisticated knowledge of their habitats and incorporated their homeland into their sense of identity. They lived in equilibrium and harmony with the environment, so much so that they thrived for hundreds of thousands of years.

A deep sense of connection

Ancient humans relied on their wits, skills, senses, and muscles to provide their next meal and to escape predators. To survive, they had to be fully present, connected to the land and its creatures. Fifty thousand years ago, when we emerged from Africa as *Homo sapiens* and spread over the entire Earth, we had to quickly adapt to new environments. Our intelligence and language made us extremely adaptable, but our abilities to connect with nature, to learn the intimate knowledge of our new habitats, and to pass this sense of connection to our offspring were key to our survival.

Hunter-gatherers' connection to their environment gave them an extreme sense of place. They had a very holistic view of the natural world. For example, the Birhor, in the jungles of India, view humans, nature, and the supernatural as all bound together to create the moral community of the universe.[1] There are no demarcations between them. The Ju/'hoansi of the Kalahari believe that, soon after God created the world, the animals were people, and the people were animals. At this time, identities were fluid. They all intermarried and preyed on each other in equal measure, and there was no separation between the Ju/'hoansi and nature.[2]

The indigenous people of the Great Rift Valley of Tanzania, the Hadza, outwardly demonstrate their deep connection to nature through a unique symbiotic relationship with honeyguide birds. Remarkably, these birds have evolved to lead humans to honeycombs so that humans can get rid of the bees for them. The Hadza smoke out the bees and take the honey, but they leave the waxy combs for the birds in appreciation for their help. After they find honey together, the Hadza whistle to the birds, then sing and dance to honor them. This is one of the most coevolved, mutually beneficial relationships between mammals and birds. The Hadza believe that the land belongs to the animals, and they are just borrowing it.[3] They are connected to nature in a way that doesn't exist in the modern world. In this way, they feel a deep belonging to the places they lived.

Reverence of nature

The reverence of nature is intricately woven into the belief systems of these hunter-gatherer societies. This connection is fundamentally demonstrated by the sheer number of hunter-gatherer groups that practice animism, a religious belief that all things, including animals, plants, rocks, rivers, and even weather, possess a spirit and are alive. The ceremonies and rituals surrounding all sustenance activities center on honoring and respecting the overarching forces—the gods and the weather—and giving gratitude to the individual animals who sacrificed themselves so the tribe might eat. Many groups believed that such honor was necessary for the animal's soul to be reborn into a new body.

In hunter-gatherer cultures, all nature is held sacred. The view that the world and all of its inhabitants are spiritually endowed and maintained, that animals and humans share a kinship, and that we should relate to both humans and nonhumans with reciprocity infuses most hunter-gatherer belief systems.[4] For example, the Innu of Northeastern Canada believe that people are not the center or the summit of the universe. Rather, they are but an integral part of it, equal with the animals and natural elements, and it is their role to maintain proper relationships between man and animal through give-and-take. In South America, the Huaorani, who live in the Amazon Rainforest of Ecuador, consider the majestic ceibo tree to be the origin and container of all life, and they worship it like a Christian would worship God. The Timbisha Shoshone of Death Valley believe that any disrespect for the land and its resources would bring about human disaster.[5] This view is eerily prophetic for the modern world.

A wealth of knowledge

Remember that hunters must know the behaviors, sounds, tracks, migration patterns, and scat of hundreds of animals. Only with this knowledge can they overpower and kill the animal because without claws or sharp teeth, strength or speed, humans had to use innovative tools and techniques. They had to outsmart the animal with knowledge.[6] Gatherers maintained the knowledge of hundreds of plants, where and when to find them, whether or not they were poisonous, which ones were edible or medicinal, their uses, how to extract them, and how to process them for consumption. Both hunters and gatherers stored this knowledge, used it, added to it, shared it, and taught it to others.[7] Anthropologist Catherine Fowler and ethnobiologist Nancy Turner even went so far as to say that the hunter-gatherer systems of knowing and explaining the universe are analogous to Western science and are the collective wisdom and experience of generations.[8]

Through the varied terrains of the past, hunter-gatherers foraged for knowledge about their surroundings, too. They possessed detailed mental maps of their territories and knew every rock and tree. They understood the signs that the weather was changing or that one season was ending and another one was beginning and what that meant for finding water. They picked up every clue and cue nature gave them.

With all of this information, hunter-gatherers had a wide and deep understanding of their surroundings and were acutely aware of their bodies and senses within those surroundings. They are so knowledgeable and connected that, according to anthropologist Daniel Everett, who studies the indigenous Pirahã of the Amazon, they "can walk into the jungle naked, with no tools or weapons, and walk out three days later with baskets of fruit, nuts, and small game."[9]

This knowledge was often the most important aspect of a leader. In the northern reaches of Russia, the Yukaghir clans were not run by the elders who were the best hunters. Rather, their elders' power came from spiritual authority and knowledge about effective coexistence with nature.

Belonging

The existential sensation that we belong to a particular place characterizes the relationship of hunter-gatherers to their homeland and their sense of themselves. With their land so incorporated into their existence through connection, respect, and knowledge, no wonder nature is wrapped into their identity. The stability of a physical environment is what led to psychological stability in these communities.[10] The loss of this identity and stability hits indigenous cultures hardest when their lands are appropriated by modern cultures and they are forced to live in resettlement camps sometimes hundreds or thousands of miles from their lands.

Geneticist and anthropologist Spencer Wells says, "People assume it doesn't really matter where they live. They're nomads, so you can take them out of here and put them over there. The problem is they accumulate this knowledge of the place where they live, and they become very closely attached to it. All of their dead are buried there. The whole place is one giant burial ground, and so they're connected intimately with their ancestors when they walk through this land. When you take that land away from them, you're taking away a critical part of their culture. It really is what defines them."[11] Removing them from the land strikes at the heart of their existence.

The loss of their environmental identity and the compulsory changes in the people's lifestyles cause rampant despair and emotional disorders, which trigger many to turn to alcohol and drugs. Tragically, suicides are on the rise in indigenous peoples separated from their traditional ways of life. Their anxiety, anger, and depression are alleviated when they can return to their lands and reconnect with their natural way of being.

For the Toba of Northern Argentina, "the bush" is constructed as a haven from the exploitation and poverty enforced on them. A return to the vast plains of their ancestors, the Pampas, is a balm that soothes their existential devastation.[12] When modern governments grant land back to indigenous groups, this return to their homeland initiates the healing of minds and a newfound ability to preserve and perpetuate their cultures. Nature is their cure, as it has always been.

Conscientious stewards

Archaeological evidence suggests that the Hadza and their ancestors have continuously occupied the Great Rift Valley since at least the beginning of the Upper Paleolithic era. These are people who still exist in the same environment in which human evolution occurred. Amazingly, when the pyramids were being built, the Hadza had already lived there for 50,000 years.

Because the Hadza leave no mark on the land as they pass through, it has sustained them for tens if not hundreds of thousands of years. Their territory may be shrinking, but they are still the conscientious stewards of the land that remains to them and never take more than they need. They never used to fear they would not be provided for, because how they managed their land ensured there would always be what they needed. Safari guide and author Daudi Peterson says, "They live in a way which represents the greater part of our human history and in a way that on both the environmental and social side achieve goals that most societies aspire to, but do not achieve."[13]

In the Kalahari Desert near the border of Namibia and Botswana, the Ju/'hoansi have also survived as hunter-gatherers for tens of thousands of years. These hunter-gatherers succeeded and survived for so long because they reached a form of dynamic equilibrium with the environment, a balance between the relative stability and harshness of the desert.[14]

Anthropologist James Suzman wrote of the Ju/'hoansi, "Something important happened here—that somehow this environment and the people who lived there had found a formula that was sustainable. And an important part of that formula was the fact that the Khoisan (Ju/'hoansi) were satisfied that their environment provided everything they desired without asking too much in return." Suzman also hypothesized that their habitat had "nurtured them in such a way that they were not driven to contrive new technologies or new ways of being."[15]

Indigenous ways of life were stable for thousands of years, until the arrival of white men. Because indigenous peoples lived sustainably for so long, Africa's megafauna (the largest mammals, such as elephants and rhinos) were preserved and maintained into present day. Sub-Saharan Africa saw only 2 out of 44 large animals go extinct, compared with the almost 80% extinction of megafauna species in other parts of the world after the arrival of man, or after colonization of an indigenous environment (figure 14.1).[16]

1500 to 1900
Extinctions: 77

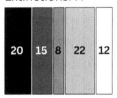

Since 1900
Extinctions: 269

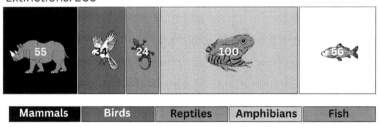

Figure 14.1. Global Extinctions from 1500 to 1900 versus since 1900

Adapted from: Palmer, G. Ceballos P.R. Ehrlich A.D. Barnosky, A. García R.M. Pringle T. 2015. "Accelerated modern human–induced species losses: Entering the sixth mass extinction." Science Advances 1 (5).

So far, we have discussed the Hadza and the Kalahari San, among others, as examples of how hunter-gatherers approach ways of being. These two groups, specifically, are the best- and longest-studied forager cultures because of their critical links to the lands where humans evolved. However, this doesn't mean they are the only models of how hunter-gatherers lived in equilibrium with nature. Most foraging cultures have similar attitudes about nature, and many of their shamans' powers mimic land management practices that sustainably transform nature into a giving entity.[17]

For the Batak of the Philippines, any wasteful or excessive use of resources is thought to cause the spirits to punish the wrongdoer with illness or death. To restore the balance among humans, forest, and spirits, a 15-day ritual of song, dance, and collective good behavior is observed.[18]

According to Aboriginal Australian belief, all life is part of Dreamtime, a vast and unchanging network of relationships traced back to the beginning of time. The great spirit ancestors in Dreamtime created the sun, moon, and stars; the land; the elements; and all plants and animals. The Aboriginal people believe they do not own the land; rather, it owns them, and they are tasked with keeping it unaltered.[19] Aboriginals who enter Dreamtime are not only taught this complex understanding of creation but are also shown how to preserve nature and maintain equilibrium with the world.[20]

Nature plays a principal role in the lives of hunter-gatherers. Their experience centers on a connection to the natural world, their respect for the environment, and their identity is strongly associated with their place. Because they are so competent and knowledgeable about the web of life, they lived sustainably and in harmony with nature, sometimes for millennia.

Why would their beliefs place such a strong emphasis on equality and equilibrium with nature? These practices were absolutely required for survival. A tribe would not endure if they did not approach their environment sustainably. A culture that destroys its environment will eventually not be able to sustain itself. Modern humans need to remember that.

Hunter-gatherers were not tree-huggers; however, a traditional society had to hold values that kept humans "as the kinsmen of plants and animals"[21] if they were to be confident that nature would always provide for them. In return, nature provided everything a human ever needed physically and psychologically for health, well-being, and vitality.

CHAPTER 15

MODERN HUMANS AND NATURE

Humans have forgotten how much the natural world means to them.

—CECILY MALLER

The Agricultural Revolution changed how people related to the environment, and humans developed a radically different understanding of their place in the world. As farmers, our home shrank from being the hills, streams, woods, and sky into cramped structures of wood, stone, or mud. We became separated from our neighbors and lived a more self-centered life.[1] We still worked outside in the fields, but that wasn't nature as we knew it.

To produce enough food to feed the growing population, farmers also had to radically modify their natural environment with irrigation and deforestation to aid cultivation. We forgot the secrets of nature because we no longer needed them. Nature itself changed in our psyche as well, becoming something to use, and our modern religious constructs declare us to have dominion over the Earth and everything on it. Becoming producers, makers, and—ultimately—consumers paved the way for our transition into being the most dominant species on Earth.[2]

Based on the area of land needed to sustain human life, the density of hunter-gatherers was about one person per square mile. But with agriculture, that restriction was broken,[3] and population growth became uncoupled from what the natural world could provide. Modern humans live at about 38 people per square mile, and in the Chinese territory of Macau, there are 48,000 people per square mile. It took only 11 years (2011 to 2022) for the Earth's population to increase by 1 billion people, and we now sit at over 8 billion. Nearly 7% of all humans who have *ever* lived are alive right now![4] Can the land provide for that many?

By 2050, two-thirds of the population are expected to live in cities.[5] In these urban zones, modernity has created its own artificial environments, where we perceive nature as "other" from us. We now see ourselves as "separate from, outside of, or above nature" and believe that it exists for us to use and manipulate as a source of wealth and jobs.[6] In fact, many modern humans believe themselves to be the pinnacle of nature,[7] as if there is nothing on the planet as important as humans.

There is a glaring problem with this perspective. Our genes, which evolved in the natural environments of hunter-gatherers, have not had time to adapt to our new artificial, urban lifestyles. The stress that our bodies and minds encounter as a result of this mismatch suggests that urban environments are not our optimal habitats. Society today has become "so estranged from its natural origins [that] it has failed to recognize our species' basic dependence on nature as a condition of growth and development," write psychologist Peter H. Kahn and social ecologist Steven Kellert.[8] We have only recently acquired the delusion that we can survive and even flourish apart from nature.[9]

Not only have we separated from nature, but our destruction of it has a direct effect on human health. A 2006 report from the WHO concluded that one-quarter of the global disease burden, including more than one-third among children, is caused by environmental degradation. Diarrhea due to unsafe drinking water, respiratory infections, cardiovascular and lung diseases, allergies and asthma due to indoor and outdoor air pollution, and malaria connected to land use practices, deforestation, and water resource management topped the list of diseases with the largest environmental contribution.[10]

This WHO report focused on the impact of environmental *degradation* on human health. How environmental *depravation* affects human health is a completely different question. However, never in all human history have humans spent so much time without regular contact with the natural world, and the consequences of this separation are unknown. Recently, more and more research has been focused on what the loss of contact with nature means to our physical and mental health.[11]

Nature deficit is our misfortune

One of the primary ways our nature deprivation harmed our health is that we've become sedentary, indoor creatures. Rectangular rooms do not suggest exercise the way wide open spaces do, and we are indeed not getting the exercise we require to stay fit and healthy while we live so much of our lives inside. The standard total daily energy expenditure of contemporary humans is only about 65% of that of late Paleolithic Stone Agers. For typical Americans to approximate the expenditure of a hunter-gatherer, we would have to add a 12-mile walk to the daily activities of an average, 150-pound man.[12]

Modernity may be affecting our children's health even more acutely. The average American kid spends five to eight hours a day on a screen, which is more than the amount of time usually spent engaged in learning at school. Unstructured play, outside, in nature has been sacrificed on the altar of screen time.[13] Over 95% of parents *think* it is important for their children to connect with nature and prefer they spend their childhood outdoors, but most modern kids spend less than half the amount of time outside than their parents did.[14] The head of the National Wildlife Federation, Collin O'Mara, writes, "The days of the free-range childhood, where kids spend hours outside playing in local parks, building forts, fording streams, and climbing trees, have been mostly replaced by video games, television watching, and organized activities such as sports and clubs. We have traded green time for screen time."[15] As kids have migrated indoors and away from nature, the percentage of children and adolescents affected by obesity has tripled since the 1970s, and now 20% of kids are considered obese.[16] Kids nowadays have a reduced chance of reaching adulthood without a chronic condition already plaguing them.

Humans in general and children specifically who spend less time in contact with the natural world may encounter a wide range of other physiological, psychological, and behavioral problems. Journalist Richard Louv coined the term *nature deficit disorder* in his book *The Nature Principle* to describe these effects. Based on theory, anecdotes, and studies that describe the restorative power of nature, Louv defines the disorder as an atrophied awareness of finding meaning in the life that surrounds us.[17] This disorder is not a medical diagnosis; rather, it is a term to describe the human costs of alienation from the natural world. In addition to obesity, the children of today face attention deficit, depression, and anxiety. Treating nature deficit disorder in these children by regularly exposing them to nature has a positive effect on everything from increasing attention span, reducing stress, and boosting cognitive development to stimulating creativity and a sense of wonder and connection to the world.

It makes sense that nature has this effect. As Louv succinctly writes, "Nature can help us feel fully alive. We are most animated when our days and nights are touched by the natural world." He wonders, "What would our lives be like if our days and nights were as immersed in nature as they are in technology?"[18] It would be a return to the nature connection of the past.

In our anxious, depressed, and unhealthy states, we wonder if modern people are suffering in similar ways, although on an infinitesimal scale, to indigenous peoples who are ripped from their way of life. Although we could never hope to understand the acute pain of their forced losses, are we experiencing the echo of a voluntary and chronic loss that started 10,000 years ago? The echo of our loss has become louder and clearer as modernization accelerates. If we return to nature, will we also find an antidote?

This idea isn't a new one. In the nineteenth century, Frederick Law Olmsted, a famous American landscape architect, believed nature to have restorative properties that "operate by unconscious processes to relax and relieve tensions created by the artificial surroundings of urban life." He claimed that parks enhanced the health and vigor of the citizens who visited them, extending their life expectancy.[19] American naturalist and philosopher John Burroughs wrote, "I go to nature to be soothed and healed and to have my senses put in order."[20]

Current scientific studies have illuminated what humans like Olmsted and Burroughs already intuitively knew: that being in nature, living near nature, or even viewing nature in pictures and videos can have positive impacts on our brains, bodies, feelings, thoughts, and social interactions.[21] Nature has positive effects on our health through countless physiological, psychological, cognitive, social, and spiritual processes.

Physiological effects of nature

Exposure to a natural setting has many positive physical effects that improve our health. Contact with nature lowers stress, decreases blood pressure and heart disease, bolsters immunity, helps prevent obesity and osteoporosis, aids the healing process, and may lower the incidence of allergy and asthma.

First, nature's ability to lower our stress may have the largest overall impact on our health. The *stress reduction theory* hypothesizes that natural environments promote recovery from stress because nature usually has low levels of information that must be processed. Conversely, a crowded city street with high levels of noise, visual complexity, intensity, and movement can produce excessive and fatiguing levels of physiological and psychological stimulation. This constant stimulus increases stress by increasing blood pressure and heart rate; inducing the production of cortisol (a primary stress hormone); or by causing fear, anger, or sadness. However, spending time in nature lowers our state of arousal and, therefore, lowers our stress.[22]

Many studies support this theory. In disadvantaged urban neighborhoods, residents with access to green space had self-reported decreases in stress levels and lower cortisol levels in their saliva than those without access.[23] Another study demonstrated that participants who took a walk in the forest had lower levels of cortisol, lower pulse rates, and lower blood pressure than those who walked in a city area.[24] Cardiac rehabilitation inpatients who were exposed to horticultural therapy had significantly reduced anxiety and heart rates compared with patients who took an education class.[25]

Lowering stress through exposure to natural settings has a trickle-down effect for improving many other health issues by boosting the immune system. Stress negatively affects the immune system because it raises levels of IL-6, a marker of inflammation and a risk factor for cardiovascular disease, depression, and autoimmune disease, and it suppresses the function of immune cells. Contact with nature and the positive feelings we associate with it were linked to reduced IL-6.[26] Being in nature also increased the activity of NK cells, which help fight off viruses and eliminate cancer cells.[27]

Urbanization has increased the incidence of obesity in our modern population. One major risk factor for obesity is being sedentary, but elevated stress is another factor due to the weight-gain effects of cortisol on the body. Exposure to nature has been found to lower the rate of obesity in communities. For instance, in one study, access to green spaces in metropolitan neighborhoods resulted in significantly lower body mass index in children ages 3 to 16 over a two-year period. The researchers concluded that this effect was due to both increased activity and a reduced stress response from exposure to nature.[28]

With more people staying indoors in urban areas, reduced exposure to natural sunlight has also led to vitamin D deficiency in both children and adults, which could cause osteoporosis, a disease where the bones become weak and brittle.[29] Don't forget that exposure to natural light helps to entrain our circadian rhythms as well, allowing us to also get enough quality sleep for the good of our health.

Nature positively affects healing, something the ancient Chinese, Greeks, and Persians knew, since hospitals in these societies maintained gardens where the sick could go to receive nature's stress-lowering effects. As modern healthcare became more and more technical, the recognition of nature's healing role declined.[30] Thankfully, this trend is reversing as more studies show its healing benefit.

Shinrin-yoku ("forest bathing") is the traditional Japanese practice of immersing yourself in nature by mindfully using all five senses. During the 1980s, shinrin-yoku became a pivotal tool in Japanese medicine, used for preventive healthcare and healing.[31] In the United States, it is called *green-care* or *nature therapy*. Richard Louv calls it *vitamin N*. Whatever you call it, forming a connection with nature is beneficial to your health.

In a large suburban Pennsylvania hospital, surgical patients who had rooms with a view of a stand of deciduous trees out their windows had shorter hospital stays by almost a full day, better pain management, and fewer negative comments than patients who had windows facing a brick wall. In another study, a group of bronchoscopy patients who experienced nature murals and sounds while sedated had measurably improved pain control over those who just experienced sedation.[32] In spite of all the evidence supporting the boost nature gives to healing, few doctors write a prescription for nature following a hospitalization or illness.[33]

Finally, affluent, industrialized countries report 20 times more allergy and asthma cases than those in poorer, underdeveloped countries.[34] Decreased time spent outdoors and the increased sterility of indoor life are a few of the reasons researchers believe this is happening. The *hygiene hypothesis* states that the early childhood exposure to a variety of microorganisms protects against allergic diseases, such as asthma, atopic dermatitis, and hay fever, by contributing to the normal development of the immune system. When such routine microbes are not encountered by children who are only exposed to indoor, sterile environments, the immune system may acquire a defect in immune tolerance, where it attacks harmless substances, like pollen, as if they were pathogens.[35] In other words, let children play outside and get dirty. Nature has diverse positive effects on the body, but what about the mind?

Psychological effects of nature

Our surroundings have an unconscious impact on our moods, positive or negative. Many studies now support a causal link between urban environments and mental illness. Residents of cities have a 20% increased risk of anxiety disorders and a 40% increased risk of mood disorders, such as depression, compared with residents of rural areas.[36]

These mental health issues are diseases of modernity; hunter-gatherers who are allowed to live the life they want do not experience anxiety and depression. Stress can lead to feelings of anxiety, fear, anger, sadness, and frustration, and many encounter chronic stress in urban areas. Perhaps due to this chronic stress, those who were raised in urban areas were found to process stress differently in the brain-imaging experiments. Researchers speculated this could account for the increased risk of these anxiety and mood disorders, even schizophrenia.[37]

In children, elevated cortisol levels caused by stress disrupt brain development, which impacts mental health and resiliency, triggers emotional and depressive problems, and negatively affects attention and inhibitory control. Lowering stress through exposure to natural settings has a trickle-down effect for improving the symptoms of anxiety, depression, and other types of mental illness. *Forbes* contributor Bill Frist writes, "Toxic stress has been called public health enemy number one, and time in nature can be an effective counterbalance."[38]

As with the positive effects of nature on the body, scientific studies demonstrate the positive psychological effects of nature. For example, researchers found significant immediate and lagged associations between feelings of well-being and exposure to nature.[39] A study of almost 1,000 residents of urban areas in Sweden showed that the more often someone visited green space in the city, the less often they reported illness due to stress.[40] A group at Stanford University found that subjects who took a 90-minute walk in a wooded, natural area had lower levels of self-reported rumination and showed reduced neural activity in areas of the brain linked to depression compared with subjects who walked in a high-traffic urban area.[41] A collection of 10 studies with 1,252 participants demonstrated that exercise in a natural environment significantly improved both self-esteem and mood compared with indoor exercise. In comparison to the indoor exercise, the outdoor exercise was also associated with an increase in the level of vigor and energy after exertion.[42]

We've all experienced the boost in mood after time spent out in the sunshine among the trees. And now there is scientific evidence that nature contributes to psychological well-being through decreasing symptoms of anxiety and depression, reducing stress, and improving self-esteem.

If there was any doubt about the importance of nature to our mental health, the devastation of our natural world is also devastating our psychological well-being. Many people are experiencing environmental grief stemming from the loss of ecosystems and the extinction of animals. Author Jordan Rosenfeld asks, "What else can we call the wrenching feeling of witnessing whales beaching themselves like toppled towers, bee populations dying off, even the death of a gorilla at a zoo?"[43] In fact, in 2012, the National Wildlife Federation estimated that 200 million Americans will be exposed to serious psychological distress from climate-related events and incidents.[44] Can nature itself help us ease our psyches and overcome our grief?

Cognitive effects of nature

From Charles Dickens to John Burroughs to Ralph Waldo Emerson, countless intellectuals have expressed how nature restores their cognitive and creative faculties.[45] One reason is because of nature's power to restore attention.

Attention restoration theory hypothesizes that our brain's executive attentional system is worn down by the demands of urban life. Journalist James Horrox writes, "Permanent background noise, compulsive and increasingly compulsory engagement with technology, the demands of multitasking and the necessity of constantly having to respond to sudden, disruptive stimuli place a severe strain on our cognitive functions."[46] In these settings, our voluntary, deliberate, and sustained attention gets overloaded and fatigued.

In contrast, a natural setting engages our involuntary attention, a kind of soft fascination that doesn't require effort. Time spent in involuntary attention allows us to gain distance, to effortlessly think about other things, to provide a scope or depth of experience to immerse ourselves in, and to rest the mind in a way that restores our voluntary attention.[47]

Spending time in nature restores our attention and reduces our mental fatigue, but it may also give us a cognitive boost. Numerous scientific studies have tested and supported this idea. Social ecologist Terry Hartig has conducted extensive experiments on cognitive restorative processes and the environments that support them. He found that, among wilderness vacationers, urban vacationers, and nonvacationers, only the wilderness group showed significant improvement on a proofreading task given both before and after their holiday.

In another study, three groups completed an attention-depleting task and then took a walk in a natural setting, took a walk in an urban setting, or sat and listened to music while reading magazines. The group who took a nature walk significantly outperformed the others at the subsequent cognitive task demonstrating their enhanced recovery in directed attention and boosted mental capabilities.[48]

Focusing on creativity, another group of study participants was asked to perform creative thinking and complex problem-solving tasks both before and after a four-day wilderness hike, completely cut off from technology. After the time in nature, their performance improved by 50%. The researchers concluded that "there is a real, measurable cognitive advantage to be realized if we spend time truly immersed in a natural setting."[49] Nature allows us to utilize our complete cognitive capacities.

Not only are attentional capacity and cognitive and creative abilities restored from time spent in nature, but memory, attention span, and productivity also benefit. In the United Kingdom alone, scientists estimate that 11.7 million days of productivity are lost due to stress, depression, or anxiety every year.[50] A study from the University of Oregon showed that 10% of absences from work can be ascribed to workspaces without connection to nature—that is, no windows or views of trees. Reduced employee absenteeism due to stress or mood disorder and increased productivity can be achieved simply by incorporating more natural light and access to green space at work.[51] For children, time in nature improves school performance, nurtures creative imagination, reduces hyperactivity, and increases attention span.[52]

Exposure to the living world can improve our senses, so we are able to better pay attention, think clearly, and be more creative. Nature calms and focuses the mind, offering a state that transcends relaxation.[53]

Social and spiritual effects of nature

Nature has been scientifically confirmed to induce positive social interaction and empowerment, reduce crime and violence, and enhance social cohesion of communities. Frances Kuo and her colleagues uncovered how residents of the poorer neighborhoods of Chicago who live near green spaces, including lawns, parks, and trees, show reductions in ADHD symptoms and have a greater sense of calm. Having access to nature, even just a tree on the grass in a small park, gave the residents a stronger sense of connection to their neighbors, with more civility between them, all leading to decreased violence in their neighborhoods. When green spaces were added to disadvantaged social housing communities, the residents experienced cognitive restoration, increased self-discipline, reduced aggression, and reduced crime.[54,55] Nature produces a cascade of positive emotions and calms our nervous systems, which helps cultivate greater openness, creativity, connection, generosity, and resilience.[56] Nature primes us to connect socially with others.

Experiencing the wonder of nature was also found to increase generosity, ethical decision-making, and prosocial behavior and lead to more feelings of humility.[57,58] This sense of awe underlies the spiritual aspects of nature and cultivates inspiration and spiritual well-being.[59]

Originally, the teachings of religions such as Judaism, Christianity, Islam, and Hinduism were grounded in a reverence for nature with an understanding of the vital relationship between humans and nature much like hunter-gatherer beliefs. In the modern world, however, it seems that our predominant religious beliefs have headed indoors and that most religions now treat individuals as separate from nature, resulting in the alienation from natural places.[60] Luckily, many are coming to realize that it's easier to find God in nature than in a building.

We may no longer live in nature, but that doesn't mean we can ignore its pull on our hearts. Michael McCarthy describes the power of this pull. In his book *The Moth Snowstorm*, he writes, "There can be occasions when we suddenly and involuntarily find ourselves loving the natural world with a startling intensity, in a burst of emotion which we may not fully understand, and the only word that seems to be appropriate for this feeling is *joy*."[61] This joy in nature can provide a grounded, connected spirituality.

Nature is disappearing from our everyday lives through both our separation from it and our destruction of it. We act as if a connection to nature is a dispensable commodity, instead of viewing it as essential to our health and well-being, our economic prosperity, and our quality of life.[62] Nature deficit, just like poor sleeping, eating, or work habits, can negatively affect us (figure 15.1). Just like when other animals lose their natural habitats, we are becoming endangered. However, we are the ones who have put ourselves on the endangered list. How can we take ourselves back off it?

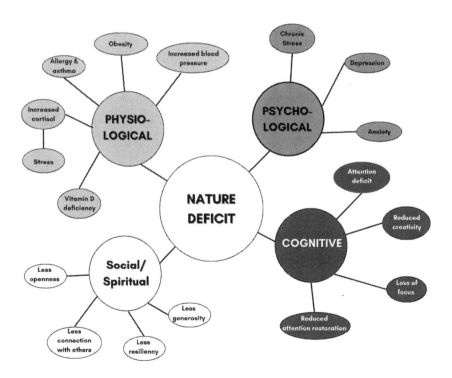

Figure 15.1. The Consequences of Nature Deficit

CHAPTER 16

REALIGNING YOUR RELATIONSHIP WITH NATURE

Thousands of tired, nerve-shaken, overcivilized people are beginning to find out that going to the mountains is going home, that wildness is a necessity, and that mountain parks and reservations are useful not only as fountains of timber and irrigating rivers but as fountains of life.

—JOHN MUIR

We may be alienated from nature in the modern world, but we still feel its pull because nature was critical to our survival and vitality as we evolved into humans in its cradle. In his book *The Nature Principle*, Richard Louv wrote, "The pleasure of being alive is brought into sharper focus when you need to pay attention to *staying* alive. Alive in the larger universe, alive in time."[1]

British environmentalist and journalist Michael McCarthy also wrote about a kind of existential experience he had during a close encounter with a black rhino in Namibia. McCarthy wrote, "I was transfixed; my heart pounded, my mouth dried, I looked around for shelter. But if I was afraid, there was a stronger and stranger feeling coursing through me. I felt in every way more alive. I felt as alive as I had ever been."[2]

Being *of* nature, we consciously or unconsciously long to return to where our physical and mental functions evolved and are naturally supported.[3] Through nature, we can achieve the well-being and vitality of eudaemonia. Hunter-gatherers can help us find the way back.

Connection

Hunter-gatherers were never apart from nature and forged a connection and sense of place with it. To reap the benefits a connection with nature has to offer us, we first must be exposed to it. This doesn't require special travel; you can begin by simply taking off your blinders and being aware of the natural world that surrounds you every day. Notice the color of the sky, the shape of the clouds, the phase of the moon, the call of local birds, the color and fragrance of gardens, the shape of the leaves on the trees, and even the complex patterns of a spiderweb. When you take breaks from work, go outside and spend time surrounded by as much green as you can, even if you simply sit on some grass or lean against a tree and breathe. When you have more time, go to parks and local open spaces or plan visits to state and national parks. To feel ourselves intertwined in the web of life, we have to see ourselves being a part of it.

A connection to nature comes in many forms. It may be as simple as appreciating and enjoying nature or having empathy for its creatures, or it may result in a feeling of oneness with it and bring about a sense of responsibility for it.[4] Joseph Campbell writes, "The goal is to make your heartbeat match the beat of the universe, to match your nature with nature."[5] The rediscovery of our connection with nature will also lead to concern for it and action to preserve it. We will be better able to see, halt, and then reverse humanity's destruction of the natural environment.[6] Our continued detachment only leads to insensitivity and indifference.

Respect

Our ancestors' respect for nature was unmistakable in their belief systems. Nature and all its plants and creatures were fundamental for their survival. There was no separation between man and animal, and nature's status was seen as equal or even above that of humans. Although they had to kill animals for food, our ancestors' ritual practices made it clear that respect for the animal, who some believed had given its life to the humans, was paramount for continued equilibrium between man and animal. Shamanistic traditions were steeped in ways to find the balance between humans and their environment, and many hunter-gatherer leaders were chosen because of their knowledge of the land and how to live in harmony with it, not their hunting prowess.

We've lost this respect for the land and its animals because we no longer connect what we need to survive, such as food and clean water, with nature. We take for granted the food we find on the shelves at a grocery store or clean water pouring out of the tap. At restaurants, who gives a silent word of thanks to the cow who died so we could eat steak? We need to expand our worldview to include the actual living world and to give this world respect for what it provides us.

For example, 70 of the top 100 human food crops are pollinated by bees. What will happen to our food supply if our lack of respect for bees—such as using pesticides that kill them off—causes their numbers to wane? Americans depend on streams and rivers to supply most of their drinking water, but many of these waterways are threatened by pollution or development. Some are fighting to roll back protections on streams and wetlands ensured by the Clean Water Act of 1972, but not only will this destroy delicate ecosystems and our natural defenses from flooding, but it puts the quality of our water in jeopardy. Water is the most essential nutrient we need, critical for every cell in our bodies. When will we realize that respect for nature is ultimately respect for ourselves? This respect will result in the preservation of our basic needs.

American astronomer Carl Sagan's point of view may help us gain a new perspective of the Earth to give it the reverence it deserves. He was inspired by the famous image taken in 1990 from the *Voyager 1* spacecraft as it turned around to take a picture of its home, 4 billion miles away. A tiny blue dot is at the center of the picture, peeking through scattered rays of light. The dot was only 12% of a single pixel in an image composed of 640,000 pixels. It was Earth. He wrote:

> From this distant vantage point, the Earth might not seem of any particular interest. But for us, it's different. Consider again that dot. That's here. That's home. That's us. On it everyone you love, everyone you know, everyone you ever heard of, every human being who ever was, lived out their lives. The aggregate of our joy and suffering, thousands of confident religions, ideologies, and economic doctrines, every hunter and forager, every hero and coward, every creator and destroyer of civilization, every king and peasant, every young couple in love, every mother and father, hopeful child, inventor and explorer, every teacher of morals, every corrupt politician, every "superstar," every "supreme leader," every saint and sinner in the history of our species lived there—on a mote of dust suspended in a sunbeam. . . .
>
> Our planet is a lonely speck in the great enveloping cosmic dark. In our obscurity—in all this vastness—there is no hint that help will come from elsewhere to save us from ourselves. The Earth is the only world known, so far, to harbor life.

There is nowhere else, at least in the near future, to which our species could migrate. Visit, yes. Settle, not yet. Like it or not, for the moment, the Earth is where we make our stand. It has been said that astronomy is a humbling and character-building experience. There is perhaps no better demonstration of the folly of human conceits than this distant image of our tiny world. To me, it underscores our responsibility to deal more kindly with one another and to preserve and cherish the pale blue dot, the only home we've ever known.[7]

Respect for nature triggers a cascade of humility, lowering our view of our own importance. This humility opens us up to feeling like we are a part of something bigger than ourselves. What Carl Sagan saw in that image didn't make him feel insignificant. Rather, it gave him a sense of respect and responsibility and a vision of connection with his fellow Earthlings.

Knowledge and competency

Hunter-gatherers knew every plant that grew and animal that roamed their territory. They memorized every rock, tree, and natural feature of the land so they could navigate their landscape to find what they needed to survive. Even though they still thought of the indigenous peoples as savages, the colonists of southern Africa documented their admiration of the natives' extraordinary knowledge of local flora and fauna after first contact.[8] The knowledge about and familiarity with the natural world led to complete competency and confidence.

Today, we don't have to know anything about the natural world to survive. Remember, that, collectively, modern humans know much more today than our ancestors did, but individually, ancient hunter-gatherers were far more knowledgeable and skillful.[9] Perhaps if we devoted more time to environmental learning, nature will move back toward the center of human culture.

Biohistory should become a part of academic curricula and community education to give humans both a framework for and a perspective on how we coevolved with nature and how it supports human life.[10] We are all attracted to learning about wildlife via the incredible documentaries from National Geographic or Nature, but these do not support our knowledge of local flora and fauna or how our food is produced. We watch survival shows on reality television with fascination, but how many of us are competent enough to survive in the wilderness for long periods of time on our own?

This education should start with children. Kids are thirsty sponges when it comes to learning about and categorizing creatures. Their tremendous capacity to memorize either natural or man-made species is evident by age eight, when on average, kids can correctly identify 80% of a sample drawn from 150 Pokémon creatures. Zoologist Andrew Balmford writes, "During their primary school years, children apparently learn far more about Pokémon than about their native wildlife and enter secondary school being able to name less than 50% of common wildlife types."

Not only do people care about what they are connected to, but they care about what they know. Balmford continues, "Conservationists need to reestablish children's links with nature if they are to win over the hearts and minds of the next generation."[11] Becoming more knowledgeable and competent about the natural world is another way to deepen our connection to it.

Environmental identity

Since all of nature was their home, and they knew everything about it, hunter-gatherers identified with their environment. Nature shaped their identities, which is why modern-day hunter-gatherer groups are hit so hard with the loss of identity when they are displaced from their homelands. In our modern, hectic lives, we go from the house to the car to the office, then back to the car and back home with only cursory glances at the sunsets, the shifting patterns of clouds, and the changing autumn leaves. We have a place blindness that we must overcome.[12]

Place identity is a psychological phenomenon. Environmental psychologist Harold Proshansky described it as "a complex pattern of conscious and unconscious ideas, feelings, values, goals, preferences, skills, and behavioral tendencies relevant to a specific environment" that define dimensions of personal identity.[13] For us to have an environmental identity, we must first cultivate in ourselves a sense of place. This ability is not a vestigial capacity, but a latent one.[14] We must establish a sense of connection to the natural environment around where we live and work based on history, familiarity, and personal connection.[15]

Although it is a personal identity, an environmental identity allows us to transcend ourselves as individuals and to incorporate ourselves into part of the natural ecosystem, making us more likely to care for and invest in the local environment. When we find our sense of place, we can achieve enduring happiness and life satisfaction through less materialistic pursuits. We don't have to go to national parks to connect with nature; nearby nature is just as important—the urban and state parks, the regional nature preserves, clean urban streams, and even the small stand of trees just beyond the cul de sac. Louv quotes *Outside* magazine: "Near is the new far."[16] We can discover who we are by knowing where we are.

Sustainability

The exponential growth of the modern human population and the technological advances of modern society do not take the long-term welfare of the Earth into account. However, there are hundreds of ways to live more sustainably like hunter-gatherers. They took only what they needed, had few possessions, and produced little waste. They consciously ensured the next generation had all that they needed.

To reduce our energy consumption, we should only use the energy we need by turning off appliances and lights, using energy-efficient appliances and light bulbs, and driving our cars less often. Going further, we could put solar panels on our homes and drive electric cars. To have fewer possessions, we can approach our lives with a minimalist mindset. We should think twice before we go shopping; every product we buy has an environmental footprint. Consider buying something used instead of new.

To produce less waste, we need to suppress our need for everything to be convenient and stop using disposable items. These days, you can buy a plastic version of any object, such as razors, utensils, cups, bags, plates, and food storage containers, which are thrown away after one use. Strikingly, about a third of all food produced in the world for human consumption ends up in the landfill as waste. This waste amounts to about $680 billion lost in industrialized countries. Every year in wealthy countries, consumers waste almost as much food as the entire net food production of sub-Saharan Africa.[17]

Finally, one of the best ways to improve sustainability is to slow population growth. If we do so, our demands for food, water, land, and fossil fuels, which are pushing other species to extinction and driving climate change, automatically decrease. If our population continues to explode, we may never achieve an ecological sustainability "in ways that promote human rights, decrease poverty and overcrowding, raise our standard of living, and allow plants, animals, and ecosystems to thrive."[18] Environmental activist and author Wendell Berry wrote, "I am speaking of the life of a man who knows that the world is not given by his fathers, but borrowed from his children."[19]

Humans and nature could have a mutually beneficial relationship. Nature provides an environment that promotes physical and psychological health while opening us up to community and spirituality. In return, we become responsible for the land. Biologist Stephen Jay Gould wrote, "We have become, by the power of a glorious evolutionary accident called intelligence, the stewards of life's continuity on Earth."[20]

Nature gave us all of our material needs and allowed us to maintain our physical and mental health. We developed biophilia, a strong sense of connection to nature. We respected nature and had detailed knowledge of our natural world as it all supported our environmental identities. These characteristics made living sustainably in our habitat second nature, and we thrived as hunter-gatherers for hundreds of thousands of years. This is why nature must be included in any discussion of human flourishing. Figure 16.1 summarizes how we can return nature to its proper place in our lives.

Psychologist Darcia Narvaez writes, "Like every other animal, human beings evolved to cooperate with the natural world, living in ecologies of give and take."[21] However, in the modern world, we must rebuild this relationship with nature. We must remember and respect what nature gives us every day to remake our connection. We must not take more than we need. In return, we must give back to nature to preserve it for generations to come.

We are the only species on Earth with the power to irrevocably change our natural habitat. But for humans to thrive, the Earth must thrive. We must return to recognizing our place in the web of life and begin to live

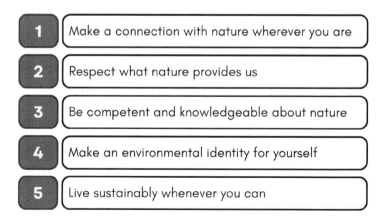

Figure 16.1. Closing the Gap on Our Relationship with Nature

in sustainable ways to not only benefit ourselves but to benefit the planet. We must return to living as creatures of the Earth, as one species in a community of species,[22] and realize that what nature gives us are gifts. Our lives depend on it.

CHAPTER 17

CLOSING THE GAP

There is grandeur in this view of life, with its several powers, having been originally breathed into a few forms or into one; and that, whilst this planet has gone cycling on according to the fixed law of gravity, from so simple a beginning endless forms most beautiful and most wonderful have been, and are being, evolved.

–CHARLES DARWIN

It may be both disheartening and overwhelming to have some of the most negative aspects of the modern world pointed out and to learn how much we are affected by the diseases of modernity. However, not everything about the modern world is doom and gloom, and as romantic as it might sound, none of us would like to go back and live 15,000 years ago. We are grateful to have plenty of food, protection from the elements and predators, air conditioning and heating, and modern sanitation practices. Modern medicine is tantamount to miraculous, and our collective human minds have made discoveries and inventions that blow our minds and infinitely improve our lives. Without the daily search for sustenance, we have the luxury to explore other rewarding facets of our existence. Many ingredients for a good life are actually found in the modern world.

However, these advancements and improvements came with an invisible cost. They are, after all, the bounties of our continuous march for progress, the products of our machines of modernity. As our machines sped up, the speed and number of changes to the way we lived accelerated too, and we began to become maladapted to our environment. Now our modern culture can evolve in the blink of an eye, but when this happens, does anyone stop to wonder how our bodies, minds, and society will be affected?

Without even realizing it, our modern machine carried us beyond where our genes could keep up. This is the reason we now encounter the physical, mental, and social pathologies never before experienced in our history. This mismatch between our genes and our environment is the reason finding a good life seems impossible.

We are no longer living as we were evolved to live, and unconsciously, we have allowed our culture to hijack many of our biological needs. We need to be entrained by the sun, so our circadian rhythms are in sync, but we stay up too late watching television. We need to eat foods that supply our bodies with the nutrients required to function at their best, but we eat cheap, processed foods in excess. We need to treat our jobs as a part of our lives, not our whole lives, yet we work longer and longer hours and do not have a work-life balance. And we need to reconnect with nature, the entity that gave us life and still provides us what we need to survive. Not only are we isolating ourselves from it, but we are also actively destroying it. When we don't meet these specific needs—and a host of others—our health and vitality suffer.

Looking through a scientific lens and grounding a new approach to life in the theory of evolution are the first steps toward reconciling our biology with our modernity. Such an evolutionary approach to life simply asks, "What are our evolved needs?" The answers lead us to understanding our natural ways of being.

With the awareness of how and why modernity is failing to fulfill these needs, combined with our new knowledge about the evolutionary history

Figure 17.1. Connect Back to Every Human, Hominid, Primate, Animal, and Cell

Kan Srijirapon, David Attenborough and Chimpanzee, 2023, watercolor

of life on Earth, we can connect ourselves back to every human, hominid, primate, animal, and cell that came before us and return to living in accord with our evolved nature. Thanks to our hominid ancestors, we know exactly how that looks (figure 17.1).

Regaining our rhythms

While many modern humans believe that we've evolved beyond the ancient timing of circadian rhythms, our bodies respond to them just like every other organism does because the rhythms are imprinted in our genetic code. These rhythms evolved to ensure that organisms—even us—timed the performance of certain tasks to when it was most beneficial for survival, like the early cells of life waiting until night to undergo the UV-sensitive mitosis. To keep internal circadian timing tied to the cycles of light and dark and to the ebb and flow of natural life, living things are required to entrain their rhythms to the sun.

Hunter-gatherers, being exposed only to whatever light (or dark) each day and night provided, were exquisitely entrained to the natural rhythms of the world. Different groups in different parts of the world had remarkable similarities in their daily patterns. They woke up at the same time every day, without an alarm clock. They got maximal sun exposure in the mornings, and the only light they were exposed to at night was firelight, moonlight, or starlight. They went to sleep a few hours after sunset. They didn't necessarily get more sleep than modern humans, but because they were so attuned to their rhythms, they were alert when they were supposed to be alert, were tired when they were supposed to be tired, and got the sleep they needed when they needed it.

Sleep is one of the most important activities regulated by circadian rhythms, and as we evolved, our sleep got shorter and more efficient. There were things to do and people to see. Modern humans aren't getting enough quality sleep because the timing of our daily light exposure—especially blue light—which entrains our rhythms, is completely backward. We get too little light during the day and too much light at night.

Restoring our natural ways of being goes beyond "sleep hygiene" because it's not just about what we do or don't provide for ourselves; it's about what we must let nature provide us: the zeitgeber sun. To entrain our bodies' circadian rhythms and get the sleep and rest we need, we must wake up every day at a consistent time and we must be exposed to bright light in the mornings. It could be as easy as opening all the curtains in the house when we wake or sitting on a deck in the morning drinking a hot beverage. Take a walk, stand in a sunbeam, and gaze out the picture window during your morning work meeting. In darker latitudes, there are sun lamps to simulate the sun, and, for the case of shift workers, there are sleep therapies that will help mitigate the effects of such wild circadian misalignment. Waking up and getting our light exposure at the same time every day will make it easier to fall asleep at night, wake up the next morning, and have better sleep in between.

At the other end of the day, we must decrease our nighttime exposure to blue light, which some go so far as to say is a carcinogen. Many apps and products exist to help improve this situation. Night Shift, Blue Shade, and the like all turn down the blue light emitted from our devices and can be set to shift automatically when the sun goes down. We can wear blue-blocking glasses, especially if our jobs are screen intensive. We can turn off any unneeded lights and use dimmer switches or warm, low—blue light bulbs in the rooms we inhabit at night. We can even buy lamps that have three different light settings for optimal morning, afternoon, and evening lighting. However, the cheapest and easiest thing to do is simply turn off or dim the lights and turn off our screens. This gives our eyes and minds a break from the constant bombardment of modern life before we go to sleep.

We also need to stop turning sleep into such a huge problem. If you have trouble sleeping one night, catch up. If we listen to our bodies, they have ways to keep the homeostatic sleep drive that will equilibrate our sleep if we need it. If you have trouble getting to sleep and waking up on a regular basis, you aren't lazy. You're not broken. You may just have a chronotype that evolved for a very specific reason: to provide protection to the members of your tribe who are fast asleep—and most likely in a very deep and efficient sleep.

It may seem that returning our sleep to match our evolved needs is an easy choice, a no-brainer. However, we also have to seriously deprogram our cultural software that has us staying up past our bedtime to binge-watch entertainment or to finish work. That will be hard, but it really comes down to the quality of our decision-making and our commitment to the pursuit of a good life. We now know how we can adapt our sleep and circadian rhythms to help us on our journey to eudaemonia. It's on us what we decide to do with this knowledge.

Remembering our foodways

There *is* a rhyme and reason to why our dietary requirements evolved the way they did. As we evolved from *Australopithecus* to *Homo erectus* to *Homo sapiens*, our nutritional goals were always the same: obtain more high-quality food in as short a time as possible. We had to feed our ravenous, expanding brains. Our brain evolution and our quest for ways to feed it formed a positive feedback loop. Our increased quality of food allowed the evolution of a bigger brain, and our bigger brains allowed us to figure out how to obtain higher-quality food.

Modern humans have taken obtaining high-quality food in as short of time as possible to pathological levels. With processed foods, we can now eat enough calories for the day in a single meal—even in a single food item. Our access to calories is unprecedented, and we take advantage of it. The ratios of our macronutrients are also out of whack because of our consumption of processed food and the way we grow crops and raise livestock. Our modern diets not only fail to give us the nutrients we need, but they also have us consuming "nutrients" our bodies did not evolve with or consuming levels of nutrients our ancestors were never exposed to. Refined sugar, trans fats, and salt, we're looking at you.

To nourish our bodies the way evolution intended, we must eat fewer industrially processed carbs, and those we do eat should come in the form of fruits and vegetables, not processed grains and sugars. Eating more fresh fruits and vegetables may sound too expensive, but remember, over a third of our food supply ends up in landfills, and that includes perfectly edible fruits and vegetables that are deemed too ugly to sell. There is a growing movement to reclaim these types of foods and sell them to people at a discount. Find places that sell "ugly produce," like Imperfect Foods or Misfits Market. Or simply grow your own.

Consuming less or eliminating added sugar in our diets will be a difficult adjustment because, just like hunter-gatherers, we are still evolutionarily programmed to want to eat as much sweet and fatty foods as we can get our hands on to help us survive leaner times. The problem is that most of us never have leaner times, and our bodies never get to burn off all the energy they've stored.

Eating more fruits and vegetables will dramatically increase the amount of fiber we consume. Raspberries have 8 grams of fiber per cup, and apples, bananas, and strawberries have 3 to 4 grams. Dark vegetables, like carrots, beets, and broccoli, tend to have high fiber content. Legumes, such as beans, peas, edamame (soybeans), and lentils are packed with fiber and are also high in protein. Whole grains, like brown rice, bulgur wheat, and barley, or even in some cereals and breads, can be good sources of fiber. Remember, the less processing a food has, the more fiber content it is likely to have. Nuts and seeds provide fiber as well. Eating these foods will help our digestion, help our guts maintain healthy bacteria, and help us feel full, stopping our sugar binge before it starts.

Modern humans and the average hunter-gatherer consumed the same relative percentage of fat in their diets—35%. But the types of fats are vastly different. We must eat less saturated fat, more monounsaturated fats, and should avoid trans fats completely. Dairy products, such as butter, cheese, and ice cream; fatty cuts of meat, cured meat, lard; coconut and palm oil; and many baked goods, such as cakes, cookies, and pastries all have high levels of saturated fats. Trans fats are not only found in those same baked goods but also in hydrogenated oils, like margarine, spreads, and shortening; fried foods; some chips and crackers; some granola bars or energy bars; and nondairy creamer. The easiest way to avoid trans fats is to read the label.

We should eat polyunsaturated fats in the way we were evolved to, and we must even out our omega-3 to omega-6 ratio by consuming more foods rich in omega-3. Good sources of omega-3s are flax or chia seeds; fish, such as salmon, herring, tuna, and trout; shellfish; walnuts; tofu and edamame; canola oil; beans; brussels sprouts; and avocados.

We must attune our protein consumption to our levels of activity, and we should get this protein from lean cuts of red meats, chicken, turkey, fish, shrimp, eggs, and some dairy products like Greek yogurt. Don't forget about high-protein plant foods, like beans, peas, chickpeas, edamame, tofu, lentils, nut butters, almonds, chia seeds, and quinoa. As our population increases, more of our protein must come from plants because increasing the production of domesticated meat is not a sustainable option for our planet.

While we are making our lower-carb, healthy-fat, balanced-protein meals, there is one more important thing that we need to learn to live with less of: salt. We can start by limiting the salt we add to food at home and by looking at the labels of prepackaged foods. Remember, salt is added to food to make it taste better, so to get your taste buds used to the transition, remove salt little by little and you may not even notice the difference.

Eating like a hunter-gatherer may seem too strict or too hard to stick to. But even the father of the Paleo diet himself, Loren Cordain, says that eating 15% non-Paleo foods is an effective nutritional change, and it may be easier to follow knowing we have this flexibility.

Returning to our nutritional evolved needs seems much more complicated than some of our other evolved needs, but we don't have to go cold turkey on our modern diet. Start small. Read labels, and start making a few different choices at the grocery store. Making one change at a time, like deciding to eat less sugar or more omega-3s, until it decides to stick is another way to ease into the complexity of a new diet. Hopefully, knowing how we evolved to need a particular nutrient or why we do not need this other nutrient will make it easier to embrace a new food and let go of an old one. The more we can eat the way evolution designed us, the better our bodies and minds will work, and the closer we will be to eudaemonia.

Reducing the grind

Contrary to popular belief, hunter-gatherers did not lead lives of constant drudgery, where the quest for food was a daily struggle. In fact, nomadic foragers worked far less than we do and enjoyed their significant leisure time. Not only this, but their approach to work was completely orthogonal to ours, and their work was seamlessly integrated into their lives.

To have this view on work, hunter-gatherers had few material wants. We, as modern humans, must reduce our needs. And it all begins with taking a hard look at all of our stuff—and especially our *relationship* with our stuff. If we could get by with less of it, we wouldn't need to work as much. Instead of thinking bigger, better, and more, we should think smaller, less, and more meaningful. Embracing a more minimalist way of life will help us sort out the really important things and what is needed to support them.

To approach work with our evolved nature in mind, we need to learn mindfulness and how to live and work in the present. With a few exceptions, nomadic forager minds were attuned to the present because that was where they could find what they needed to survive. In the modern world, we are obsessed with our mistakes of the past or stressing about a future that may not even happen. We are never in the moment, and this affects the choices we make about work, how much we enjoy the work, and our job performance.

Living in this more mindful way, we will notice the most pressing tasks so we can prioritize better. We will also notice the needs of our bodies and minds, especially when it comes to taking a break. Taking breaks—within a day, over a weekend, or over a vacation—will improve efficiency and performance, so we must ditch the cultural belief that someone who takes breaks is being lazy. To actually enjoy our breaks from work, we have to separate our identities from our work so we can put our work down long enough to recharge.

Hunter-gatherers' work was infused with a playful spirit. To match this spirit, we need to challenge ourselves intellectually and try to expand the parameters of our jobs to include more variety and flexibility, even choice. In a world where more and more people work from home, we also must make special effort to connect and socialize with our peers at work. This will make work more fun and keep our jobs more in the realm of play.

If we live with less, keep work in the present moment, rest and relax, and approach work with a playful spirit, we can stop the cycle of work for the sake of work. Returning to our evolved needs surrounding our work, we can reduce the pathologies brought about by overwork. Emulating how hunter-gatherers approached work will get us one step closer to eudaemonia.

Reclaim the natural world

We must reclaim the natural world as our own, work to restore it to its prominence in our lives, and return it to a more unspoiled state. Because our ancestors were never *not* connected to the natural world, it all starts with connection. Connections can be made as simply as noticing the nature around you in your everyday life: the parks and open spaces in your area, a man-made garden, or even the patch of grass with a few trees outside your office. We can briefly connect with all living things we see or hear around us, like the bugs scurrying through the grass beneath our feet, the owl we hear when out walking at night, or the elusive fox we see out of the corner of our eyes darting into the scrub at the side of the road.

Go further. Go on a hike. Learn about the indigenous plants and animals in your area. Learn to camp. Visit a national park. Develop an understanding of the ecologies of the region you live in. Discover the efforts of others to preserve them. Join these people. Nurture an environmental identity through conscious behavior to both maximize the positive impacts and minimize the negative impacts of our actions on the environment.

Approach life sustainably. We can recycle, shop at thrift stores before Amazon, save electricity, not waste food, and reduce our carbon footprint. It is possible to be conscientious of what you buy and who are you buying it from. With a little digging, we can learn how a company contributes to sustainability and make informed decisions about our consumerism.

When we are connected, respectful, and knowledgeable and have an environmental identity, we will not only benefit from the positive effects of nature, we will also be more likely to take the actions necessary to save it. Nature is an indispensable resource that we are both essential to and responsible for its preservation. It is an essential element of returning to a more evolved way of being.

It's all connected

Every aspect of our lives is part of an interwoven spiderweb of connections. Behaviors developed from meeting evolved needs surrounding our sleep, diet, work, and interactions with nature all inform each other in complex ways.

If we don't do work on our screens long into the night, our decreased nighttime light pollution won't affect our sleep quality, and we can fall asleep and wake up more easily. If we get better-quality sleep, our work performance and efficiency improve, meaning we can spend less time at work. Our circadian rhythms would be better aligned if we stopped working 70-hour weeks. If we have less stuff, we can work less, and we will also live more sustainably. When we need to take a break at work, we can take a walk in nature to restore our attention and creativity while getting exposed to natural sunlight and entraining our rhythms. If we increase our fruit and vegetable intake by growing our own or finding ways to buy produce on its way to the landfill, we will reduce the carbon footprint of food waste.

If our circadian rhythms are entrained to our lives, the daily cycle of digestion hormones will be aligned to when we eat. If we are mindful of the present at work, this will carry over so we will be more attuned to our sleep and nutritional needs and make better decisions. Consuming foods mindfully produced and sourced will positively impact our nutrition and sustainability. Eating according to our natures will decrease our risk of obesity, which also decreases our risk of disturbed sleep via sleep apnea. The list goes on (figure 17.2).

Deficient sleep, poor diet, overwork, and a nature deficit are also inter-connected as the root causes of the diseases of modernity. Each has been tied in some way to cardiovascular disease, obesity, metabolic syndrome, type 2 diabetes, hypertension, cancer, depression, and anxiety.

The sheer number of these connections tells us how it is essential to live holistically, or in a way that takes care of our entire person in all aspects of our well-being—the physical, the mental, and the social—at the same time, if we want to close the gap and search for eudaemonia.

Again, we look to hunter-gatherers for confirmation. Every part of a hunter-gatherer's life was integrated into a whole. Their holistic life flowed naturally from their present needs, and they are remarkable examples of how living in touch with our bodies, with others, and with the world around us contributes to well-being and vitality. Not only were their lives integrated, but they viewed themselves as an integral part of the web of life, and critical play no more and no less important than the other parts.

Figure 17.2. It's All Connected

A good foundation

A return to our evolved ways of being for sleep, nutrition, work, and the natural world will reconcile our Paleolithic genes with our modern world and provide us with a strong foundation. These foundational, evolved needs are much like the base tiers of Abraham Maslow's 1943 psychological theory, called *Maslow's hierarchy of needs*. He illustrated his theory as a pyramid with five stacked tiers representing human needs in the progression of human growth. Physiological needs were at the base of the hierarchy, then safety and security needs, love and belonging, self-esteem, and finally, at the top, self-actualization. Maslow theorized that the needs lower down in the hierarchy must be satisfied before we could attend to the higher ones.[1] Each tier supports the one above it.

If sleep, nutrition, work, and the natural world are analogous to Maslow's base tier of physiological needs, what evolved needs correspond to safety, belonging, self-esteem, and self-actualization? What other areas of our lives do our basic, evolved needs support (figure 17.3)? And the bigger question: Are we meeting our evolved needs in those areas? (For more information, visit www.ontheoriginofbeing.com.)

Figure 17.3. Hierarchy of Ways of Being

Hidden breadcrumbs are scattered throughout our lives, left behind on our evolutionary journey to becoming human. These are the genetic instructions evolved and honed over millions of years that will help us bridge the gap between our evolved natures and the modern world. It is up to us to discover them, understand them, and put them into action in our quest to find our ultimate goal—a good life.

Every single one of us is descended from the hunter-gatherer ancestors who roamed the Earth for millions of years. There is no doubt that a little hunter-gatherer still resides within us. We still have their evolved needs, and—lucky for us—we also still have their genome. Using their behavior as a guide, you can adapt aspects of your behavior the way you want by using your flexibility, intellect, and creativity, then take this evolutionarily aligned version of yourself into the modern world.

We want more than just to survive in life. We want to flourish. Once our mismatch has diminished, our health and vitality will return, and more of us can experience eudaemonia in our lifetime.

Kan Srijirapon, 2023, watercolor

ACKNOWLEDGMENTS

This book would never have existed without the support of many people. A huge thank-you to Kelly McLaughlin for keeping the gears turning at The Aurignacian, LLC and always being positive and kind. The interviews with David Samson and Peter Gray were incredible, and we are so appreciative that they took time out of their day to talk with us.

Everyone at Greenleaf Book Group provided tremendous encouragement and expertise at every step of the publication process. Brian Welch and Lee Reed Zarnikau were excellent project managers, and Neil Gonzalez created an amazing cover and laid out a great design. We cannot thank Nathan True enough for his unwavering support in our substantive edit. He made the book so much better. Elizabeth Brown's copyedits were thorough and detailed, and she helped plow through the endless endnotes, and our proofreader, Kimberlene Francis, was meticulous. Thank you both! And a big thank-you to the publicity team at Greenleaf and to Sharon Bially and her team at Book Savvy for leading us through the publicity craziness.

To all the scientists who did the research that enabled this book to be written, thank you so much! And of course, we must thank Charles Darwin, the Father of Evolution, for the theory that has allowed us to discover how we came to be.

From Jenny

First, I'd like to express my gratitude to Luke Comer for the amazing opportunity to bring his vision for this book into being. His passion for the subject was contagious, and I have learned so much. I want to thank my friends in every niche of my life who listened to me and encouraged me over the years it took to write this book. My parents always told me I could do anything I wanted to do and have been behind me in everything I've ever attempted or done in my life. Writing this book has been no different. Thank you for being my rocks. My sister was my first and continues to be my most fervent of cheerleaders. I'm not sure I would've had the courage to pursue writing if she hadn't been in my corner. I am forever grateful for her. When I told my husband I wanted to be a writer, he told me to go for it, and my kids' endless curiosity inspires me every day, and their sweet, unconditional support makes me smile. I love you all so much . . . you are my world!

NOTES

Introduction

1. Herberg, W. 1955. *Protestant, Catholic, Jew: An Essay in American Religious Sociology*. University of Chicago Press.

2. Putnam, R.D. Romney Garrett, S. 2020. *The Upswing: How America Came Together a Century Ago and How We Can Do It Again*. New York: Simon & Schuster.

3. Curtis, L. 2012. "Happiness Is the New Success: Why Millennials Are Reprioritizing." Accessed July 9, 2019. https://www.forbes.com/sites/85broads/2012/01/23/happiness-is-the-new-success-why-millennials-are-reprioritizing/#6f686df43de6.

4. Fox, J. 2012. "The Economics of Well-Being." Accessed July 10, 2019. https://hbr.org/2012/01/the-economics-of-well-being.

5. Schwartz, B. 2000. "Self-Determination. The Tyranny of Freedom." *Am Psychol* 55 (1): 79-88.

6. Centers for Disease Control and Prevention. 2018. "Adult Obesity Facts." Accessed October 7, 2019. https://www.cdc.gov/obesity/data/adult.html.

7. Centers for Disease Control and Prevention. 2019. "Type 2 Diabetes." Accessed October 7, 2019. https://www.cdc.gov/diabetes/basics/type2.html.

8. Centers for Disease Control and Prevention. 2017. "Heart Disease Facts." Accessed October 7, 2019. https://www.cdc.gov/heartdisease/facts.htm.

9. Sullivan, A. 2018. "The World Is Better Than Ever. Why Are We Miserable?" Accessed April 15, 2019. https://nymag.com/intelligencer/2018/03/sullivan-things-are-better-than-ever-why-are-we-miserable.html.

10. Centers for Disease Control and Prevention. 2017. "Mental Health." Accessed October 7, 2019. https://www.cdc.gov/nchs/fastats/mental-health.htm.

11. Centers for Disease Control and Prevention, "Adult Obesity Facts."

12. Knick, S. 2010. "Traditional Culture and Modern Culture: Man's Fall from Grace." Accessed February 20, 2019. https://www.huffingtonpost.com/stanley-knick/traditional-culture-and-m_b_655992.html.

13. World Health Organization. 1946. *Preamble to the Constitution of the WHO as Adopted by the International Health Conference.* Vol. 2, in *Official Records of the WHO*, 100. New York: WHO.

14. The Association of Faculties of Medicine of Canada. 2023. "Chapter 1: Concepts of Health and Illness." Accessed May 24, 2023. https://phprimer.afmc.ca/en/part-i/chapter-1/.

15. Campbell, J. Moyers, B.D. 1988. *The Power of Myth.* New York: Doubleday.

16. Deci, E.L. Ryan, R.M. 2008. "Hedonia, Eudaimonia, and Well-Being: An Introduction." *J. Happiness Stud* 9: 1-11.

17. Deci, "Hedonia, Eudaimonia, and Well-Being."

18. Curtis, "Happiness Is the New Success: Why Millennials Are Reprioritizing."

19. Sullivan, "The World Is Better Than Ever."

20. Sullivan, "The World Is Better Than Ever."

Chapter 1

1. Hidaka, B.H. 2012. "Depression as a Disease of Modernity: explanations for increasing prevalence." *J Affect Disord* 140 (3): 205-214.

2. Hill, K.B. Barton, M. Hurtado, A.M. 2009. "The Emergence of Human Uniqueness: characters underlying behavioral modernity." *Evol Anthropol* 18 (5): 187-200.

3. Panel, ASU Origins Project. 2013. *The Great Debate: The Storytelling of Science.* Accessed June 1, 2019. https://www.youtube.com/watch?v=_J4QPz52Sfo.

4. Lee, R.B. Daly, R. 2004. *The Cambridge Encyclopedia of Hunters and Gatherers.* Edited by Richard B. Daly, Richard Lee. Cambridge: Cambridge University Press.

5. Lee, R.B. DeVore, I. Wenner-Gren Foundation. 1966. *Man the Hunter.* Chicago: Aldine Pub. Co.

6. Suzman, J. 2017. *Affluence without Abundance: The Disappearing World of the Bushmen.* New York: Bloomsbury USA.

7. Lee et al., *Man the Hunter.*

8. Strauss, I. 2019. "Does Medicine Actually Make People Live Longer?" Accessed July 11, 2019. https://www.huffpost.com/entry/medication-live-longer-longevity_n _5c1a9231e4b0ce5184b9bcc1.

9. Strauss, "Does Medicine Actually Make People Live Longer?"

10. Centers for Disease Control and Prevention. 2017. "Heart Disease Facts." Accessed October 15, 2019. https://www.cdc.gov/heartdisease/facts.htm.

11. University of California Museum of Paleontology. 2023. "Misconceptions about evolution." Accessed May 24, 2023. https://evolution.berkeley.edu/evolibrary/ misconceptions_faq.php.

12. Gibbons, A. 2010. "Human Evolution. Tracing Evolution's Recent Fingerprints." *Science* 329 (5993): 740-742.

13. Uyeda, J.C. Hansen, T.F. Arnold, S.J. Pienaar, J. 2011. "The Million-Year Wait for Macroevolutionary Bursts." *Proc Natl Acad Sci U S A* 108 (38): 15908-15913.

14. Junger, S. 2016. *Tribe: On Homecoming and Belonging.* First edition. New York: Twelve.

15. Harari, Y.N. 2015. *Sapiens: A Brief History of Humankind.* First U.S. edition. New York: Harper.

16. Lee, *The Cambridge Encyclopedia of Hunters and Gatherers.*

Part 1

1. Gery, S. Koeffler, H.P. 2010. "Circadian Rhythms and Cancer." *Cell Cycle* 9 (6): 1097-1103.

2. Roenneberg, T. Foster, R.G. 1997. "Twilight Times: Light and the Circadian System." *Photochem Photobiol* 66 (5): 549-561.

3. Terman, M. McMahan, I. 2012. *Chronotherapy: Resetting Your Inner Clock to Boost Mood, Alertness, and Quality Sleep.* New York: Avery.

4. Holzman, D.C. 2018. "What's in a Color? The Unique Human Health Effect of Blue Light." *Environ Health Perspect* 118 (1): A22-A27.

5. Terman et al., *Chronotherapy.*

6. Terman et al., Chronotherapy.

7. Terman et al., Chronotherapy.

8. Frank, M.G. Benington, J.H. 2006. "The role of sleep in memory consolidation and brain plasticity: dream or reality?" *Neuroscientist* 12 (6): 477-488.

9. Samson, D.R. Nunn, C.L. 2015. "Sleep Intensity and the Evolution of Human Cognition." *Evol Anthropol* 24 (6): 225-327.

10. Samson et al., "Sleep Intensity and the Evolution of Human Cognition."

11. Epstein, L. 2015. "The Biology of Sleep: Circadian Rhythms, Sleep Stages, and Sleep Architecture." Accessed June 23, 2020. https://www.helpguide.org/harvard/biology-of-sleep-circadian-rhythms-sleep-stages.htm.

12. Samson et al., "Sleep Intensity and the Evolution of Human Cognition."

13. Epstein, "The Biology of Sleep."

14. Obringer, L.A. Jeffcoat, Y. 2021. "How Dreams Work." Accessed May 26, 2023. https://science.howstuffworks.com/life/inside-the-mind/human-brain/dream2.htm.

15. Obringer, "How Dreams Work."

16. Samson, David, interview by Jenny Powers. 2020. "Interview about primate sleep." (February 12).

Chapter 2

1. Maor, R. Dayan, T. Ferguson-Gow, H. Jones, K.E. 2017. "Temporal niche expansion in mammals from a nocturnal ancestor after dinosaur extinction." *Nat Ecol Evol* 1 (12): 1889-1895.

2. Shultz, S. Opie, C. Atkinson, Q.D. 2011. "Stepwise evolution of stable sociality in primates." *Nature* 479 (7372): 219-222.

3. Samson et al., "Sleep Intensity and the Evolution of Human Cognition."

4. Zimmer, Carl. 2015. "Down from the Trees, Humans Finally Got a Decent Night's Sleep." Accessed February 11, 2020. https://www.nytimes.com/2015/12/22/science/down-from-the-trees-humans-finally-got-a-decent-nights-sleep.html.

5. Samson et al., "Sleep Intensity and the Evolution of Human Cognition."

6. Zimmer, "Down from the Trees."

7. Samson et al., "Sleep Intensity and the Evolution of Human Cognition."

8. Samson et al., "Sleep Intensity and the Evolution of Human Cognition."

9. Lynn, C.D. 2014. "Hearth and campfire influences on arterial blood pressure: defraying the costs of the social brain through fireside relaxation." *Evol Psychol* 12 (4): 983-1003.

10. Beck, K. 2020. "What Are the Colors of a Fire & How Hot Are They?" February 24. Accessed May 26, 2023. https://sciencing.com/colors-fire-hot-8631323.html.

11. Samson et al., "Sleep Intensity and the Evolution of Human Cognition."

12. Zimmer, "Down from the Trees."

13. Zimmer, "Down from the Trees."

14. Samson, "Interview about primate sleep." (February 12).

15. Samson, "Interview about primate sleep." (February 12).

16. Samson et al., "Sleep Intensity and the Evolution of Human Cognition."

17. Samson et al., "Sleep Intensity and the Evolution of Human Cognition."

18. Samson, D.R. Crittenden, A.N. Mabulla, I.A. Mabulla, A.Z.P. Nunn, C.L. 2017. "Chronotype variation drives night-time sentinel-like behaviour in hunter-gatherers." *Proc Biol Sci* 284 (1858): 1-8.

19. Yetish, G. Kaplan, H. Gurven, M. Wood, B. Pontzer, H. Manger, P.R. Wilson, C. McGregor, R. Siegel, J.M. 2015. "Natural sleep and its seasonal variations in three pre-industrial societies." *Curr Biol* 25 (21): 2862-2868.

20. Samson, D.R. Crittenden, A.N. Mabulla, I.A. Mabulla, A.Z. Nunn, C.L. 2017. "Hadza sleep biology: Evidence for flexible sleep-wake patterns in hunter-gatherers." *Am J Phys Anthropol* 162 (3): 573-582.

21. Samson, "Interview about primate sleep." (February 12).

22. Samson et al., "Hadza sleep biology."

23. Samson, "Interview about primate sleep." (February 12).

24. Samson et al., "Hadza sleep biology."

25. Samson, "Interview about primate sleep." (February 12).

26. Samson et al., "Hadza sleep biology."

27. Samson, "Interview about primate sleep." (February 12).

28. Yetish et al., "Natural sleep and its seasonal variations in three pre-industrial societies."

29. Yong, Ed. 2015. "What You Can Learn from Hunter-Gatherers' Sleeping Patterns." Accessed March 19, 2020. https://www.theatlantic.com/science/archive/2015/10/the-many-myths-of-paleo-sleeping/410707/.

30. Samson, "Interview about primate sleep." (February 12).

31. de la Iglesia, H.O. Fernández-Duque, E. Golombek, D.A. Lanza, N. Duffy, J.F. Czeisler, C.A. Valeggia, C.R. 2015. "Access to Electric Light Is Associated with Shorter Sleep Duration in a Traditionally Hunter-Gatherer Community." *J Biol Rhythms* 30 (4): 342-350.

32. de la Iglesia, "Access to Electric Light."

Chapter 3

1. Harvard-Health. 2017. "Blue Light Has a Dark Side." Accessed February 21, 2020. https://www.health.harvard.edu/staying-healthy/blue-light-has-a-dark-side.

2. Holzman, "What's in a Color?"

3. Holzman, "What's in a Color?"

4. Terman et al., *Chronotherapy.*

5. Skeldon, A. Phillips, A. Dijk, D.J. 2017. "The effects of self-selected light-dark cycles and social constraints on human sleep and circadian timing: a modeling approach." *Sci Rep* 7: 45158.

6. Holzman, "What's in a Color?"

7. Carter, S.B. 2012. "The Dangers of Using Electronics at Night and What We Can Do about It." Accessed April 12, 2018. https://www.psychologytoday.com/blog/high-octane-women/201205/the-dangers-using-electronics-night-and-what-we-can-do-about-it.

8. Capatides, C. 2016. "Beyond early bird or night owl: Expert says there are 4 types of sleepers." Accessed August 20, 2019. https://www.cbsnews.com/news/early-bird-night-owl-4-types-of-sleepers-dr-michael-breus/.

9. Leigh, S. 2019. "1 in 300 Thrives on Very-Early-to-Bed, Very-Early-to-Rise Routine." Accessed August 20, 2019. https://www.ucsf.edu/news/2019/08/415091/1-300-thrives-very-early-bed-very-early-rise-routine.

10. Harvard-Health, "Blue Light Has a Dark Side."

11. Holzman, "What's in a Color?"

12. Morin, C.M. Espie, C.A. 2011. *The Oxford Handbook of Sleep and Sleep Disorders.* Oxford: Oxford University Press.

13. Phillips, A.J.K. Clerx, W.M. O'Brien, C.S. Sano, A. Barger, L.K. Picard, R.W. Lockley, S.W. Klerman, E.B. Czeisler, C.A. 2017. "Irregular sleep/wake patterns are associated with poorer academic performance and delayed circadian and sleep/wake timing." *Sci Reps* 7 (1): 1-13.

14. Morin et al., *The Oxford Handbook of Sleep and Sleep Disorders.*

15. Jackson, M.L. Croft, R.J. Kennedy, G.A. Owens, K. Howard, M.E. 2013. "Cognitive components of simulated driving performance: Sleep loss effects and predictors." *Accid Anal Prev* 50: 438-444.

16. Morin et al., *The Oxford Handbook of Sleep and Sleep Disorders.*

17. Morin et al., The Oxford Handbook of *Sleep* and Sleep Disorders.

18. Fullagar, H.H. Skorski, S. Duffield, R. Hammes, D. Coutts, A.J. Meyer, T. 2015. "Sleep and athletic performance: the effects of sleep loss on exercise performance, and physiological and cognitive responses to exercise." *Sports Medicine* 45 (2): 161-186.

19. Fullagar, "Sleep and athletic performance."

20. The Nobel Assembly. 2017. "The Nobel Assembly at Karolinska Institutet has today decided to award the 2017 Nobel Prize in Physiology or Medicinejointly to Jeffrey C. Hall, Michael Rosbash and Michael W. Young for their discoveries of molecular mechanisms controlling the circadian rhythms." Accessed August 20, 2019. https://www.nobelprize.org/prizes/medicine/2017/press-release/.

21. Gery et al., "Circadian rhythms and cancer," 1097-1103.

22. Silver, K. 2022. "Why Good Sleep Matters for Your Heart's Health." WebMD Magazine. Accessed June 24, 2023. https://www.webmd.com/sleep-disorders/features/how-sleep-affects-your-heart#1.

23. Holzman, "What's in a Color?"

24. Larson, J. 2023. "Cancer and Sleep." The Sleep Doctor. Accessed June 24, 2023. https://sleepdoctor.com/physical-health/cancer-and-sleep/#:~:text=Sleep%20and%20Cancer%20Treatment&text=Other%20drugs%20may%20make%20people,affect%20how%20well%20treatment%20works.

25. Gery et al., "Circadian rhythms and cancer."

26. Sloan, M. "Prolonged stress may increase the risk of death from cancer." 2023. Accessed January 31, 2024. https://www.health.harvard.edu/cancer/prolonged-stress-may-increase-the-risk-of-death-from-cancer.

27. Gery et al., "Circadian rhythms and cancer."

28. Morris, C.J. Purvis, T.E. Hu, K. Scheer, F.A. 2016. "Circadian misalignment increases cardiovascular disease risk factors in humans." *Proc Natl Acad Sci U S A* 113 (10): E1402-1411.

29. Cappuccio, F.P. Miller, M.A. 2017. "Sleep and Cardio-Metabolic Disease." *Curr Cardiol Rep* 19: 110.

30. Daghlas, I. Dashti, H.S. Lane, J. Aragam, K.G. Rutter, M.K. Saxena, R. Vetter, C. 2019. "Sleep Duration and Myocardial Infarction." *J A Coll Cardiol* 74 (10): 1304-1314.

31. Wei, R. Duan, X. Guo, L. 2022. "Effects of sleep deprivation on coronary heart disease." *Korean J Physiol Pharmacol* 26 (5): 297-305.

32. Yetish et al., "Natural sleep and its seasonal variations in three pre-industrial societies."

33. Buxton, O.M. Cain, S.W. O'Connor, S.P. Porter, J.H. Duffy, J.F. Wang, W. Czeisler, C.A. Shea, S.A. 2012. "Adverse metabolic consequences in humans of prolonged sleep restriction combined with circadian disruption." *Sci Transl Med* 4 (129): 1-19.

34. Scheer, F.A. Hilton, M.F. Mantzoros, C.S. Shea, S.A. 2009. "Adverse metabolic and cardiovascular consequences of circadian misalignment." *Proc Natl Acad Sci U S A* 106 (11): 4453-4458.

35. Griffin, R.M. 2010. "The Health Risks of Shift Work." Accessed August 21, 2019. https://www.webmd.com/sleep-disorders/features/shift-work#1.

36. Buxton et al., "Adverse metabolic consequences in humans of prolonged sleep restriction."

37. Scheer et al., "Adverse metabolic and cardiovascular consequences of circadian misalignment."

38. Huang, T. Redline, S. 2019. "Cross-sectional and Prospective Associations of Actigraphy-Assessed Sleep Regularity With Metabolic Abnormalities: The Multi-Ethnic Study of Atherosclerosis." *Diabetes Care* 42 (8): 1422-1429.

39. Yetish et al., "Natural sleep and its seasonal variations in three pre-industrial societies."

40. Kronfeld-Schor, N. Einat, H. 2012. "Circadian rhythms and depression: human psychopathology and animal models." *Neuropharmacology* 62 (1): 101-114.

41. Griffin, "The Health Risks of Shift Work."

42. Terman et al., *Chronotherapy.*

43. Kronfeld-Schor et al., "Circadian rhythms and depression."

44. Shokri-Kojori, E. Wang, G. Wiers, C.E. Demiral, S.B. Guo, M. Kim, S.W. Lindgren, E. Ramirez, V. Zehra, A. Freeman, C. Miller, G. Manza, P. Srivastava, T. De Santi, S. Tomasi, D. Benveniste, H. Volkow, N.V. 2018. "β-Amyloid accumulation in the human brain after one night of sleep deprivation." *Proc Natl Acad Sci U S A* 115 (17): 4483-4488.

45. Kujovic, M. Lipka, T. Zalman, M. Baumann, L. Jänner, M. Baumann, B. 2023. "Treatment of hypertension and obstructive sleep apnea counteracts cognitive decline in common neurocognitive disorders in diagnosis-related patterns." *Sci Rep* 13 (1): 7556.

46. Leslie, M. 2012. "Circadian rhythms. Sleep study suggests triggers for diabetes and obesity." *Science* 336 (6078): 143.

Chapter 4

1. Terman et al., *Chronotherapy.*

2. Wright, K.P. McHill, A.W. Birks, B.R. Griffin, B.R. Rusterholz, T. Chinoy, E.D. 2013. "Entrainment of the human circadian clock to the natural light-dark cycle." *Curr Biol* 23 (16): 1554-1558.

3. Samson, "Interview about primate sleep." (February 12).

4. "Why Sleep Consistency May Be More Important Than Duration." 2023. Accessed January 31, 2024. https://www.psychiatrist.com/news/why-sleep-consistency-may-be-more-important-than-duration/#:~:text=Prioritizing%20Consistency,consistency%20in%20sleep%2Dwake%20timing.

5. Wright et al., "Entrainment of the human circadian clock to the natural light-dark cycle."

6. Worthman, C.M. Brown, R.A. 2007. "Companionable sleep: social regulation of sleep and cosleeping in Egyptian families." *J Fam Psychol* 21 (1): 124-135.

7. Faraut, B. Andrillon, T. Vecchierini, M.F. Leger, D. 2017. "Napping: A public health issue. From epidemiological to laboratory studies." *Sleep Med Rev* 35: 85-100.

8. Carter, "The Dangers of Using Electronics at Night and What We Can Do About."

9. Harvard-Health, "Blue Light Has a Dark Side."

10. Yetish et al., "Natural sleep and its seasonal variations in three pre-industrial societies."

11. Braun, A. 2017. "The Once-Common Practice of Communal Sleeping." Accessed August 19, 2019. https://www.atlasobscura.com/articles/communal-sleeping-history-sharing-bed.

12. Worthman et al., "Companionable sleep."

13. Kurina, L.M. Knutson, K.L. Hawkley, L.C. Cacioppo, J.T. Lauderdale, D.S. Ober, C. 2011. "Loneliness is associated with sleep fragmentation in a communal society." *Sleep* 34 (11): 1519-1526.

14. Hsu, C. 2010. "Surprising Reasons Why Sleeping with Someone Is Better than Sleeping Alone." Accessed August 22, 2019. https://www.medicaldaily.com/surprising-reasons-why-sleeping-someone-better-sleeping-alone-240711.

15. Terman et al., *Chronotherapy*.

16. Griffin, "The Health Risks of Shift Work."

17. Howard, J. 2016. "What's the Best Work Schedule for Your Age?" Accessed August 21, 2019. https://www.cnn.com/2016/09/08/health/best-work-schedule-sleep-schedule-age/index.html.

18. Samson, "Interview about primate sleep." (February 12).

19. Samson, "Interview about primate sleep." (February 12).

20. Samson, "Interview about primate sleep." (February 12).

Part 2

1. 2004. *Super Size Me.* Directed by Morgan Spurlock. Produced by Morgan Spurlock.

2. O'Sullivan, M. 2004. "'Super Size Me': I'm Loving It." Accessed November 8, 2020. https://www.washingtonpost.com/archive/lifestyle/2004/05/07/super-size-me-im-loving-it/7e1dee67-1fcb-454c-9846-ed163393a285/.

3. Molina, B. 2018. "More than 1 in 3 adults eat fast food on a given day, CDC survey finds." Accessed December 21, 2020. https://www.usatoday.com/story/news/nation-now/2018/10/03/americans-eat-fast-food-daily-cdc-survey/1507702002/.

4. O'Sullivan, "'Super Size Me': I'm Loving It."

5. Cordain, L. Eaton, S.B. Sebastian, A. Mann, N. Lindeberg, S. Watkins, B.A. O'Keefe, J.H. Brand-Miller, J. 2005. "Origins and Evolution of the Western Diet: health implications for the 21st century." *Am J Clin Nutr* 81 (2): 341-354.

6. Centers for Disease Control and Prevention, "Adult Obesity Facts."

7. Centers for Disease Control and Prevention, "Type 2 Diabetes."

8. Centers for Disease Control and Prevention. 2020. "High Cholesterol Facts." Accessed December 22, 2020. https://www.cdc.gov/cholesterol/facts.htm.

9. Centers for Disease Control and Prevention, "High Cholesterol Facts."

10. Centers for Disease Control and Prevention. 2021. "Leading Causes of Death." Accessed January 31, 2024. https://www.cdc.gov/nchs/fastats/leading-causes-of-death.htm.

11. Diamond, J.M. 2012. *The World Until Yesterday: What Can We Learn From Traditional Societies?* New York: Viking.

12. Eaton, S.B. Konner, M. 1985. "Paleolithic Nutrition. A consideration of its nature and current implications." *N Engl J Med* 312 (5): 283-289.

13. Cordain et al., "Origins and Evolution of the Western Diet."

14. Konner, M. Eaton, S.B. 2010. "Paleolithic Nutrition: twenty-five years later." *Nutr Clin Pract* 25 (6): 594-602.

15. de Menezes, E.V.A. Sampaio, H.A.C. Carioca, A.A.F. Parente, N.A. Brito, F.O. Moreira, T.M.M. de Souza, A.C.C. Arruda, S.P.M. 2019. "Influence of Paleolithic diet on anthropometric markers in chronic diseases: systematic review and meta-analysis." *Nutr J* 18 (1): 41-53.

16. Bennett, B.J. Hall, K.D. Hu, F.B. McCartney, A.L. Roberto, C. 2015. "Nutrition and the science of disease prevention: a systems approach to support metabolic health." *Ann N Y Acad Sci* 1352: 1-12.

17. Leonard, W.R. 2014. "The global diversity of eating patterns: human nutritional health in comparative perspective." *Physiol Behav* 134: 5-14.

Chapter 5

1. Milton, K. 1993. "Diet and Primate Evolution." *Sci Am* 269 (2): 86-93.

2. Milton, "Diet and Primate Evolution."

3. Zihlman, A.L. Cronin, J.E. Cramer, D.L. Sarich, V.M. 1978. "Pygmy chimpanzee as a possible prototype for the common ancestor of humans, chimpanzees and gorillas." *Nature* 275 (275): 744-746.

4. Milton, K. 2020. "Back to Basics: why foods of wild primates have relevance for modern human health." *Nutrition* 16 (7-8): 480-483.

5. Carlson, B.A. Rothman, J.M. Mitani, J.C. 2013. "Diurnal variation in nutrients and chimpanzee foraging behavior." *Am J Primatol* 75 (3): 342-349.

6. Milton, "Diet and Primate Evolution."

7. Watts, D.P. Mitani, J.C. 2002. "Hunting Behavior of Chimpanzees at Ngogo, Kibale National Park, Uganda." *Int J Primatol* 23 (1): 1-28.

8. Milton, "Back to Basics."

9. Bogart, S.L. Pruetz, J.D. 2011. "Insectivory of savanna chimpanzees (Pan troglodytes verus) at Fongoli, Senegal." *Am J Phys Anthropol* 145 (1): 11-20.

10. Ulijaszek, S.J. Mann, N. Elton, S. 2012. "Evolving *Human* Nutrition: implications for public health." New York: Cambridge University Press.

11. Ulijaszek, "Evolving Human Nutrition."

12. Go, Y. Niimura, Y. 2008. "Similar numbers but different repertoires of olfactory receptor genes in humans and chimpanzees." *Mol Biol Evol* 25 (9): 1897-1907.

13. Perry, G.H. Dominy, N.J. Claw, K.G. Lee, A.S. Fiegler, H. Redon, R. Werner, J. Villanea, F.A. Mountain, J L. Misra, R. Carter, N.P. Lee, C. Stone, A.C. 2007. "Diet and the evolution of human amylase gene copy number variation." *Nat Genet* 39 (10): 1256-1260.

14. Perry et al., "Diet and the evolution of human amylase gene copy number variation."

15. Kawamura, S. 2016. "Color vision diversity and significance in primates inferred from genetic and field studies." *Genes Genomics* 38: 779-791.

16. Sanz, C. Call, J. Morgan, D. 2009. "Design complexity in termite-fishing tools of chimpanzees (Pan troglodytes)." *Biol Lett* 5 (3): 293-936.

17. Sanz, C.M. Morgan, D.B. "Flexible and Persistent Tool-using Strategies in Honey-gathering by Wild Chimpanzees." *Int J Primatol* 30: 411-427.

18. Boesch, C. Bombjaková, D. Boyette, A. Meier, A. 2017. "Technical intelligence and culture: Nut cracking in humans and chimpanzees." *Am J Phys Anthropol* 163 (2): 339-355.

19. Napier, J.R. Napier, P.H. 1985. *The natural history of the primates.* Cambridge, Mass: MIT Press.

20. Milton, "Diet and Primate Evolution."

21. Roth, G. Dicke, U. 2005. "Evolution of the brain and intelligence." *Trends in Cognitive Sciences* 9 (5): 250-257.

Chapter 6

1. Sepulchre, P.R. Flatueu, G. Schuster, F. Tiercelin, M. Michel, J.J.B. 2006. "Tectonic Uplift and Eastern Africa Aridificaiton." *Science* 313: 1419-1423.

2. Leonard, W.R. 2002. "Food for Thought: Dietary change was a driving force in human evolution." *Scientific American* 289 (6): 108-115.

3. Foley, R. Elton, S. 1998. "Time and energy: the ecological context for the evolution of bipedalism." In *Primate Locomotion: Recent Advances*, by E. Fleagle, J. Rosenberger, A. McHenry, H. Strasser, 419-433. New York: Plenum Press.

4. Sockol, M.D. Raichlen, D.A. Pontzer, H. 2007. "Chimpanzee locomotor energetics and the origin of human bipedalism." *Proc Natl Acad Sci U S A* 104 (30): 12265-12269.

5. Skinner, M.M. Stephens, N.B. Tsegai, Z.J. Foote, A.C. Nguyen, N.H. Gross, T. Pahr, D.H. Hublin, J.J. Kivell, T.L. 2015. "Human evolution. Human-like hand use in Australopithecus africanus." *Science* 347 (6220): 395-399.

6. Ulijaszek, "Evolving Human Nutrition."

7. Ulijaszek, "Evolving Human Nutrition."

8. Finch, C.E. Stanford, C.B. 2004. "Meat-adaptive genes and the evolution of slower aging in humans." *Q Rev Biol* 79 (1): 3-50.

9. Leonard, "Food for Thought."

10. Leonard, "Food for Thought."

11. Dennis, M.Y. Nuttle, X. Sudmant, P.H. Antonacci, F. Graves, T.A. Nefedov, M. Rosenfeld, J.A. Sajjadian, S. Malig, M. Kotkiewicz, H. Curry, C.J. Shafer, S. Shaffer, L.G. de Jong, P.J. Wilson, R.K. Eichler, E.E. 2012. "Evolution of human-specific neural SRGAP2 genes by incomplete segmental duplication." *Cell* 149 (4): 912-922.

12. Leonard, "Food for Thought."

13. Leonard, "Food for Thought."

14. Bramble, D.M. Lieberman, D.E. 2004. "Endurance running and the evolution of Homo." *Nature* 432 (7015): 345-352.

15. Ulijaszek, "Evolving Human Nutrition."

16. Ulijaszek, "Evolving Human Nutrition."

17. Ungar, P.S. 2012. "Dental Evidence for the Reconstruction of Diet in African Early Homo." *Curr Anthropol* 53 (S6): S318-S329.

18. Ulijaszek, "Evolving Human Nutrition."

19. Milton, "Back to Basics."

20. Ulijaszek, "Evolving Human Nutrition."

21. Finch et al., "Meat-adaptive genes and the evolution of slower aging in humans."

22. Bramble et al., "Endurance running and the evolution of Homo."

23. Perry et al., "Diet and the evolution of human amylase gene copy number variation."

24. Steudel-Numbers, K.L. 2006. "Energetics in Homo erectus and other early hominins: the consequences of increased lower-limb length." *J Hum Evol* 51 (5): 445-453.

25. Shipman, P. Walker, A. 1989. "The costs of becoming a predator." *J Hum Evol* 18: 373-392.

26. Ulijaszek, "Evolving Human Nutrition."

27. Eaton, S. Boyd Eaton, Stanley B. 2004. "Hunter-Gatherers and Human Health." In *The Cambridge Encyclopedia of Hunters and Gatherers*., edited by Richard B. Daly, Richard Lee. Cambridge, U.K.; New York, NY: Cambridge University Press.

28. Ulijaszek, "Evolving Human Nutrition."

29. Wrangham, Richard W. 2009. *Catching Fire: How Cooking Made Us Human*. New York: Basic Books.

30. Leonard, "Food for Thought."

31. Leonard, "Food for Thought."

32. Carroll, S.B. 2003. "Genetics and the making of Homo sapiens." *Nature* 422 (6934): 849-857.

33. Ulijaszek, "Evolving Human Nutrition."

34. Leonard, "Food for Thought."

Chapter 7

1. Jenike, M. 2001. "Nutritional ecology: diet, physical activity and body size." In *Hunter-gatherers: an interdisciplinary perspective*, by Catherine Layton, Robert Rowley-Conwy, P. Panter-Brick. Cambridge, UK; New York: Cambridge University Press.

2. Ulijaszek, "Evolving Human Nutrition."

3. Milton, "Back to Basics."

4. Leonard, "Food for Thought."

5. Ulijaszek, "Evolving Human Nutrition."

6. Connor, T. 2022. "Forget the Macronutrient Ratios. Here's Why." April 7. Accessed May 27, 2023. https://thepaleodiet.com/forget-the-macronutrient-ratios-you-are-what-you-were-designed-to-eat.

7. Eaton, J.C. Iannotti, L.L. 2017. "Genome-Nutrition Divergence: Evolving Understanding of the Malnutrition Spectrum." *Nutr Rev* 75 (11): 934-950.

8. Jamka, M. Kulczyński, B. Juruć, A. Gramza-Michałowska, A. Stokes, C.S. Walkowiak, J. 2020. "The Effect of the Paleolithic Diet vs. Healthy Diets on Glucose and Insulin Homeostasis: A Systematic Review and Meta-Analysis of Randomized Controlled Trials." *J Clin Med* 9 (2): 296-317.

9. Lee et al., *Man the Hunter.*

10. Cordain, L. Miller, J.B. Eaton, S.B. Mann, N. Holt, S.H. Speth, J.D. 2000. "Plant-animal subsistence ratios and macronutrient energy estimations in worldwide hunter-gatherer diets." *Am J Clin Nutr* 71 (3): 682-692.

11. Cordain et al., "Plant-animal subsistence ratios."

12. Ulijaszek, "Evolving Human Nutrition."

13. Crittenden, A.N. Schnorr, S.L. 2017. "Current views on hunter-gatherer nutrition and the evolution of the human diet." *Am J Phys Anthropol* 162 (S63): 84-109.

14. Eaton, S.B. Eaton III, S.B. Konner, M.J. 1997. "Paleolithic Nutrition revisited: a twelve-year retrospective on its nature and implications." *Eur J Clin Nutr* 51 (4): 207-216.

15. Cordain et al., "Origins and Evolution of the Western Diet," 341-354.

16. Ulijaszek, "Evolving Human Nutrition."

17. Cordain et al., "Origins and Evolution of the Western Diet," 341-354.

18. Eaton et al., "Paleolithic Nutrition revisited," 207-216.

19. Jenike, "Nutritional ecology."

20. Ulijaszek, "Evolving Human Nutrition."

21. Leonard, "Food for Thought."

22. Ulijaszek, "Evolving Human Nutrition."

23. Leonard, "Food for Thought."

24. Kopp, W. 2019. "How Western Diet And Lifestyle Drive The Pandemic Of Obesity And Civilization Diseases." *Diabetes Metab Syndr Obes* 12: 2221-2236.

25. Cordain et al., "Origins and Evolution of the Western Diet."

26. Eaton et al., "Paleolithic Nutrition."

27. Eaton et al., "Hunter-Gatherers and Human Health."

28. Eaton et al., "Hunter-Gatherers and Human Health."

29. Eaton et al., "Hunter-Gatherers and Human Health."

30. Konner et al., "Paleolithic Nutrition."

31. Leonard, "Food for Thought."

32. Ulijaszek, "Evolving Human Nutrition."

33. Milton, "Back to Basics."

34. Leonard, "Food for Thought."

35. O'Keefe, J.H. Cordain, L. 2004. "Cardiovascular disease resulting from a diet and lifestyle at odds with our Paleolithic genome: how to become a 21st-century hunter-gatherer." *Mayo* Clin *Proc* 79 (1): 101-108.

Chapter 8

1. Suzman, *Affluence without Abundance*.

2. Ulijaszek, "Evolving Human Nutrition."

3. Scott, J.C. 2017. Against the Grain: A Deep History of the Earliest States. New York: Yale UP.

4. Cordain et al., "Origins and Evolution of the Western Diet."

5. Turner, B.L. Thompson, A.L. 2013. "Beyond the Paleolithic prescription: incorporating diversity and flexibility in the study of human diet evolution." *Nutr Rev* 71 (8): 501-510.

6. Svizzero, S. Tisdell, C. 2014. "The Neolithic Revolution and Human Societies: Diverse Origins and Development Paths." Working papers on Economics, Ecology, and the Environment: School of Economics, The University of Queensland (School of Economics, The University of Queensland) 192: 1-38.

7. Harari, *Sapiens*.

8. Eaton et al., "Genome-Nutrition Divergence."

9. Harari, *Sapiens*.

10. O'Keefe et al., "Cardiovascular disease resulting from a diet and lifestyle at odds with our Paleolithic genome."

11. Harlan, Jack R. 1992. Crops & Man. Madison, Wisconsin, USA: American Society of Agronomy: Crop Science Society of America.

12. Suzman, *Affluence without Abundance*.

13. Page, A.E. Viguier, S. Dyble, M. Smith, D. Chaudhary, N. Salali, G.D. Thompson, J. Vinicius, L. Mace, R. Migliano, A.B. 2016. "Reproductive trade-offs in extant hunter-gatherers suggest adaptive mechanism for the Neolithic expansion." Proc Natl Acad Sci U S A 113 (17): 4694-4699.

14. Svizzero et al., "The Neolithic Revolution and Human Societies," 1-38.

15. Harari, *Sapiens*.

16. Eaton et al., "Genome-Nutrition Divergence."

17. Harari, *Sapiens*.

18. Cordain et al., "Origins and Evolution of the Western Diet."

Chapter 9

1. Challa, Hima J. Bandlamudi, Manav Uppaluri, Kalyan R. 2020. *Paleolithic Diet*. Accessed December 8, 2020. https://www.statpearls.com/articlelibrary/viewarticle/38816/.

2. Greenfield, P. 2017. "Cultural Change Over Time: Why Replicability Should Not Be the Gold Standard in Psychological Science." *Perspect Psychol Sci* 12 (5): 762-771.

3. Ulijaszek, "Evolving Human Nutrition."

4. Ulijaszek, "Evolving Human Nutrition."

5. Eaton et al., "Genome-Nutrition Divergence."

6. De Oliveira, O.M.C. Anderson, C.A.M., Dearborn, J.L Ferranti, E.P. Mozaffarian, D. Rao, G. Wylie-Rosett, J. Lichtenstein, A.H. 2018. "American Heart Association Behavioral Change for Improving Health Factors," Dietary Diversity: Implications for Obesity Prevention in Adult Populations: A Science Advisory from the American Heart Association. *Circulation* 138 (11): e160-e168.

7. Eaton et al., "Genome-Nutrition Divergence."

8. Cordain et al., "Origins and Evolution of the Western Diet."

9. Moon, J. Koh, G. 2020. "Clinical Evidence and Mechanisms of High-Protein Diet Induced Weight Loss." *J Obes Metab Syndr* 29 (3): 166-173.

10. Mittendorfer, B. Klein, S. Fontana, L. 2020. "A word of caution against excessive protein intake." *Nat Rev Endocrinol* 16: 59–66.

11. Koh, G.J. Rhee, C.M. Kalantar-Zadeh, K. Joshi, S. 2020. "The Effects of High-Protein Diets on Kidney Health and Longevity." *J Am Soc Nephrol* 31 (8): 1667-1679.

12. Cordain et al., "Origins and Evolution of the Western Diet."

13. Ulijaszek, "Evolving Human Nutrition."

14. Cordain et al., "Origins and Evolution of the Western Diet."

15. Dunn, Rob. 2012. "How to Eat Like a Chimpanzee." Accessed January 10, 2021. https://blogs.scientificamerican.com/guest-blog/how-to-eat-like-a-chimpanzee/.

16. Cordain et al., "Origins and Evolution of the Western Diet."

17. Lawton, Graham, New Scientist. 2020. *This Book Could Save Your Life: the science of living longer better*. London Boston: John Murray Press Nicholas Brealey Publishing.

18. Cordain et al., "Origins and Evolution of the Western Diet."

19. Lawton et al., *This Book Could Save Your Life*.

20. Mozaffarian, D. Rosenberg, I. Uauy, R. 2018. "History of modern nutrition science-implications for current research, dietary guidelines, and food policy." *BMJ* 361: k2392.

21. Eaton et al., "Genome-Nutrition Divergence."

22. Lawton et al., *This Book Could Save Your Life*.

23. Ulijaszek, "Evolving Human Nutrition."

24. Ulijaszek, "Evolving Human Nutrition."

25. Diamond, *The World Until Yesterday*.

26. Cordain et al., "Origins and Evolution of the Western Diet."

27. Cordain et al., "Origins and Evolution of the Western Diet."

28. Eaton et al., "Genome-Nutrition Divergence."

29. Cordain et al., "Origins and Evolution of the Western Diet."

30. Tungland, B. 2018. "Short-Chain Fatty Acid Production and Functional Aspects on Host Metabolism." In *Human gut microbiota in health and disease: from pathogenesis to therapy*, 37-106. Waltham, MA: Elsevier, Academic Press.

31. Di Rienzi, S.C., Britton, R.A. 2020. "Adaption of the Gut Microbiota to Modern Dietary Sugars and Sweeteners." *Adv Nutr* 11(3): 616-629.

32. Cordain et al., "Origins and Evolution of the Western Diet."

33. Bennett et al., "Nutrition and the science of disease prevention."

34. Ulijaszek, "Evolving Human Nutrition."

35. Ulijaszek, "Evolving Human Nutrition."

36. Lawton et al., *This Book Could Save Your Life.*

37. Ulijaszek, "Evolving Human Nutrition."

38. Cordain et al., "Origins and Evolution of the Western Diet."

39. Lawton et al., *This Book Could Save Your Life.*

40. Diamond, *The World Until Yesterday.*

41. Wigmore, A. 1985. *Why suffer?* Wayne, N.J.: Avery Pub. Group.

42. Kopp, "How Western Diet And Lifestyle Drive The Pandemic Of Obesity And Civilization Diseases."

43. Kopp, "How Western Diet And Lifestyle Drive The Pandemic Of Obesity And Civilization Diseases."

44. Bennett et al., "Nutrition and the science of disease prevention."

45. Ulijaszek, "Evolving Human Nutrition."

46. Kopp, "How Western Diet And Lifestyle Drive The Pandemic Of Obesity And Civilization Diseases."

47. Eaton et al., "Genome-Nutrition Divergence."

48. Ulijaszek, "Evolving Human Nutrition."

49. Diamond, *The World Until Yesterday.*

50. Diamond, The World Until Yesterday.

51. Cordain et al., "Origins and Evolution of the Western Diet."

52. Lawton et al., *This Book Could Save Your Life.*

53. The American Cancer Society Medical and Editorial Team. 2020. "Does Body Weight Affect Cancer Risk?" Accessed March 15, 2021. https://www.cancer.org/cancer/cancer-causes/diet-physical-activity/body-weight-and-cancer-risk/effects.html#:~:text=Being%20overweight%20or%20obese%20is%20clearly%20linked%20to,well%20as%20about%207%25%20of%20all%20cancer%20deaths.

54. National Cancer Institute. 2015. "Cancer Causes and Prevention; Risk Factors; Diet." Accessed March 14, 2021. https://www.cancer.gov/about-cancer/causes-prevention/risk/diet.

55. Eaton et al., "Hunter-Gatherers and Human Health."

56. Eaton et al., "Hunter-Gatherers and Human Health."

57. Lawton et al., *This Book Could Save Your Life.*

58. National Cancer Institute, "Cancer Causes and Prevention; Risk Factors; Diet."

59. Lawton et al., *This Book Could Save Your Life.*

60. Ulijaszek, "Evolving Human Nutrition."

61. Cordain et al., "Origins and Evolution of the Western Diet."

62. Cordain et al., "Origins and Evolution of the Western Diet."

63. Eaton et al., "Genome-Nutrition Divergence."

64. Ulijaszek, "Evolving Human Nutrition."

65. Ulijaszek, "Evolving Human Nutrition."

Chapter 10

1. Eaton et al., "Hunter-Gatherers and Human Health."

2. Ulijaszek, "Evolving Human Nutrition."

3. Cabot, L. Erlenbeck-Dinkelmann, J. Fenselau, H. 2023. "Neural gut-to-brain communication for postprandial control of satiation and glucose metabolism." *J Endocrinol* 258 (3): e220320.

4. Cordain et al., "Origins and Evolution of the Western Diet."

5. Connor, *Forget the Macronutrient Ratios.*

6. Ulijaszek, "Evolving Human Nutrition."

7. Wu, G. 2016. "Dietary protein intake and human health." *Food Funct* 7 (3): 1251-1265.

8. Wu, "Dietary protein intake and human health."

9. Huang, J. Liao, L.M. Weinstein, S.J. Sinha, R. Graubard, B.I. Albanes, D. 2020. "Association Between Plant and Animal Protein Intake and Overall and Cause-Specific Mortality." *JAMA Intern Med* 180 (9): 1173-1184.

10. Harvard T.H. Chan School of Public Health. 2021. "The Nutrition Source: Collagen." Accessed October 25, 2023. https://www.hsph.harvard.edu/nutritionsource/collagen/.

11. Paul, C. Leser, S. Oesser, S. 2019. "Significant Amounts of Functional Collagen Peptides Can Be Incorporated in the Diet While Maintaining Indispensable Amino Acid Balance." *Nutrients* 11 (5): 1079.

12. Gordon, B. 2021. "Choose healthy fats." Accessed August 4, 2023. https://www.eatright.org/food/food-groups/fats/choose-healthy-fats.

13. Simopoulos, A.P. 2002. "The importance of the ratio of omega-6/omega-3 essential fatty acids." *Biomed Pharmacother* 56 (8): 365-379.

14. Gunnars, K. Chin, K. 2023. "How to Optimize Your Omega-6 to Omega-3 Ratio." Accessed November 1, 2023. https://www.healthline.com/nutrition/optimize-omega-6-omega-3-ratio.

15. Mayo Clinic Staff. 2022. "Trans fat is double trouble for heart health." Accessed October 28, 2023. https://www.mayoclinic.org/diseases-conditions/high-blood-cholesterol/in-depth/trans-fat/art-20046114.

16. El Bacha, T., Luz, M. Da Poian, A. 2010. "Dynamic Adaptation of Nutrient Utilization in Humans." *Nature Education* 3 (9): 8.

17. El Bacha et al., "Dynamic Adaptation of Nutrient Utilization in Humans."

18. Nothaft, D. 2023. "How many carbs should you eat a day? We spoke with an expert." Accessed September 17, 2023. https://www.usatoday.com/story/life/health-wellness/2023/06/04/how-many-carbs-per-day-should-i-eat/70259227007/.

19. Lawton et al., *This Book Could Save Your Life*.

20. Eaton et al., "Hunter-Gatherers and Human Health."

21. O'Keefe et al., "Cardiovascular disease resulting from a diet and lifestyle at odds with our Paleolithic genome."

22. Cordain et al., "Origins and Evolution of the Western Diet."

23. Fellows, L. 2022. *Defining the Paleo Diet: Paleo 101*. Accessed May 27, 2023. https://thepaleodiet.com/paleo-101/what-is-paleo.

24. Smith, M.L. 2019. "The Paleo Diet: Designed by Nature, Built By Science." Accessed March 17, 2021. https://thepaleodiet.com/designed-by-nature-built-by-science.

25. Eaton et al., "Genome-Nutrition Divergence," 934-950.

26. Jamka et al., "The Effect of the Paleolithic Diet vs. Healthy Diets on Glucose and Insulin Homeostasis."

Part 3

1. Kantor, J. Streitfeld, D. 2015. "Inside Amazon: Wrestling Big Ideas in a Bruising Workplace." Accessed August 9, 2019. https://www.nytimes.com/2015/08/16/technology/inside-amazon-wrestling-big-ideas-in-a-bruising-workplace.html?_r=0.

2. Kantor, "Inside Amazon."

3. Thompson, D. 2019. "Workism Is Making Americans Miserable." Accessed August 26, 2019. https://www.theatlantic.com/ideas/archive/2019/02/religion-workism-making-americans-miserable/583441/.

4. Moodie, A. 2016. "Why Are Americans Spending Too Much Time at Work?" Accessed August 9, 2019. https://www.theguardian.com/sustainable-business/2016/jun/30/america-working-hours-minimum-wage-overworked.

5. Francis, L. 2019. "When So-Called Work Ethic Replaces Productivity, American Families Suffer." Accessed March 26, 2020. https://www.fatherly.com/love-money/work-ethic-productivity-american-families-suffer#:~:text=Life-,When%20So%2DCalled%20Work%20Ethic%20Replaces%20Productivity%2C%20American%20Families%20Suffer,do%20with%20unhappy%2C%20overworked%20families.&text=Americans%20spend%20390%20more%20hours,than%20did%2030%20years%20ago.

6. Francis, "When So-Called Work Ethic Replaces Productivity."

7. Moodie, "Why Are Americans Spending Too Much Time at Work?"

8. Boushey, H. Ansel, B. 2016. "Overworked America: The economic causes and consequences of long work hours." Accessed March 19, 2018. http://equitablegrowth.org/report/overworked-america/.

9. Cohan, W. 2015. "Deaths Draw Attention to Wall Street's Grueling Pace." Accessed March 19, 2018. https://www.nytimes.com/2015/10/04/business/dealbook/tragedies-draw-attention-to-wall-streets-grueling-pace.html.

10. Suzman, *Affluence without Abundance*.

11. Thompson, "Workism Is Making Americans Miserable."

12. Suzman, *Affluence without Abundance*.

13. Moodie, "Why are Americans Spending Too Much Time at Work?"

14. Thompson, "Workism Is Making Americans Miserable."

15. Schulte, B. 2018. "The Way We Work Is Killing Us." Accessed April 5, 2020. https://slate.com/human-interest/2018/04/is-your-work-killing-you.html.

16. The Organization for Economic Co-operation and Development (OECD), OECD. 2022. "Hours worked." Accessed July 8, 2023. https://data.oecd.org/emp/hours-worked. htm#indicator-chart.

17. Schulte, "The Way We Work Is Killing Us."

18. CBS/AP. 2016. "These jobs have the highest rate of suicide." Accessed August 27, 2019. https://www.cbsnews.com/news/these-jobs-have-the-highest-rate-of-suicide/.

19. Newman, T. 2018. "What is a cell?" Accessed March 20, 2020. https://www. medicalnewstoday.com/articles/320878.

20. Pusey, A.B. Walker, E.K. 2019. "Chimpanzee Behavior and Conservation: 'Making a Living in the Forest.'" Accessed August 26, 2019. https://www.coursera.org/learn/ chimp#syllabus.

21. Tweheyo, M. Lye, K.A. Weladji, R.B. 2004. "Chimpanzee diet and habitat selection in the Budongo Forest Reserve, Uganda." *For Ecol Manag* 188: 267-278.

22. Goodall, J. 1986. *The chimpanzees of Gombe: patterns of behavior.* Cambridge, Mass.; London: Belknap Press of Harvard University Press.

23. Pusey et al., "Chimpanzee Behavior and Conservation."

24. Pusey et al., "Chimpanzee Behavior and Conservation."

Chapter 11

1. Lee et al., *Man the Hunter*.

2. Lee et al., Man the Hunter.

3. Harari, *Sapiens*.

4. Mostert, N. 1992. *Frontiers: The Epic of South Africa's Creation and the Tragedy of the Xhosa People.* New York: Knopf.

5. Suzman, *Affluence without Abundance*.

6. Suzman, Affluence without Abundance.

7. Junger, *Tribe*.

8. Lee et al., *Man the Hunter*.

9. Lee et al., Man the Hunter.

10. Lee et al., Man the Hunter.

11. Lee et al., Man the Hunter.

12. 2014. *The Hadza: The Last of the First.* Directed by Bill Benenson. Produced by Bill Laurie, Benenson Benenson.

13. Suzman, *Affluence without Abundance*.

14. Lee et al., *Man the Hunter*.

15. Suzman, *Affluence without Abundance*.

16. Gray, Peter. 2009. "Play as a Foundation for Hunter-Gatherer Social Existence." *American Journal of Play* 1 (4): 476-522.

17. Suzman, *Affluence without Abundance*.

18. Suzman, Affluence without Abundance.

19. Suzman, Affluence without Abundance.

20. Suzman, Affluence without Abundance.

21. Lee et al., *Man the Hunter*.

22. Mostert, *Frontiers: The Epic of South Africa's Creation and the Tragedy of the Xhosa People*.

23. Gray, Peter, interview by Jenny Powers. 2020. "Interview about hunter-gatherer play." (March 27).

24. Gray, "Play as a Foundation for Hunter-Gatherer Social Existence."

25. Suzman, *Affluence without Abundance*.

26. Gray, "Interview about hunter-gatherer play." (March 27).

27. Gray, "Play as a Foundation for Hunter-Gatherer Social Existence."

28. Gray, "Play as a Foundation for Hunter-Gatherer Social Existence."

29. Gray, "Play as a Foundation for Hunter-Gatherer Social Existence."

30. Harari, *Sapiens*.

31. Gray, "Play as a Foundation for Hunter-Gatherer Social Existence."

32. Gray, "Interview about hunter-gatherer play." (March 27).

33. Suzman, *Affluence without Abundance*.

34. Gray, "Play as a Foundation for Hunter-Gatherer Social Existence."

35. Gray, "Play as a Foundation for Hunter-Gatherer Social Existence."

36. Gray, "Interview about hunter-gatherer play." (March 27).

37. Gray, Peter. 2009. "Play Makes Us Human." Accessed December 27, 2019. https://www.psychologytoday.com/blog/freedom-learn/200906/play-makes-us-human-i-ludic-theory-human-nature.

38. Gray, "Play Makes Us Human."

Chapter 12

1. Svizzero et al., "The Neolithic Revolution and Human Societies."

2. Harari, *Sapiens*.

3. Suzman, *Affluence without Abundance*.

4. Gray, "Interview about hunter-gatherer play." (March 27).

5. Widrich, L. 2013. "The Origin of the 8-Hour Work Day and Why We Should Rethink It." Accessed December 14, 2019. https://blog.bufferapp.com/optimal-work-time-how-long-should-we-work-every-day-the-science-of-mental-strength.

6. Saad, L. 2014. "The '40-Hour' Workweek Is Actually Longer—by Seven Hours." Accessed December 14, 2019. http://news.gallup.com/poll/175286/hour-workweek-actually-longer-seven-hours.aspx.

7. Snyder, B. Jones, S. 2015. "Americans Work Hard, but People in these 15 Countries Work Longer Hours." Accessed December 13, 2019. http://fortune.com/2015/11/11/chart-work-week-oecd/.

8. Kivimäki, M. Jokela, M. Nyberg, S.T. Singh-Manoux, A. Fransson, E.I. Alfredsson, L. Bjorner, J.B. Borritz, M. 2015. "Long working hours and risk of coronary heart disease and stroke: a systematic review and meta-analysis of published and unpublished data for 603,838 individuals." *Lancet* (Lancet) 386 (10005): 1739-1746.

9. Francis, "When So-Called Work Ethic Replaces Productivity."

10. C.W. and A.J.K.D. 2023. "Get a life. If you're more productive, you get to work less." *The Economist*. Accessed July 8, 2023. https://www.economist.com/free-exchange/2013/09/24/get-a-life.

11. Schulte, "The Way We Work Is Killing Us."

12. Adams, J.T. 1931. *The epic of America*. Boston, Mass: Little, Brown, and Company.

13. Schiller, R. 2017. "The Transformation of the 'American Dream.'" Accessed December 15, 2019. https://www.nytimes.com/2017/08/04/upshot/the-transformation-of-the-american-dream.html.

14. Tucker, P. 2003. "The impact of rest breaks upon accident risk, fatigue and performance: a review." *Work and Stress* 17 (2): 123-137.

15. Schulte, "The Way We Work Is Killing Us."

16. Siegrist, J. 2008. "Effort-reward imbalance and health in a globalized economy." *Scandinavian Journal of Work* 6: 163-168.

17. Kivimäki et al., "Long working hours and risk of coronary heart disease and stroke."

18. Kivimäki et al., "Long working hours and risk of coronary heart disease and stroke."

19. Virtanen, M. Heikkilä, K. Jokela, M. Ferrie, J.E. Batty, G.D. Vahtera, J. Kivimäki, M. 2012. "Long working hours and coronary heart disease: a systematic review and meta-analysis." *Am J Epidemiol* 176 (7): 586-596.

20. Howard, "What's the Best Work Schedule for Your Age?"

21. Maruyama, T. 2017. "Depressive symptoms and overwork among physicians employed at a university hospital in Japan." *Journal of Health and Social Sciences* 2 (3): 243-256.

22. Schulte, "The Way We Work Is Killing Us."

23. Waters, S. Karanikolos, M. McKee, M. 2016. "When Work Kills." *Journal of Public Mental Health* 15 (4): 229-234.

24. Boushey, H. Ansel, B. 2016. "Overworked America: The economic causes and consequences of long work hours." Accessed December 15, 2019. http://equitablegrowth.org/report/overworked-america/.

25. Dembe, A.E. Erickson, J.B. Delbos, R.G. Banks, S.M. 2005. "The impact of overtime and long work hours on occupational injuries and illnesses: new evidence from the United States." *Occup Environ Med* 62 (9): 588-597.

26. Boushey et al., "Overworked America."

27. Francis, "When So-Called Work Ethic Replaces Productivity."

28. Boushey et al., "Overworked America."

29. Boushey et al., "Overworked America."

30. Boushey et al., "Overworked America."

31. Kantor, "Inside Amazon."

32. Siegrist, "Effort-reward imbalance and health in a globalized economy."

33. Waters et al., "When Work Kills."

34. Waters et al., "When Work Kills."

35. Boushey et al., "Overworked America."

36. Siegrist, "Effort-reward imbalance and health in a globalized economy."

37. Randolph, S.A. 2016. "The Importance of Employee Breaks." *Workplace Health and Safety* 64 (7): 344.

38. Fritz, C. Ellis, A.M. Demsky, C.A. Lin, B.C. Guros, F. 2013. "Embracing Work Breaks: Recovering from work stress." *Organizational Dynamics* 42: 274-280.

39. Francis, "When So-Called Work Ethic Replaces Productivity."

40. Fritz et al., "Embracing Work Breaks."

41. Fritz et al., "Embracing Work Breaks."

42. Green, Marc. 2013. "The Seven Laws Of Attention." Accessed December 20, 2019. https://www.visualexpert.com/Resources/lawsofattention.html.

43. Bureau of Labor Statistics, U.S. Department of Labor. 2022. "Employee Benefits in the United States - March 2022." Accessed July 9, 2023. https://www.bls.gov/news.release/pdf/ebs2.pdf.

44. U.S. Department of Labor, "Vacation Leave." Accessed July 9, 2023. https://www.dol.gov/general/topic/workhours/vacation_leave.

45. Maye, A. 2019. "No-Vacation Nation, Revised." Center for Economic and Policy Research (CEPR). Accessed July 18, 2023. https://cepr.net/report/no-vacation-nation-revised/.

46. Miller, G.E. 2017 "American Paternity & Maternity Leave vs. The Rest of the World." Accessed July 9, 2023. https://20somethingfinance.com/american-paternity-maternity-leave/.

47. Pencavel, J. 2015. "The Productivity of Working Hours." *The Economic Journal* 2052-2076.

48. Moodie, "Why are Americans Spending Too Much Time at Work?"

49. Caruso, C.C. Hitchcock, E.M. Dick, R.B. Russo, J.M. Schmit, J.M. 2004. "Overtime and Extended Work Shifts: Recent Findings on Illnesses, Injuries, and Health Behaviors." Accessed August 14, 2019. https://www.cdc.gov/niosh/docs/2004-143/pdfs/2004-143.pdf.

50. Hill, G. 2013. "Living With Less. A Lot Less." Accessed August 14, 2019. https://www.nytimes.com/2013/03/10/opinion/sunday/living-with-less-a-lot-less.html.

51. Sisson, P. 2018. "Self-Storage: How Warehouses for Personal Junk Became a $38 Billion Industry." Accessed August 7, 2019. https://www.curbed.com/2018/3/27/17168088/cheap-storage-warehouse-self-storage-real-estate.

52. Wilder, L.I. Hines, S.W. 2007. *Laura Ingalls Wilder, farm journalist: writings from the Ozarks.* Columbia, Missouri: University of Missouri Press.

53. Hill, "Living With Less."

54. Bauer, M.A. Wilkie, J.E. Kim, J.K. Bodenhausen, G.V. 2012. "Cuing consumerism: situational materialism undermines personal and social well-being." *Psychol Sci* 23 (5): 517-523.

55. Hill, "Living With Less."

Chapter 13

1. Hill, "Living With Less."

2. Millburn, J.F. Nicodemus, R. n.d. "Minimalism: An Elevator Pitch." Accessed August 30, 2019. https://www.theminimalists.com/pitch/.

3. Balmain, M. 2017. "How Living With Less Can Give You More." Accessed September 1, 2019. http://www.success.com/article/how-living-with-less-can-give-you-more.

4. Hill, "Living With Less."

5. Millburn et al., "Minimalism."

6. Moodie, "Why Are Americans Spending Too Much Time at Work?"

7. Corbley, M. 2018. "Work Less, Accomplish More: New Zealand Firm's 4-Day Work Week an 'Unmitigated Success.'" Accessed August 17, 2018. https://www.goodnewsnetwork.org/work-less-accomplish-more-new-zealand-firms-4-day-work-week-an-unmitigated-success/.

8. Howard, "What's the Best Work Schedule for Your Age?"

9. Balmain, "How Living With Less Can Give You More."

10. James, A. 2018. "How to Escape Being a Victim of Time and Truly Live in the Present Moment." Accessed September 15, 2019. https://www.pocketmindfulness.com/live-in-the-present-moment/.

11. James, "How to Escape Being a Victim of Time."

12. Grover, S.L. Teo, S.T.T. Pick, D. Roche, M. 2017. "Mindfulness as a personal resource to reduce work stress in the job demands-resources model." *Stress Health* 33(4): 426-436.

13. Chester, L. n.d. "Mindfulness at Work." Accessed August 3, 2018. http://mindfulnessatwork.com/.

14. Hume, D. 1777. *An Enquiry concerning the Human Understanding, and an Enquiry concerning the Principles of Morals.* Oxford: Clarendon Press.

15. Randolph, "The Importance of Employee Breaks."

16. Kuhnel, J. Zacher, H. de Bloom, J. Bledow, R. 2017. "Take a break! Benefits of sleep and short breaks for daily work engagement." *European Journal of Work and Organizational Psychology* 481-491.

17. Tucker, "The impact of rest breaks upon accident risk, fatigue and performance."

18. Randolph, "The Importance of Employee Breaks."

19. Kuhnel, "Take a break!"

20. Randolph, "The Importance of Employee Breaks."

21. Seiter, C. 2014. "The Science of Taking Breaks at Work: How to Be More Productive By Changing the Way You Think About Downtime." Accessed August 29, 2019. https://open.buffer.com/science-taking-breaks-at-work/.

22. Fritz et al., "Embracing Work Breaks."

23. Fritz et al., "Embracing Work Breaks."

24. Kreider, T. 2012. "The 'Busy' Trap." Accessed September 3, 2019. https://opinionator.blogs.nytimes.com/2012/06/30/the-busy-trap/.

25. Harari, *Sapiens*.

26. Gray, "Interview about hunter-gatherer play." (March 27).

27. Rosengren, C. 2012. "Why You Must Challenge Yourself." Accessed April 23, 2020. https://money.usnews.com/money/blogs/outside-voices-careers/2010/02/18/why-you-must-challenge-yourself.

28. Wooll, M. 2022. "43% of us don't feel connected at work. Here's what to do about it." Accessed January 31, 2024. https://www.betterup.com/blog/connection-crisis-what-you-can-do.

29. Gray, "Play as a Foundation for Hunter-Gatherer Social Existence."

30. Gray, "Play as a Foundation for Hunter-Gatherer Social Existence."

31. Gray, "Play Makes Us Human."

32. "The Value of Play as a Driver of Innovation." Accessed January 31, 2024. https://fs.blog/value-play-driver-innovation/.

33. Suzman, Affluence without Abundance.

Part 4

1. Kesebir, S. Kesebir, P. 2017. "How Modern Life Became Disconnected from Nature." Accessed January 16, 2018. https://greatergood.berkeley.edu/article/item/how_modern_life_became_disconnected_from_nature.

2. Yale Environment 360. 2017. "U.S. Study Shows Widening Disconnect with Nature, and Potential Solutions." Accessed January 20, 2018. https://e360.yale.edu/digest/u-s-study-shows-widening-disconnect-with-nature-and-potential-solutions.

3. Pyle, R.M. 1993. *The Thunder Tree: Lessons from an Urban Wildland.* Boston, Mass: Houghton Mifflin.

4. 1963. *The Silent Spring of Rachel Carson.* Directed by CBS News. Performed by Rachel Carson.

5. Carrington, D. 2016. "The Anthropocene Epoch: scientist declare dawn of human-influenced age." Accessed July 26, 2020. https://www.theguardian.com/environment/2016/aug/29/declare-anthropocene-epoch-experts-urge-geological-congress-human-impact-earth.

6. Keeling, R. Tans, P. Shindell, D. 2022. "Peak CO2 & Heat-trapping Emissions." Accessed December 16, 2023. https://www.climatecentral.org/climate-matters/peak-co2-heat-trapping-emissions.

7. Maller, C. Townsend, M. St. Leger, L. Herderson-Wilson, C. Pryor, A. Prosser, L. Moore, M. 2008. "Healthy Parks, Healthy People: The health benefits of contact with nature in a park context." Deakin University and Parks Victoria, Burwood, Melbourne: Deakin University and Parks Victoria.

8. Smith, L. 2014. "Zoos Drive Animals Crazy." Accessed September 6, 2019. https://slate.com/technology/2014/06/animal-madness-zoochosis-stereotypic-behavior-and-problems-with-zoos.html.

9. Smith, "Zoos Drive Animals Crazy."

10. U.S. Fish & Wildlife Service. 2023. "Endangered Species Act Basics: 50 Years of Conserving Endangered Species." Accessed July 11, 2023. https://www.fws.gov/media/endangered-species-act-basics-50-years-conserving-endangered-species.

11. Carrington, "The Anthropocene Epoch."

12. Morell, V. 2007. "The Discover Interview: Jane Goodall." Accessed February 3, 2018. https://www.discovermagazine.com/planet-earth/the-discover-interview-jane-goodall.

13. Wilson, Edward O. 1984. *Biophilia.* Cambridge, Mass.: Harvard University Press.

14. Kellert, S.R. Wilson, E.O. 1993. *The Biophilia hypothesis.* Washington, D.C.: Island Press.

15. Wilson, *Biophilia.*

16. Newell, P.B. 1997. "A Cross Cultural Examination of Favourite Places." *Environment and Behavior* 29: 495-515.

17. Moore, R. 1986. "The power of nature orientations of girls and boys toward biotic and abiotic play settings on a reconstructed schoolyard." *Children's Environments Quarterly* 3-6.

18. Wilson, *Biophilia.*

19. Wilson, Biophilia.

20. Green, K. Keltner, D. 2017. "What Happens When We Reconnect with Nature." Accessed February 3, 2018. https://greatergood.berkeley.edu/article/item/what_happens_when_we_reconnect_with_nature.

21. Kellert, The Biophilia hypothesis.

Chapter 14

1. Lee, *The Cambridge Encyclopedia of Hunters and Gatherers.*

2. Suzman, *Affluence without Abundance.*

3. 2014, *The Hadza.*

4. Wishart, D.J. 2007. *Encyclopedia of the Great Plains Indians.* Lincoln: University of Nebraska Press.

5. Wishart, *Encyclopedia of the Great Plains Indians.*

6. Harari, *Sapiens.*

7. Gray, "Play as a Foundation for Hunter-Gatherer Social Existence."

8. Fowler, C.S. Turner, N.J. 2004. "Ecological/cosmological knowledge and land management among hunter-gatherers." In *The Cambridge Encyclopedia of Hunters and Gatherers*, by Richard B. Daly, Richard Lee, 419-424. Cambridge: Cambridge University Press.

9. Everett, D. 2008. *Don't Sleep, There Are Snakes.* New York: Pantheon Books.

10. Wishart, *Encyclopedia of the Great Plains Indians.*

11. 2014, *The Hadza.*

12. Lee, *The Cambridge Encyclopedia of Hunters and Gatherers.*

13. 2014, *The Hadza.*

14. Suzman, *Affluence without Abundance.*

15. Suzman, Affluence without Abundance.

16. Palmer, G. Ceballos, P.R. Ehrlich, A.D. Barnosky, A. García, R.M. Pringle, T. 2015. "Accelerated modern human–induced species losses: Entering the sixth mass extinction." *Science Advances* 1 (5).

17. Lee, *The Cambridge Encyclopedia of Hunters and Gatherers.*

18. Lee, The Cambridge Encyclopedia of Hunters and Gatherers.

19. Aboriginal Art & Culture, Alice Springs Australia. 2023. "Dreamtime Meaning." Accessed July 11, 2023. https://www.aboriginalart.com.au/culture/dreamtime2.html.

20. Lee, *The Cambridge Encyclopedia of Hunters and Gatherers.*

21. Knick, "Traditional Culture and Modern Culture."

Chapter 15

1. Harari, *Sapiens.*

2. Suzman, *Affluence without Abundance.*

3. Lee et al., *Man the Hunter.*

4. Nelson, B. 2019. "How Many People Are There in the World?" Accessed September 9, 2020. https://www.rd.com/article/how-many-people-on-earth/.

5. United Nations Population Fund. 2022. "World Population Trends." Accessed May 28, 2023. www.unfpa.org/pds.

6. Maller, "Healthy Parks, Healthy People."

7. Knick, "Traditional Culture and Modern Culture."

8. Kahn, P.H. Kellert, S.R. 2002. *Children and nature: psychological, sociocultural, and evolutionary investigations.* Cambridge, Mass.: MIT Press.

9. Maller, "Healthy Parks, Healthy People."

10. Prüss-Ustün, A. Corvalan, C. 2006. "Preventing Disease through Healthy Environments: Towards an estimate of the environmental burden of disease." Geneva, Switzerland: World Health Organization.

11. Maller, "Healthy Parks, Healthy People."

12. Panter-Brick, C. 2002. "Sexual division of labor: energetic and evolutionary scenarios." *Am J Hum Biol* 14 (5): 627-640.

13. O'Mara, C. 2018. "Kids Do Not Spend Nearly Enough Time Outside. Here's how (and why) to change that." Accessed August 30, 2019. https://www.washingtonpost.com/news/parenting/wp/2018/05/30/kids-dont-spend-nearly-enough-time-outside-heres-how-and-why-to-change-that/.

14. The Guardian Press Association. 2016. "Children spend only half as much time playing outside as their parents did." July 27. Accessed August 30, 2019. https://www.theguardian.com/environment/2016/jul/27/children-spend-only-half-the-time-playing-outside-as-their-parents-did#:~:text=Children%20today%20spend%20half%20the,developing%20a%20connection%20with%20nature.

15. O'Mara, "Kids Do Not Spend Nearly Enough Time Outside."

16. Centers for Disease Control and Prevention. 2019. "Healthy Schools: Childhood Obesity Facts." Accessed September 10, 2019. https://www.cdc.gov/healthyschools/obesity/facts.htm.

17. Louv, Richard. 2011. *The nature principle: human restoration and the end of nature-deficit disorder.* 1st. Chapel Hill, N.C.: Algonquin Books of Chapel Hill.

18. Louv, *The Nature Principle.*

19. Maller, "Healthy Parks, Healthy People."

20. Burroughs, J. 1900. *The light of day; religious discussions and criticisms from the naturalist's point of view.* Boston & New York,: Houghton, Mifflin and Co.

21. Green, "What Happens When We Reconnect with Nature."

22. Ulrich, R.S. Simons, R.F. Losito, B.D. Fiorito, E. Miles, M.A. Zelson, M. 1991. "Stress recovery during exposure to natural and urban environments." *J. Environ. Psychol.* 11 (3): 201-230.

23. Thompson, C.W. 2012. "More green space is linked to less stress in deprived communities: Evidence from salivary cortisol patterns." *Landsc Urban Plan* 105 (3): 221-229.

24. Park, B.J. Tsunetsugu, Y. Kasetani, T. Kagawa, T. Miyazaki, Y. 2010. "The physiological effects of Shinrin-yoku (taking in the forest atmosphere or forest bathing): evidence from field experiments in 24 forests across Japan." *Environ Health Prev Med* 15 (1): 18-26.

25. Wichrowski, M. Whiteson, J. Hass, F. Mola, A. Rey, M. 2005. "Effects of Horticultural Therapy on Mood and Heart Rate in Patients Participating in an Inpatient Cardiopulmonary Rehabilitation Program." *J. Cardiopulm. Rehabil* 25 (5): 270-274.

26. Stellar, J.E. John-Henderson, N. Anderson, C.L. Gordon, A.M. McNeil, G.D. Keltner, D. 2015. "Positive affect and markers of inflammation: discrete positive emotions predict lower levels of inflammatory cytokines." *Emotion* 15 (2): 129-133.

27. Louv, *The Nature Principle.*

28. Bell, J.F. Wilson, J.S. Liu, G.C. 2008. "Neighborhood greenness and 2-year changes in body mass index of children and youth." *Am J Prev Med* 35 (6): 547-553.

29. Louv, *The Nature Principle.*

30. Townsend, Mardie Weerasuriya, Rona. 2010. "Beyond Blue to Green: The benefits of contact with nature for mental health and well-being." Government brief, Deakin University, VIC Australia, Melbourne, Australia: Beyond Blue Limited.

31. Hansen, M.M. Jones, R. Tocchini, K. 2017. "Shinrin-Yoku (Forest Bathing) and Nature Therapy: A State-of-the-Art Review." *Int J Environ Res Public Health* 851-899.

32. Louv, *The Nature Principle*.

33. Frist, Bill. 2017. "The Science Behind How Nature Affects Your Health." Accessed September 23, 2017. https://www.forbes.com/sites/billfrist/2017/06/15/the-science-behind-how-nature-affects-your-health/#b0d6e3415aeb.

34. Lambrecht, B.N. Hammad, H. 2017. "The immunology of the allergy epidemic and the hygiene hypothesis." *Nat Immunol* 18 (10): 1076-1083.

35. Lambrecht, "The immunology of the allergy epidemic and the hygiene hypothesis."

36. Jordan, Rob. 2015. Accessed September 23, 2019. https://news.stanford.edu/2015/06/30/hiking-mental-health-063015/.

37. Lederbogen, F. Kirsch, P. Haddad, L. Streit, F. Tost, H. Schuch, P. Wüst, S. Pruessner, J.C. Rietschel, M. Deuschle, M. Meyer-Lindenberg, A. 2011. "City living and urban upbringing affect neural social stress processing in humans." *Nature* 474 (7352): 498-501.

38. Frist, "The Science Behind How Nature Affects Your Health."

39. Bakolis, I. Hammund, R. Smythe, M. Gibbons, J. Davidson, N. Tongin, S. Mechelli, A. 2018. "Urban Mind: Using Smartphone Technologies to Investigate the Impact of Nature on Well-Being in Real Time." *Bioscience* 68 (2): 134-145.

40. Grahn, P. Stigsdotter, U. 2003. "Landscape planning and stress." *Urban Forestry & Urban Greening* 2 (1): 1-18.

41. Bratman, G.N. Hamilton, J.P. Hahn, K.S. Daily, G.C. Gross, J.J. 2015. "Nature experience reduces rumination and subgenual prefrontal cortex activation." *Proc Natl Acad Sci U S A* 112 (28): 8567-8572.

42. Barton, J. Pretty, J. 2010. "What is the best dose of nature and green exercise for improving mental health? A multi-study analysis." *Environ Sci Technol* 44 (10): 3947-3955.

43. Rosenfeld, J. 2016. "Facing Down 'Environmental Grief': Is a traumatic sense of loss freezing action against climate change?" Accessed 24, 2019. September. https://www.scientificamerican.com/article/facing-down-environmental-grief/.

44. Rosenfeld, "Facing Down 'Environmental Grief.'"

45. Horrox, J. 2017. "The Science of Hiking." Accessed August 20, 2019. https://medium.com/@jameshorrox/the-science-of-hiking-53e8260ab46d.

46. Horrox, "The Science of Hiking."

47. Townsend et al., "Beyond Blue to Green."

48. Horrox, "The Science of Hiking."

49. Atchley, R.A. Strayer, D.L. Atchley, P. 2012. "Creativity in the wild: improving creative reasoning through immersion in natural settings." *PLoS One* 7 (12): e51474.

50. Frist, "The Science Behind How Nature Affects Your Health."

51. Frist, "The Science Behind How Nature Affects Your Health."

52. O'Mara, "Kids Do Not Spend Nearly Enough Time Outside."

53. Louv, *The Nature Principle*.

54. Kuo, F. Sullivan, W. 2001. "Environment and Crime in the Inner City." *Environment and Behavior* 33 (3): 343-367.

55. Kuo, F. Faber Taylor, A. 2004. "A Potential Natural Treatment for Attention-Deficit/Hyperactivity Disorder: Evidence From a National Study." *American Journal of Public Health* 94 (9): 1580-1586.

56. Green, "What Happens When We Reconnect with Nature."

57. Piff, P.K. Dietze, P. Feinberg, M. Stancato, D.M. Keltner. "Awe, the small self, and prosocial behavior." *J Pers Soc Psychol* 108 (6): 883-899.

58. Stellar, J.E. Gordon, A. Anderson, C.L. Piff, P.K. McNeill, G.D. Keltner, D. 2017. "Awe and Humility." *J Pers Soc Psychol* 114 (2): 258-269.

59. Keniger, L.E. Gaston, K.J. Irvine, K.N. Fuller, R.A. 2013. "What Are the Benefits of Interacting with Nature?" *Intl Enviro Res and Public Health* 10 (3): 913-935.

60. Maller, "Healthy Parks, Healthy People."

61. McCarthy, Ml. 2016. *The Moth Snowstorm: Nature and Joy.* New York: New York Review Books.

62. Yale Environment 360, "U.S. Study Shows Widening Disconnect with Nature."

Chapter 16

1. Louv, *The Nature Principle*.

2. McCarthy, *The Moth Snowstorm*.

3. Hansen et al., "Shinrin-Yoku (Forest Bathing) and Nature Therapy."

4. Gelsthorpe, J. 2017. "Disconnect from nature and its effect on health and well-being: A public engagement literature review." *Natural History Museum: Learning and Audience Research Department*. Accessed August 21, 2019. https://www.nhm.ac.uk/content/dam/nhmwww/about-us/visitor-research/Disconnect%20with%20nature%20Lit%20review.pdf.

5. Campbell, J. Osbon, D.K. 1991. *A Joseph Campbell companion: reflections on the art of living*. New York, NY: HarperCollins.

6. Maller, "Healthy Parks, Healthy People."

7. Sagan, Carl. 1994. *Pale Blue Dot*. New York: Random House.

8. Suzman, *Affluence without Abundance*.

9. Harari, *Sapiens*.

10. Boyden, S. 2001. "Nature, Society, History and Social Change." *Innovation* 14 (2): 103-116.

11. Balmford, A. Clegg, L. Coulson, T. Taylor, J. 2002. "Why conservationists should heed Pokémon." *Science* 295 (5564): 2367-2369.

12. Louv, *The Nature Principle*.

13. Proshansky, H.M. 1978. "The City and Self-Identity." *Environ Behavr* 10 (2): 147-169.

14. Louv, *The Nature Principle*.

15. Gelsthorpe, "Disconnect from nature and its effect on health and well-being."

16. Louv, *The Nature Principle*.

17. Food and Agriculture Organization of the United Nations. 2019. "SAVE FOOD: Global Initiative on Food Loss and Waste Reduction, Resources, Key Findings, Key facts on food loss and waste you should know." Accessed September 30, 2019. https://www.fao.org/3/i4068e/i4068e.pdf.

18. Center for Biological Diversity. n.d. "12 Ways to Live More Sustainably." Accessed September 30, 2019. https://www.biologicaldiversity.org/programs/population_and_sustainability/sustainability/live_more_sustainably.html.

19. Berry, W. Meatyard, R.E. 1971. *The Unforeseen Wilderness: An Essay on Kentucky's Red River Gorge.* Lexington, KY: University Press of Kentucky.

20. Gould, S.J. 1985. *The Flamingo's Smile: Reflections in Natural History.* New York: Norton.

21. Narvaez, D. 2017. "Getting Back on Track to Being Human." *Interdisciplinary Journal of Partnership Studies* 4 (1): 5.

22. Narvaez, "Getting Back on Track to Being Human."

Chapter 17

1. Maslow, A.H. "A theory of human motivation," *Psychol Rev* 50 (4): 370-396.

ABOUT THE AUTHORS

Jenny Powers

Jenny Powers has embodied many incarnations in her life: an athlete, a scientist, a wife, a mom, and a writer. Each one led her closer to discovering her genuine self. Collegiate basketball trained her to push her body beyond physical limits. Earning her PhD in immunology taught her to push her mind past mental barriers and soak in how research works. Becoming a mom caused a tectonic shift in her identity, as she learned what is truly important in life, which included finally pursuing her passion for writing.

Photo by Benjamin Buren

Taking advantage of the opportunity to combine many of her "incarnations" into one purpose, Jenny researched and wrote *On the Origin of Being*. She is continually toppled over in awe by the research and discovery of human nature and humbled by the study of our amazing ancestors. She lives in Colorado with her human and furry family.

Luke Comer

Luke Comer is an independent producer, writer, and director who owns all of his own projects and works in different mediums. He was the author of the novel, *Yoke of Wind*; the creator and director of the multimedia production, "The Portal," which toured the country for several years; the producer and director of the Arise Music and Arts  Festival that took place in Colorado for ten years; and the originator and conceptualizer for the book, *On the Origin of Being*. He is currently in production on his next book, *Sapient: How to Design the Optimum Meal*. In the background, he also works on another series of books called *The First Supper*, subtitled *How Evolution Designed You to Eat*. He is also one of the original investors in "Meow Wolf."

He also works towards providing "freedom of assembly" in the state of Colorado for artistic and alternative cultures that, he knows from experience, are persecuted by the government without cause, other than their own prejudice.

He was born and raised in small towns in Alabama, where he ran around with his buddies, building forts, racing bikes, throwing mudpies, and always playing football or other games. He loved books, drew pictures, and played drums in rock and roll bands. Later, he was shipped to prep school where he felt imprisoned and bided his time reading books. He soon dropped out, traveled through Southeast Asia for many months, and soon thereafter attended Oberlin College, where he studied as many things as he could. After college, he ran 30-day, therapeutic wilderness courses for adjudicated teenagers from Philly for several years. After some time in the corporate world, he moved to Boulder, CO, where he supported his climbing and skiing habit with his own restaurant, called "Native," serving organic and nourishing fast food. In his late 20s and early 30s, he faced a crisis in life where he suffered from insomnia, senseless anxiety, and other maladies—but then dedicated himself to healing, experimenting with many different modalities: yoga, psychotherapy, psychedelics, nutrition, trance dancing, and festival culture.

He always engaged in multiple forms of outdoor sports and adventures, attaining upper levels of expertise in white-water paddling, rock climbing, and snow skiing—as well as multiple ocean sports, including windsurfing and kitesurfing.

He splits his time between Boulder, CO; Cabarete, Dominican Republic; and New York City.

Made in United States
Orlando, FL
28 February 2025

58995523R00173